D1188343

Marguerite De La Roque

A STORY OF SURVIVAL

Elizabeth Boyer

ISBN: 0-915964-01-5
LIBRARY OF CONGRESS CATALOG CARD NUMBER 75-20805

FIRST EDITION

Veritie Press
Post Office Box 222
Novelty, Ohio 44072

2500 SOUTH STATE STREET / ANN ARBOR, MICHIGAN 48104

Dedicated to Marguerite's husband

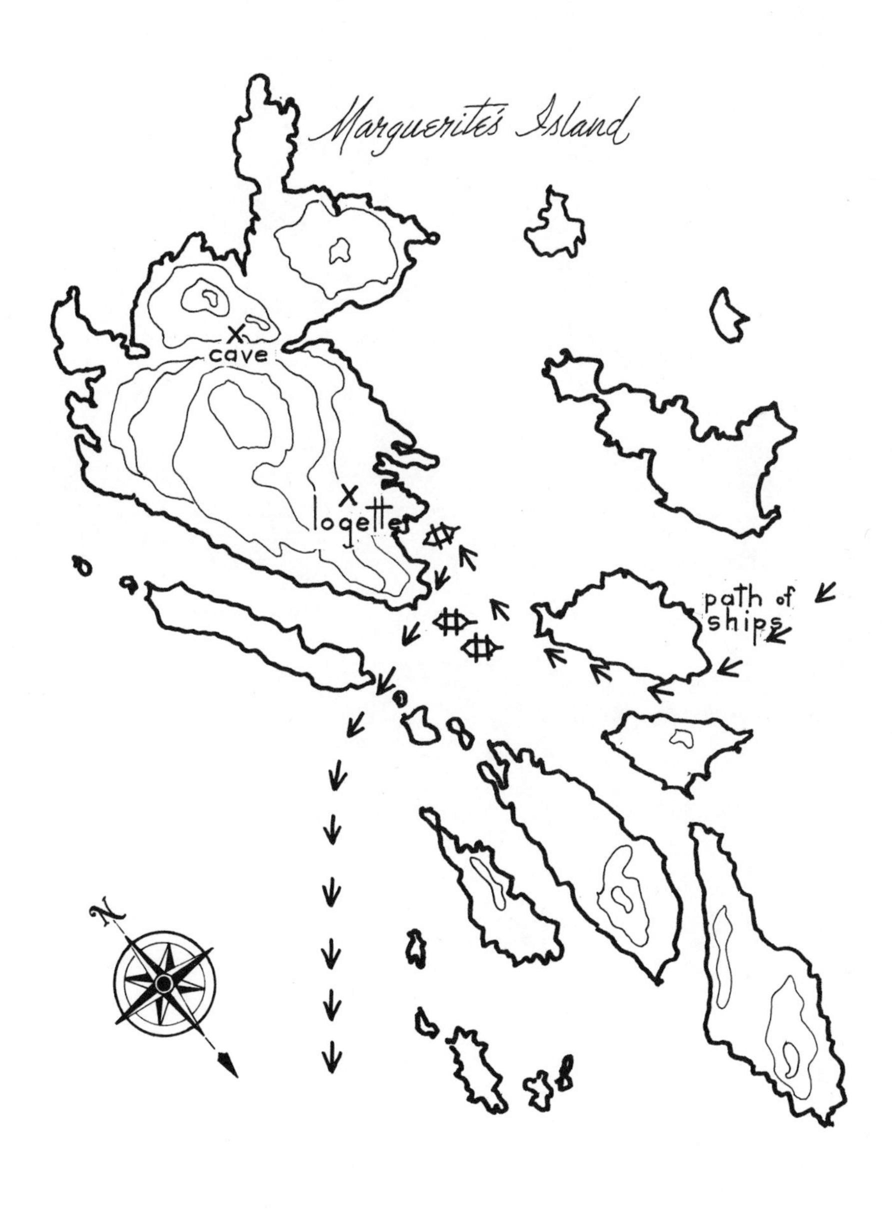

Marguerite's Island
cave
logettes
path of
ships
N

AUTHOR'S NOTE

The story of Marguerite de la Roque is true. It is incredible that such an event could have occurred, equally incredible that this early episode on our shores has been for the most part disregarded and forgotten.

As a story of courage, love and endurance it deserves to take its place in history.

The story as I have written it is a reconstruction and an assembling of actual fact. When possible I have used exact quotations of statements made by the historical personages involved. While all known data has been included, I have added only very minor incident, and conversations, in areas of probability or fair assumption.

All names, places, dates, relationships, conditions, and sequences of events, are correct insofar as present research discloses.

A listing of persons who were of assistance in the research undergirding this history is an impossibility, since perhaps as many as a thousand persons gave varying amounts of data or assistance. The librarians of Ohio, Canada, France and The Library of Congress were without exception helpful, as were many of the personnel in the various Archives and museums of France.

So far as I am aware, every available document or writing, original or derivative, on the subject of Marguerite de la Roque or Jean-François de la Roque was researched in connection with the writing of this book, including several original findings of my own. The places where it is probable that Marguerite lived were visited, including the island where she was marooned, Roberval, Rhuis, Compèigne, Paris, Le Havre, Honfleur, Harfleur, Périgueux, Angoulême, Carcassonne and Nontron.

The heroine of this book must have combined great charm with magnificent stamina and staunchness of soul. Her achievement was incredible. And to find not one book about her among the thousands of volumes which have been written since her day, on far less worthy subjects, seems to me to be a further injustice which I have attempted to remedy.

Novelty, Ohio
March 19, 1975

MARGUERITE DE LA ROQUE

A STORY OF SURVIVAL

July, 1542

—1—

The three castaways watched in silence as the ship's boat made its return trip to the *vaisseau*, roiling the smooth, dark water of the cove with little whirlpools left behind by its oars. As soon as its clumsy, round prow touched the side of the larger vessel it was hauled aboard and a trumpet sounded to signal the other two ships in the little fleet to prepare for departure. Then the anchor hawser tightened until it was nearly vertical, to the faintly-heard command, "*Levez l'aussiere!*"

Across Marguerite's shoulders her young cavalier had placed his arm, and he now drew her body more closely against him in shock and pity. At her other side stood Damienne, her old nurse, ashen-faced and silent. Unbelief numbed them.

Faces at the rail of the *Marye* now looked across the brown water at the three left behind on shore as the ship was pulled briefly toward land on its anchor-line. Some of their former shipmates appeared shocked, some impassive, some pitying. Marguerite wondered which of them had brought about her downfall by carrying a tale to her cousin, Jean-François de la Roque, leader of the expedition to New France. Someone currying favor? Perhaps even a seaman? Anger and resentment mingled with the fear and dismay that had filled her since her public disgrace. Dazedly she recalled it.

Earlier that morning Jean François had climbed onto the *gaillard d'arriere* of the ship in full ceremonial armor. He had read the order of exile to the assembled ship's company, saying that she, Marguerite de la Roque, who was of his blood, had made a tort against him, and therefore against the whole expedition to the New World, and that by her behavior with a certain *compagnon* of the party she had misconducted herself in a way which did not become a Christian gentlewoman. In doing this, he had intoned in pompous accents, she had been aided by her nurse and *duègne,* whose duty it was to stand at the side of her lady and prevent such indiscretions.

What disgrace! thought Marguerite, to be publicly denounced as an adulteress, and by one's own kinsman. He should be the last, she thought, scoundrel that he was, unjustly to accuse another. She remembered his numerous and unsavory misdoings, some of which even François Premier, the King of France, had not dared to overlook.

But even so, her cousin Roberval had this morning crossed her name and Damienne's from the *role d'equipage,* and had said that to expiate their guilt, and as an example to the rest of the company, the Damoiselle Marguerite de la Roque and her nurse, Damienne, were to be set ashore, alone, on this island, the Isle of Demons. Then he had ordered two seamen to row them landward, after he had mockingly tossed four arquebuses into the boat—guns for their protection which neither woman knew how to fire.

Shuddering, Marguerite laid her head against the broad shoulder beside her. Ah, my love, she thought, when they set us ashore, alone, I never thought to see you again. Utter desolation and despair had overwhelmed her as she stood on the shore with Damienne and watched the ship's boat draw away, leaving them with scant food and useless weapons to face death on this barren land in the New World.

But her love had come to her! He had fought his way above-decks, threatening with his own loaded arquebus all who would have interfered, and had forced the landing-party to return to shore, bringing him to share her exile.

All her life, Marguerite was sure, she would remember the feelings of relief and gratitude which had surged through her when she saw him leap into the ship's boat and come ashore to this lonely island to share her disgrace and danger. Now, in the midst of this nightmare, love for him, and pride, filled her with its warmth as she leaned against his velvet-clad shoulder, now tense with his anger and dismay.

He, for his part was grim and silent while he boiled with inner fury. Dignity must be maintained, but his hand which enclosed Marguerite's trembling body felt stiff with outrage. He longed to shoulder his arquebus and shoot Jean-François where he stood. From Marguerite's kinsman he himself had expected little good, but yet no such flagrant outlawry as this! And against one of his own blood! Viceroy or no, the young nobleman said to himself, the man is a swine, and I should have spitted him with my sword rather than submit to this.

Across the small harbor the windlass creaked again, and a cry from the mate indicated that the anchor was now ready to be lifted. The *grand'hunier* had been set, and the yard of the *petite hunier* was now fully hauled aback. At the command to break out the anchor, the ship pivoted and the *petite hunier* was rapidly hauled around to catch the wind. The tall ship slowly started to move forward, bubbling a brownish wake toward the watchers on the shore.

In silence the exiles stared at it, transfixed by a sense of utter unreality, watching the ship as onlookers from the shore. The *ecoutes* of the huge triangular *artimon* were fed slowly through their pulleys and the big sail caught the light breeze. Now the heavy ship moved out toward the west and south where a seaman in a sounding-boat was gesturing toward a safe channel. On the *Marye's* stern as she drew away the glitter of her ornaments seemed to mock them—the lilies of France, in azure and gold. Her split pennons fluttered as she crossed the narrow channel to the southwest of their island and passed through the strait between the larger western island and another islet to the south.

Without coming closer inshore the two other ships in the

little fleet lifted anchor and followed the flagship in stately order, leaving a rapidly subsiding wake behind them which rippled against the sloping granite of the strand.

The castaways stood on the same spot as if turned to stone, not looking into each other's faces, as the ships drew farther away, the *Saincte Anne* and the *Valentyne* picking up their ships' boats beyond the outer islands. Then all three vessels continued toward the southwest where a safe channel had been found by the leadsmen.

Marguerite wildly imagined, in the midst of her shock, Jean Alfonce de Xanctoine standing on the after-deck of the *Marye,* dutifully marking the soundings on his charts as the ships departed. He had seemed fond of her, she thought, but he had done nothing to interfere with her cousin Roberval's action. Now Jean Alfonce would no doubt duly record her marooning as though it were a harbor depth to be noted. A strange sound, almost a laugh, burst from her throat, and shivering she thrust her fingers upward through her blowing hair. A strong arm pressed beneath hers, and turned her away.

As though by common consent the three exiles walked uphill through the trees for a last desperate view of the receding ships. Damienne followed the young pair who climbed with their arms clutched around each other, through the scrubby bushes and across the granite slopes, up to the southern summit of the island.

They walked as if in a deadly trance, not hastening overmuch; the ships moved slowly in the light wind, and, against all reason, the three hoped that they would veer about and return.

There were no trees at the island's summit, only worn, bare granite domes, with lichens and moss around them, and it did not take the exiles long to wind their way to the top. From there they could see the ships far to the south. As they watched, the *Marye,* still in the lead, changed her course to the westward, setting her *voile á livarde* before turning. Now the *misaine* and the huge *grand'voile* also fell into place and filled. This meant, the watchers knew, as surely as if it had been a signal given to them, that the ships would not turn back. The breeze had stiffened and the three ships now moved smartly along, upriver, in the direction of Stadacona and Hochelaga.

The exiles stood immobile, transfixed, beyond conscious thought, as the three *vaisseaux* dimmed and diminished in the distance and the sea-mist. Then Marguerite looked at the incredulous faces beside her, one sternly contained, one tremulous with shock and dismay.

"They will never come back," she said.

*

Slowly, as though be-dazed, the three castaways had wandered aimlessly down the hill again, to the shore of the cove where their belongings lay piled on the rock strand. Their trunks and bundles looked scanty and forlorn, outlined against the dark trees like the salvage of a shipwreck. The elegance of the young courtier's glossy *citre,* with its ivory insets and gold trimmings, looked piteous to him in these wild surroundings, glittering strangely from the top of the pile.

A huge cargo had been loaded into the expedition's ships in France; food, tools, livestock, armaments and even dis-assembled carts and boats had been stowed into the huge ships from *quais* stacked from end to end before the loading. And well did all three castaways know the careful planning and provisioning which had gone forward to insure survival in the harsh New World, as well as the size of the company which was deemed necessary. Even convicts, *forcats,* had been taken from their prisons and sent along to round out the numbers of workers and fighting-men. A colony needed many men.

For only three, alone on this northern island, there could be no hope. Even the hardy fisher-folk and the settlers at St. John went home from these latitudes in the wintertime.

Although his own heart was sick with foreboding her love concealed his despair from Marguerite. Again he drew her head down upon his shoulder and absently stroked her windblown hair, thinking of the desperate straits into which they would shortly be reduced as they fought to survive in this forlorn nest of islands. Over the top of Marguerite's head he looked into Damienne's eyes. Terror glazed them as she peered back at him.

But he murmured reassuringly to Marguerite, "This cannot

be for long, *ma ame.* Even your kinsman cannot do this, Viceroy of Canada though he may be."

Damienne's lips trembled, and Marguerite remained silent, her long hair blowing its gently-scented strands across his face. "Figure to yourself," he added, "The questions which would arise if Jean-François returned to France without his cherished cousin and friend. He must return here, or send someone for us." Resentfully he told himself that even a scoundrel with influence at Court must expect to be called to account for such a deed as this.

For a grateful moment Marguerite slumped against her lover, blessing his staunchness, his very presence at her side. Then she straightened and looked into his face. "I do not think my cousin Roberval will come back," she repeated dully, "And mayhap some day I will tell you why."

The look on Damienne's face made her regret her words. Damienne agreed with her; that was clear, and Damienne was on the verge of terror.

Ah, my love, thought Marguerite, you must already know that I am often more honest than wise, and thus I have spoiled your attempt to reassure Damienne. But as she looked out across the bright, empty sea and the desolate wilderness around them she told herself that they might well abandon themselves to a lingering and lonely death.

On the whole face of the earth it was probable that no three people were more alone.

But on that thought Marguerite suddenly rebelled. Here with her were the two souls who loved her, whom she loved. She must not let their despair overcome them. Slowly she turned back to her companions, forcing a show of *gaiete d'esprit* to raise their spirits, to make amends for her hopeless words. "*Allons!*" she cried desperately. "At least we are out from under my cousin's eye and off his reeking ship!" She paused and considered what next to say.

"I know my kinsman well, and I can vow to you truly that those who are with him will have little cause for gaiety. They may not fare much better than we."

Tossing back her hair, she added wildly, "Now we are free

from him! It is cause for gladness!" Feverishly she flung open her round-topped *coffre de voyage,* took out her flute, and trilled a few notes, then skipped down the shore, her heavy skirts swinging around her feet. A few more notes rippled forth. Her audience looked startled, unamused.

"Ah, *ma Damoiselle,*" Damienne conceded at last, "It was ever hard to punish you!" They were the first words she had spoken since the marooning.

Marguerite played on and after a moment her chevalier picked up his *citre* and strummed an accompaniment, humming the tune as he did so, in an effort to match her strange insouciance. But he soon laid the ornate instrument aside and turned toward Damienne. "I must build us a shelter," he murmured apprehensively. As they all knew it rained a great deal in these parts and a dry place to sleep would be necessary.

Doomed though they were perhaps their daily needs could be met for a while, the young nobleman thought, and it was for this that he had forced his way ashore. But he assumed a confident air. "We will have much to do today," he said in his firmest tones, "And few hands to do it. We must set to work." Looking about him, he hardly knew how to start the impossible tasks which must be done. He had never truly worked with his hands at home in France, and never alone.

Almost to himself, he added, "And tonight we must sign our marriage contract."

Only Damienne heard him, since Marguerite was still wandering in an aimless trance along the shoreline, playing a few strange notes at intervals, and looking upward at the soaring wildfowl.

Damienne was startled out of her despair. "It were well so to do, *mon Sieur,*" she admitted in confusion, "But there is none here to read the lines. It belongs to the clergy to do that." But as she said these words her old eyes began to resume a somewhat more natural expression, her thoughts diverted to the saving of her own reputation as a *duègne* and that of her mistress.

Her young companion replied with increasing assurance, "Since there is no-one here with authority to marry us, we will marry ourselves."

Damienne now cast a bemused glance at Marguerite, who

had returned to their side, and he addressed his next words to both of them. "It is not unheard-of, in our new religion, for couples to read their own marriage lines when a parson cannot be found. It is called a marriage by word and gift. The bride and groom exchange rings." This one thing we can now do, he thought, in despite of Jean-François. Since we are to die for our love, it can now at least be as a married pair.

He continued determinedly, looking into Marguerite's wide eyes. "We are to be alone here, and I hold your honor too dear that there should be further doubt cast upon it." Quaintly he added, "This touches upon my honor as well." And in France an alliance with my family would have been accepted by your cousin Roberval if he had held your interests more dear than his own, he thought. Resentment and confusion warred in his mind but he kept a composed demeanor.

With a certain awkward, half-teasing dignity, bizarre in their deadly predicament, her suitor faced Marguerite and requested her hand in marriage, bowing his head in formal address as he uttered the stately phrases, omitting no courtly expression, while raucous gulls wheeled and cried over his head and dived for fish at the water's edge. With brimming eyes Marguerite looked into his set and serious face and said that she gave him her hand, and gladly.

Then for a moment both were silent. It was a strange and overwhelming thought to betroth oneself thus hastily, even in such a setting. Marriages of the nobility in France came only after ceremonious negotiations in advance, sometimes lasting for years, between the families involved. Representations were made and properties were appraised before such agreements were settled upon. Between these two, they were well aware, titles were held and seigneuralties would be conjoined. In France the betrothal would have been a long-awaited and solemn moment. Indeed it was a solemn moment here. If they were to die, they would die as married lovers.

The young couple finally turned toward Damienne, who stood before them speechless. Matters had moved too fast for her, matters in which the customs of France would have allotted her no part, except to follow her Lady to a different *château.*

"Now we are properly betrothed," the bold young voice announced, "Before you, Damienne, as our witness." He paused. "The wedding will be tonight."

The women gave each other one dumbfounded look, then almost smiled. "There is much to be done," said Marguerite.

—2—

The day passed rapidly. All three castaways sorted their gear and decided what would have to be gotten under cover. They changed their clothing and the women kilted up their trailing skirts to walk more freely on the uneven stones underfoot. Marguerite's betrothed took off his shipboard jacket and his embroidered shirt as well, removing his encumbering sword-belt with its scabbard and *escorcelle.* He put on a plain linen shirt and a leather vest, rolling up the shirt-sleeves to free his arms.

"It is a sunny day," he remarked, "None too common, in truth, on this northern shore." The *Grande Baye* of Hochelaga was all too chill, even in July.

Whistling a Court air which the women recognized as "Soothe me, my Sweet Lovely Brunette," the young Courtier took his axe and strode uphill toward the woodland. His manner was more sanguine than his thoughts as he approached the task before him. He could not recall that he had ever actually cut down a tree.

The forest was fir and pine, he found, trees growing close together and not much taller than a ship's tallest mast, nor thicker at the base than a man's body. The woodland was confined to the valley, which spread northwestward between two red granite hills to the north and south of it.

In their walk to the summit the castaways had almost unconsciously noticed rocky pools of clear water, some as large as ponds. At least they would have water. And so Marguerite now returned up the hill with a kettle to bring down drinking water. When she reached a pond she found that the water tasted peaty, but good. And suddenly standing beside the little pool halfway up the hill she felt a strange sense of relief from the strain which had built up during the voyage, especially during the last few days.

Dimly she had realized that all was not well but the closed face of her cousin had not warned her of what was to come, as he had silently planned this act of punishment, shocking in its finality. But now her spirits rallied, a natural resilience raising her from her despair. Straightening her shoulders Marguerite looked about her, taking deep breaths of the clean air. It was so clear that she could see for miles in all directions, over the surrounding islands, red cliffs, dark green trees, blue water, and swooping white birds. The sea looked peaceful.

Perhaps we can survive, she told herself hopefully, gazing across her small domain, at least until other colonists come, or some of the fisher-folk.

Slowly, changing the heavy kettle from hand to hand as it cut into her soft palms, she walked down the hill. Water dampened the side of her long skirt by the time she reached the shore.

"You should not have gone so far alone." Her affianced husband's voice was grim. "There are beasts of all kinds in this country, and savages as well, who may wish us ill." He looked toward Damienne, including her in his warning. But the older woman's fear, he thought gloomily, might keep her from mistakes and foolhardiness, while his affianced bride was behaving like a child at play within the secure confines of her father's woodlot.

So he faced Marguerite sternly, showing by his demeanor what an appalling risk she had taken. "Until you have learned how to fire an arquebus you must stay within call of me," he told the two women, giving them an uncompromising stare to add emphasis to his words.

For one frightened moment the women peered into the wilderness surrounding them, newly aware that even on this sunny day savage beasts might be concealed there, stalking them for the attack if they were found alone.

In a chastened mood the women followed their protector soberly up the path to the shelter which he was building for them.

For one man, alone, he had done a great deal. On a little

mound in the middle of the valley, close to the shore, two trees had been lopped off at head-height, and across their high stumps he had laid a bar made of the trimmed top of one of them. The women noticed that the earth was fairly dry underfoot in the spot he had chosen, while the soil of the valley was wet and spongy elsewhere.

Now their woodsman was chopping down saplings and laying them side by side, slanting them upward to lie with their narrow ends on the crossbar, and sticking their lower ends deep into the mossy soil, so that they would stay in place against the winds which seldom ceased from blowing on this northern shore, as well as the gales which were said to come frequently from the northwest.

The shelter had been faced toward the southeast, its builder explained, so that most of the winds would blow right over it, while it would catch the brief, northern sunlight. They would thus have a dry place to sleep and it would be large enough to store their belongings. It was just such a shelter as hunters built in France, he told the two women.

They seemed pleased, he thought, and they asked him what they could do to help. Looking at Marguerite's soft, be-ringed hands, and Damienne's knotted ones, the man thought, nothing. The question seemed to him to betray a touching naiveté, poignant in the circumstances. Beings such as they could not long survive in the wild, nor could they even do their part in protecting themselves here, he thought. It would be only a question of time. But he thrust the dark thoughts from his mind and answered them briskly.

"You can cut spruce branches for our beds," he said.

Even in the summer-time this shelter could be only a temporary one, he knew; the winds and the cold would be too severe for them to stay in it for long. The nights were chill even now, in midsummer, and the summer itself would be short. But beds they must have.

Returning to the shore the young man took from his scanty stores a coil of hemp rope and two knives, and on his reappearance he gave Marguerite and Damienne the knives somewhat dubiously. Then he showed the women how to select long, springy boughs for the lower layer in the beds, and brushy ones for softness above. But he was surprised at the determined way in which the women set to work, using the tops of the saplings he had cut down for their branches.

Marguerite sensibly removed her rings, he noticed, and put them in the purse dangling from her belt.

When the supports of the shelter had been solidly spaced from tree to tree, the young man tied them into place with a rope by winding them against the crossbar. The one rope on the island, he had suddenly realized, was too valuable to be cut apart. It could not be replaced. As he thought of this the young exile's hands hung for an instant at his sides in discouragement. Nothing we have brought here can be replaced, he thought; we must lose or break nothing. On this our lives depend.

He glanced at the women, happily trundling their branches to the shelter, like girls at play. Let them have a few happy days, he thought. Unless they were rescued, trouble would be upon them soon enough

And so he did not cut the rope at all, but coiled the remainder into a hank and hung it on a branch-stub.

*

The women had gone down to the shore and were calling to him to come. They wanted him to start a fire, it seemed, so that they could prepare food to break the morning fast since it was nearly noon. They had gathered wood and twigs; he found dry moss under a stone and soon had a fire flaming up with the aid of a pinch of powder and a spark from his fusil.

The food was oddly assorted. The young nobleman had brought ashore his full share of ship's biscuit, several hundredweights of it, the least tasty food known to man, he said, but the most unlikely to spoil. They had some wine in large basket-covered bottles, smoked sausage and bacon, no great amounts of either, some cereals, beans, some sacks of dried herbs, a pot of honey, dried fruit, and little else. All were voyage-foods, of which they were heartily wearied.

Surprisingly, Damienne reached into her hitched-up skirt and brought forth several eggs. "Fresh ones," she said with satisfaction. "I have shaken them, and they are good. Birds nest here, and I followed one to her nest." Beaming at the young couple, she added, "We will have an omelette."

They propped stones for Damienne's heavy griddle, and the smell of bacon soon floated on the air, followed by the sizzling of the eggs. A scattering of herbs was sprinkled in, and the servings were laid on the metal plates they had used on the ship. They took their tiny forks from the purses at their belts and ate the savory food with relish.

All three then returned to work on the shelter with better heart, having eaten more tasty food than they would have had on shipboard.

Between them they now carried uphill the large rectangle of canvas which had been among the stores brought ashore. It was very big and heavy, long enough to spread over the whole shelter and to hang down at the sides and front, reaching the ground all around. On the slanted end which lay against the ground they placed heavy chunks of stone to hold the canvas down, and on the triangular ends the canvas was folded and held down in the same way, without being cut. The front was draped back over the log bar at the top, to be lowered in case of need, or propped out as an awning.

Their shelter, Marguerite decided, was a kind of log-framed tent, as her woodsman cut small logs from the tops of the trees, and laid them on the ground under the shelter to make a sort of floor. Many a hunter's shelter in France, they told each other, was not so snug.

But the sea-chests were too heavy for one man to carry, so they laid a short bough under one end and Marguerite and Damienne shared the weight at the front as they carried them to the shelter. It seemed very wrong to the young cavalier to have women do such work, but they persuaded him, and in truth there was little choice.

Their shelter was partitioned into two sections by the tool-chest, because it was longest and heaviest, and the leather chests of

Damienne and Marguerite were placed at the ends to help hold the canvas in place. Their other belongings were ranged along the back, where the roof met the ground, and the beds were laid in place with Damienne's on one side of the chest and the double bed on the other.

When they were covered with bedding they looked reassuringly homelike. None of the exiles found the proximity of the beds disturbing. Marriage beds in France were semi-public and throughout their lives married couples had little privacy in the drafty castles and châteaux.

After many trips everything was now under cover, arranged as seemed best, with the flute and *citre* laid on the partitioning chest. It was late afternoon before they finished, and after a last look at the shelter, Damienne turned away to walk down to the shore. She intended to hunt more eggs, she said, and to build up the fire.

As Damienne disappeared down the path Marguerite stepped nearer to her love and laid her head against the curve of his neck where his linen shirt lay open against his throat. They stood silently for a moment in the deepening shade of the dark trees, until Marguerite drew away, holding both his arms as she did so.

"What you have done today, no man has ever done for his love, that I have ever heard," she said, "And if such a thing had been done, songs would have been sung of it." She paused, adding as if to herself, "If I die in this place I care not, for it is a kindly fate to marry a man who would do for his wife what you have done."

—3—

Their preparations for the wedding were both solemn and gay. Damienne found her smoothing-stone and prepared the marriage garments, which were crumpled into folds from their long storage. Marguerite had chosen her gayest dress, suitable for the ballroom of a provincial Court, with its low, square neckline, tight basque waist, puffed peplum, and sleeves that flared so long and wide that they almost swept the ground when she lowered her arms. She even planned to wear her mother's jewels.

Her bridegroom's garments, she found, were as splendid as her own, with puffed over-sleeves, embroidered open short-robe, slashings, and round-toed shoes with straps over the insteps.

Damienne's modest finery, appropriate to her station, included a satin under-petticoat meant to show at the front, and an embroidered hood.

The food would be lavish, the women had decided. Twice the arquebus had sounded, and a hare was turning on the spit, accompanied by a goose which was filled with savory stuffing made of pounded hard-tack mixed with bacon, garlic and herbs. A hot potion of berries and cloves was simmering in a kettle, and the wine-bottle had been wiped off and set in readiness. A *sallet* of fresh greens had been made, and other dainties had been contrived from the figs, raisins and sugar-biscuits carried on the voyage as remedies for sea-sickness.

Heavy blue and white dishes had been removed from their careful packing and were sitting on the white tablecloth which had been spread over a large, flattish stone. Damienne bustled about, almost happily, in accustomed work. If one closed one's eyes, she thought, the smells and sounds were those of home.

And her lady, she reflected comfortably, was at least to be properly wed.

*

Marguerite brought out the tiny New Testament which had been given to her by her grandfather at the time of its first printing. She did not remember receiving it; it had been hers since her infancy, and the marriage record would be written in its pages, together with the names of the children she bore.

The marriage contract, of course, would have to be put on a larger page, since it would have to recite all the holdings of husband and wife, seigneuralty by seigneuralty.

Finally Marguerite walked up to the woodland and consulted

her bridegroom. "What lands do you hold?" she asked him.

He replied teasingly, arms crossed over his axe-handle, that she had been improvident indeed, not to have asked this question before the betrothal. But then he recited his holdings so that his bride could write them down.

She had puzzled over the wording of the contract, since this work was usually done by lawyers. It was extraordinary to be writing one's own agreement, but Marguerite thought she could recall the essential phrases. Had she ever anticipated that such a need would occur, she thought ruefully, she would have paid more attention to the marriage-contracts she had happened to see. But it was not considered seemly, in a girl, to pay much heed to such matters. It belonged to others to arrange the marriage terms.

Finally, after much thought, she wrote in a careful, clear slant the opening lines of formal phraseology, followed by her name and titles:

> *Damoiselle Marguerite de la Roque, Dame de Sermet, de Sauveterre, d'Allais and de la Mothe, et Co-Seigneuresse de Saint-Popoing . . .*

This was followed by the words of contract and espousal to her Seigneur, giving his name and titles, followed by his holdings, the formal words of consideration, the mutual consents, and the date. Space was left for the signatures, with Damienne's as witness.

As Marguerite finished her writing, she held the document in her hands for a moment, looking out dreamily over the empty harbor and the *Grande Riviere* beyond it. This would be the first Christian marriage to be solemnized in the New World, she reflected, except, perhaps, for the southern lands held by Spain, and those would be Catholic marriages, performed by priests.

Perhaps it was fitting, she thought, that in the New World, in their new religion, she and her husband should perform the ceremony for themselves.

*

As evening drew near, the island took on a festive air. The wind died down, and the sea was still. All three exiles bathed, taking turns in the shelter, using their perfumed soap and dressing in their finery. Tapers were lighted for the feast-table, although the sky was still bright.

Finally the bride and groom stood facing each other to repeat the traditional prayer:

> "*Dieu, le pere tout-pouissant, createur du Ciel et de la terre* . . ."

The sea-birds still soared overhead, uttering their harsh cries in the long northern twilight as the ancient vows were exchanged and hands were placed, in turn, on Marguerite's tiny leather-bound Testament, its gold-colored edge glimmering in the firelight. Each gave the other a family ring, long-cherished and long-used for espousals in their separate families.

With the traditional ban: "Whom God hath brought together no man may put asunder," they concluded their pledging.

At this time it seemed strangest of all not to have a parson to pronounce them man and wife, and to conclude the service. After a pause, and somewhat awkwardly, they pronounced themselves man and wife and kissed each other on the lips.

Then they nodded to Damienne, and all repeated the well-remembered words of dismissal:

> "*Seigneur, tu laissez maintenant aller ton serviteurs en paix* . . ."

After the final *prou face* was said, they walked to the marriage contract, lying on the feast-table, with the inkwell and pen on a plate beside it. Both signed with bold flourishes, Damienne signing afterward, on the left side, as a witness.

The three of them looked at each other, then, with a long, solemn regard. This thing which they had done was a serious matter, and might well invite royal reprisals when they returned to France. And the Seigneur de Roberval, Marguerite's cousin, would not be pleased at their effrontery if he ever came to hear of it; that was clear, and he was a dangerous enemy to have. All pondered this.

Marguerite, whose gaiety was never far beneath the surface, was the first to smile. "What a sour-faced bridegroom," she cried teasingly. "Is the bride, then, so ill-favored? Too bad. These family-arranged marriages, you know, always chancy, except for the land-holdings!"

She poked a slim finger at the clauses in the marriage contract. "*These* are first considered; the bride's charms come second!"

It was a remark that no-one would have dared to make at a wedding in France, as possibly coming too near to the mark, not only for the bridal pair, but for many of the wedding-guests. But here on this island his bride's remarks seemed to the young bridegroom to be droll and amusing, and to show a high-hearted flouting of the adversity in which they found themselves. He tried to respond in an amusing way, although seriousness had always come more easily to him than humor. "If you are to be a good bargain here," he said, "You will have to make a showing of wifely qualities other than your land-holdings. They do not count for much while we are on this island."

A shadowy look of dismay passed across the face of his bride, and he thought that as usual his attempts at lightness and levity were foredoomed to failure.

But the maladroit moment passed quickly, since Damienne was now placing food on the plates. So the new bridegroom carved the goose and took a drumstick, first laying the other ceremoniously on Marguerite's plate. The tapers flickered, and orange eyes began to reflect the flame from the dark woodland. It seemed an incongruous affair to the young groom, such a wedding-feast as had never been heard-of, nor was like to be heard-of unless they lived to tell of it.

He thrust the somber thought aside, and bent his efforts to accustomed gallantry. They ate; they played the flute and *citre;* they danced.

Up and down the smooth rock shore they frolicked, an elegant pair, first in the court dances, the *branle* and the *pavane,* then in the stamping rhythms of tap dances and gallops done to village tunes. Damienne sat tapping and clapping as though for a crowd of guests assembled. Even the echoes from the dark woods chimed in with sounds of gaiety, and the firelight flickered in reflections on their swirling silks and satins, dipping and bouncing over the red granite shore.

Only once did a darker moment intrude. Damienne glanced over her shoulder, when the dancers had stopped to regain their breath, and said, "The Sieur de Roberval called this place 'The Isle of Demons' when he read the order putting us ashore. Do you think our prayers can drive away the demons, if they have long held sway here . . ." her voice trailed apprehensively away, as her gaze drifted to the unblinking orange eyes peering out from the dark forest.

"Tales written by old men, to frighten old women." Damienne's new Lord was not one to coddle superstition. She looked somewhat abashed.

Marguerite placed a hand on the old woman's shoulder and added soothingly, "Jean-François often says these things to frighten folk, as you well know." Seeing that Damienne was still disturbed, she added, "The Isle of Demons to which he referred is far away from here, in a different latitude, if indeed it exists at all, or is well-charted. I saw the maps, and I know that our islands here are the *Ysles Saincte Martre.*"

Looking at her young husband, Marguerite added, "Jacques Cartier named them for Saint Martha when he passed by here on his second voyage, several years ago."

Damienne looked doubious. Like many older folk in France, she still half-believed in demons, Marguerite knew, and as a recent convert to the new religion, she still had ties to the old. If the islands had long borne a Saint's name it should comfort Damienne, since Saints were thought to give special protection to those places which were named for them, even including the bridges and the ships which bore their names.

So Marguerite went on, addressing herself to Damienne. "Jacques Cartier is a good Catholic, as you know, and he often named islands and rivers for the Saints' days on which they were discovered. Many of these names are marked on Jean Alfonce's charts.'' Glancing at her bridegroom, she noticed that even he seemed to be impressed by her words. To him she added, ''Jacques passed here on July the twenty-ninth, which is the day of Saint Martha; that is why he named the island for her.'' She repeated her words firmly to Damienne, ''So the island is named for a saint, and has been so named since 1535.''

Glancing at the old woman whimsically she added, ''Ample time, I should think, to drive away the demons.''

''*Ysles de Saincte Martre,*'' Damienne repeated the homely words. ''And it is so written on the charts. That is where we are.'' Somehow the words bore comfort for all of them, as though the recordings on the maps insured that they were inhabiting a place now known to man.

Taking her young bridegroom's hand Marguerite drew him back toward the feast-table to select a dainty, then continued the dance.

*

A Saint's name, thought Damienne. That was indeed a fortunate thing. She believed the words of her young mistress, who would not lie to her even to ease her troubled mind. And, indeed, the girl had pored over the charts endlessly with Jean Alfonce de Xanctoigne.

New faith or old, they were in no position, Damienne told herself, to dispense with a Saint's protection. Dutifully she returned to tidy the feast-table, then again added her hearty voice to the rollicking old tunes as the married pair danced and sang.

It was unlucky, Damienne knew, to make a long face at a wedding feast, even though this festal-board was a sad showing compared to what she could have done for her lady had they been at home in France.

But now the night was already growing chill; since the married pair had long since drunk each other's health, Damienne threw her shawl around her shoulders and sat sipping her wine, occasionally lifting her glass in the direction of the bride and groom, as was seemly.

*

Later, during the night, the exiles had good cause to believe that this might indeed be the Isle of Demons. Bursts of demoniacal laughter echoed over their bay, answered from the shoreline by a higher peal of insane mirth. The evil spirits of the place seemed to have returned, and to be taunting them with their exile.

Deep in each other's arms, the newly-married pair were hardly aware of the sounds that came from the woodland behind their shelter, crackles and growls, sounds of creatures killing and being killed. To Damienne it was not reassuring. Once during the night she saw a winged creature with a head like a cat floating over them in complete soundlessness, as if swung by a string from the heavens.

At this she covered her head in her bedding and inched closer to the marriage-bed. She made up her mind to open her package of roots and herbs, and to hang up a sprig of Saint John's Wort over the front of the shelter to ward off evil spirits, as it was known to do. Yes, and a sprig of garlic as well, she thought, would do no harm.

But her young mistress, lying beyond the sea-chest on her bridal-bed of pine boughs, was well content, as was her bridegroom, as though they lay on goose-down, under velvet coverlets, in one of their own *châteaux* in France. After long months of delay and denial they had now come into each other's arms in their own marriage chamber, and neither cared, during these spell-bound hours, what might come afterward.

—4—

During the next few days the castaways did not delay in planting their garden. Summers in this latitude would be very short, they knew. Blanc Sablon was only about thirty or forty leagues to the north of them, they thought, and it was too cold for gardens there. Even much farther south, at Sainct Croix, where Jacques Cartier had set up his settlement, the time for gardening was short.

Marguerite had heard the argument between Jacques and Jean-François, and Jacques had made it clear that her cousin had come to the New World too late to depend on raising a crop. The cold of autumn and the winter came on earlier here than they did even in the North of France.

The castaways hoped that in a sheltered spot, with much care, they might raise some of the familiar foods of home. These would, indeed, be necessary to their survival.

So the seeds and rootlings were brought out and soaked in water from the pond while the ground was prepared. All three of the exiles worked. The rising from the marriage-bed, for all its delights, could not be a languid one, and by wordless consent all three recognized the urgency of the gardening.

Marguerite and her new husband had never made a garden, but Damienne had helped in her family's garden in her girlhood. She searched her memory and took the lead in the planning. All three of them had noticed that when the breeze came from offshore, over the land, the wind was warmed by the mainland over which it passed, but when it came from the sea it was very cool. Therefore they searched out a garden-spot which would be sheltered by a rocky shelf between it and the sea, with the forest to shelter it from the west, and where, from the look of the vegetation, the soil was good.

When they tried to spade the ground they encountered an unfamiliar condition. Even the very earth of the island seemed strange and savage. It was not like any soil they had ever seen—there was nothing in it that they would have considered as earth. When it was turned over it was found to be a mat of brown, peaty fibers and root-ends of all sizes, like coarse stubbles.

As they got this turfy earth turned they planted their seeds in careful rows, tearing the soil into feather-like shreds to cover the seeds and pounding shells to weigh down and mark the rows. Carefully they handled their precious seeds from home, the flat, whitish parsnip seeds, the brown seeds of the carrots, and, most carefully of all, the tiny, round turnip seeds. Since all of these vegetables could be stored for winter they were precious indeed. The cabbage and lettuce seeds would give them tender greens for *salats,* although it was doubtful that the cabbage would have time to head, or, indeed, than any of the vegetables would have time to bear seed.

When she realized this Marguerite quietly saved aside some of each kind of seed for the next summer. The others might still be thinking that Jean François would return; no need to lower their spirits by repeating her conviction that they might be a long time on this island.

Breaking the soil for the first time was slow work and it went along endlessly. They wanted to get all their planting done as quickly as possible, so that they worked almost throughout the long northern daylight, falling into bed weary, sore and blistered, for the short nights.

"We should have spread dung from our own beasts," Damienne worried, and added that she doubted that plants would grow when this custom could not be followed. But she sought out all the dead fish she could find at the tide's edge, some of them dry and brittle enough to crumble along the seed-rows. She broke up eggshells too, having little confidence in this strange soil.

At last they got the cabbage planted, and even a few rows of millet and barley. Without oxen to plough it was impossible to raise enough of these grains to do more than thicken soup, they knew, but they thought that they might thus insure enough fresh seed for another year. The garlic and shallots had early been pressed into the ground by Damienne, with eggshells dug in around them as was customary, and their homely green shoots had already appeared.

Damienne searched the island for deposits of clay or sand to bring to the garden and thus to turn it into the kind of soil she knew. But while here and there she found a sort of crumbled granite which she laboriously gathered, there was apparently no clay nor sand at all on the island, even along the shores. There water met rock, with no sandy beach such as was found at Blanc Sablon.

*

Most of Damienne's time was now spent in the garden, hovering over the seeds with a small jar of water which she splashed over the rows, lest the seedlings wither. Until they took deep root, she feared that they would shrivel and die in this peaty soil which drained so rapidly on the surface during the heat of the day.

At last the small sprouts came into view, the twin, kidney-shaped first leaves of the turnips, the long double blades of the carrots and parsnips, and the oval leaves of the lettuce. As Marguerite and her husband stood arm-in-arm viewing them he was astonished at his own flooding sense of relief to see the garden growing. It seemed a hopeful sign.

—5—

While the women worked at their unaccustomed tasks in the garden their young Lord explored and hunted, taking time each day for one duty which he said must be done. A lookout must be kept from the very topmost point of the island, almost a league to the north of them. The summit there was also bare of trees, and from it one could see for countless miles when the weather was clear. A pyre must be built there, he said, to be lighted if they caught sight of passing vessels. Ships could be seen from a great distance from there, so that they could know of their approach for a long time before their arrival.

Thus explaining himself to the women, he built the pyre and made daily trips to his lookout. To himself he thought anxiously that his observations would also serve to give timely warnings of the approach of parties of savages, which were known to pass this way, and of the movements of various wild beasts which their activities had temporarily driven to the north of the island. He feared they would return to seek human prey when the odor of mankind became more familiar to them.

So once each day he bounded up the path to the north of the shelter, through the woodland and up beyond the tangled scrub and underbrush, until he reached the slanting, rocky cliff which led northwestward, up to the highest part of the island.

His trips were hasty; he did not like to leave the women alone for long.

It took no great time to scan the horizon. Nothing was to be seen but the sea and the sky, and the barren islands which spread out around him. He never saw so much as a wisp of smoke.

*

The women had been promised that they would all explore the island when the garden was well on its way. After a few rainy days, during which they sat around in the shelter, playing cards, singing, and talking, the sky dawned clear, and they set out for what seemed almost a holiday.

First they walked southwestward by the water's edge, turning east around the little cove where Jean-François had set them ashore. The tongue of land at the southeast tip of the island did not extend very far, and ended in a rocky cliff that climbed steeply toward the west and north, forming the southern boundary of their island. It dropped off in a sheer, vertical wall along a narrow inlet, beyond which, on the south, lay a long, narrow, island, also steep-sided. The channel between the islands pointed as straight as a spear out to the east and south, through the passage by which the *Marye* had entered the harbor. Straight south of where they now stood was the passage by which she had left.

The three exiles now climbed the high cliff toward the west, quickly reaching the summit, which was not far away at that point. Then they turned northward on the crest and went to the highest southern summit of the island, from which they could look out over the lower parts of the coasts to the east and west.

It was a frighteningly small place, all of them secretly thought, on which to spend the rest of their lives.

And the very soil underfoot was strange. It sprang up and

down as they stepped on it, the women found, and once in a while a foot would slip through it, down into a crevice in the granite below, which sometimes held a well of cold water.

At the crest of the hill the rock was scoured clear even of lichens; farther down, the low mosses started to cover the stone, and still lower there were strange masses of growth, the like of which none of them had ever seen before. These consisted of shrubby bushes which looked like stunted trees, but which lay close to the ground, matted and intertwined together in a solid tangle, so that one could walk right across their matted tops by taking care not to let a foot slip. In that case the whole leg plunged down through the twigs into thin air.

On a lower level than this the first trees grew, scrawny and spindling, also clinging to the ground, so that one spruce tree spread along the ground for several paces, only growing upward for a foot or so near to its tip.

Below this was woodland as the French exiles knew it, with closely-space trees filling only the lower parts of the valleys.

The walking was difficult, and once Marguerite fell, when her foot slipped down into a deep, wet cranny under the moss. When she stood up her shoe had been pulled off. It was no mean task for her young husband to regain it for her. As he groped for it, lying on his face in the damp moss, and reaching down at arm's length to find the shoe, he realized that he was dealing with no casual, courtly matter. The shoe must be found. It could not be replaced. And no-one could walk far on this island without shoes.

As he lay there he realized that they would have to take extremely good care of their clothing, especially of their shoes. He knew no way that they could be replaced.

When he finally straightened up, the dripping shoe in his hand, the look on Marguerite's face told him that she had been visited by the same discomforting thoughts as he.

*

In a less festive mood the three climbed carefully down through the valley which cut across the island from west to east and clambered up the bare rock of the northern dome. For the first time the women saw the signal-pyre and viewed the very tip of the island to the north. They looked across to the mainland, as well, less than a league away. It was a swampy shore, stretching along in low, irregular scallops northeasterly toward Blanc Sablon, and southwesterly toward where, hundreds and hundreds of leagues away, there stood the native villages of Saguenay, Hochelaga and Stadacona, and the settlements set up by Jacques Cartier.

Suddenly all three thought of Roberval, Marguerite with clear resentment of his injustice to her, Damienne with fear for the results of his harsh edict, but their young Lord's feelings were those of an unplumbed hatred and contempt, too profound for him to put into words. So their mention of him was cursory, and they turned their eyes to the east, away from where his upriver settlement, with all the comforts he had carried there, was as out of reach as France, itself.

To the east the sea was scattered with countless islets, like stepping-stones, the larger ones to the south fronting on the open sea.

Since the day was sunny the sea was a clear blue, and the outcroppings of granite looked almost soft and crumbled, while the sea-birds swooped low overhead, not pleased to have unfamiliar creatures walking across the heights they considered their own.

All three of the castaways now looked about for plants that could be eaten, and Damienne was asked to judge of their similarity to plants in France. They discovered blueberries, strawberries, blackberries, and even gooseberries, many still unripe.

One of the berry plants was strange to them, with its scalloped leaves which made a sort of half-circle. The berries were round, but had large lobes, somewhat like a blackberry, and a few of them had ripened, turning from red to yellow. Their taste was tart, like a well-baked apple, and somehow satisfying.

As the three turned back toward their shelter Damienne found a patch of mushrooms of a kind she recognized. From her outcries, Marguerite said, one would have thought she had found a mine of Canadian diamonds.

Damienne's young Lord did not jest about the matter. He suspected already that their diet of fish and game would soon become monotonous, plentiful though such food was.

Already they missed their good white bread.

*

When Damienne and Marguerite were alone they often discussed their new Lord. He was an easy, kindly man, as Roberval had never been, they both agreed. Even cast away on this island as they were, they felt fortunate, even protected, in his company. When they returned to France with him they hoped that they would never need to see Jean-François de la Roque, Sieur de Roberval and Viceroy of Canada, again.

Damienne had folded away the sheets from the marriage-bed, with their stains of her Lady's blood, over the objections of Marguerite who believed these old customs could well be dispensed with. But Damienne had grimly set her lips and had said that she did not intend to relinquish this proof of her Damoiselle's honor, which Marguerite's cousin, a man of her own blood, had so gravely sullied.

"This is my proof that I did not fail in my duty," she said in a flat and obdurate tone of voice as she packed the sheets away in her own sea-chest for safe-keeping.

As Damienne spoke Marguerite felt a re-awakened anger against her kinsman. In her happiness with her husband she had almost forgotten her resentment of Roberval, unless some reminder brought him back into her mind. "Roberval did me no great honor," she now remarked, "To think I would yield *pucelage* on his stinking ship, crowded on one side by convicts and on the other by gossipy noblemen and swine!"

She laughed, not without some bitterness at the memory. "There was no place on that *nef* that could claim to be a virgin's bower. My love and I were hard put to it to exchange a clasp of hands without being elbowed while we did so—and as to the awkward business of making first love to a virgin!" She paused, with an embarrassed smile toward her old nurse.

"It is absurd," she concluded. "Anyone with sense would know as much. One could doubt that Jean-François ever made love to a woman, if he could so believe."

She did not disclose her further thoughts to Damienne. More and more, as she thought on the matter, she believed that Roberval had seized a pretext to rid himself of her and of Damienne as well. As she considered it, Marguerite no longer believed that it was because of her behavior, nor even to get rid of two useless mouths when the expedition was short of food.

*

After the first few days on the island the young married pair had decided that they had best mark off a calendar for themselves, so as not to have to judge plantings and harvestings by the weather on the island, which was so different from that of France. Counting off the days, they came close to agreement as to the date. On one of their few sheets of paper they began a calendar, showing its record of days of planting.

It gave all three exiles a strange and meager comfort to know what days, and holidays, were going by for them as well as for the rest of their countrymen back in France.

Although she still kept a close watch over the garden, along with Damienne, Marguerite often sought out her husband to be near him as he worked at building rude bridges over the bogs for their pathways or searched for the fish and game for their meals.

It was an unending miracle for her to be with him, alone and undisturbed, and she did not regret their isolation nor the solitude around them, in his nearness. And her bridegroom, for his part, was happier than he had thought to be in his exile, doomed as they were. While he was halfway countryman, fretful at being away from his lands in France, his other half was Courtier and romantic, counting his life well laid forfeit if his last days could be spent with his love.

So he toiled to prolong their days of comfort, followed as they were by nights of dalliance and long-denied assuagement.

One day he made a rude basket of pine branches and scrub willow withes, since he had found that just offshore the fish were so plentiful that he could catch them in a basket by wading out and setting it down for a few moments. When it was quickly raised, it was usually full of fish. As he performed this feat for Marguerite, who remained on the shore, he remarked, "This place is surely well named *Baccalaos*, for these fish of that name that fill the seas hereabouts." Before long, he thought, he would suggest that they dry and smoke some fish and game for winter, but he felt a certain reluctance to put this thought into words, with its implied loss of hope for rescue before winter.

And he hated to turn his thoughts to the coming of winter, with its deadly hardships. Even in France, he had always minded the cold.

Let the women think of this as a short, pleasant interval, he told himself, for a while more. And so, without mentioning it to them, he started notching suitable trees to build a permanent *logette* for warmer shelter.

August, 1542

—1—

Wolves had been heard nearby in the forest, their chilling cries borne on the northwest wind, and Marguerite's young husband had decided that he could no longer delay in teaching her to fire the arquebus. And Marguerite was as eager to learn as he was to teach her, since both knew that here in this savage land, their lives might depend on the fire-power of a second gun.

But so far as they knew no woman had ever been taught to fire the heavy weapons. Fortunately Marguerite was tall, and she seemed to have gained strength from her hard work since coming to the island. Otherwise firing such a gun would have been unthinkable. For one thing the firearms were heavy. Many men used a standard, fastened on the bottom of the gun, to prop it up and carry its weight. By good fortune one of their own arquebuses was so equipped. To start with, at least, this would be a great help.

The firing operation was complicated. Marguerite was taught to remove the rope-like slow-match from the jaws of the moveable serpentine at the stock of the gun, in which it was ordinarily held. This reduced the ever-present chance of accidental misfiring. The slow-match was to be kept lighted at both ends, in case one end did not stay lighted. And the match had to be held in the left hand, at the same time as that hand must hold up the barrel of the gun for loading.

Most men, Marguerite's husband told her, used the little finger to hold the slow-match away from the barrel. This was awkward, he agreed, but the match could not be laid on the wet earth, or it would go out, and on dry ground it might start a fire.

Next, with her right hand Marguerite was to pour a charge of powder from the powder-flask down the barrel. Fortunately they had one of the new flasks which had a little brassbound nozzle with a steel cut-off, which measured the charge. Overcharging was also a grave danger, Marguerite's husband told her gravely, worried at the unheard-of task he had set her, but certain of her need to be able to protect herself from the wild beasts or even savages who might visit the island.

So he continued his instruction, telling her that a ball from the bullet-pouch, or from her mouth if she was in a hurry, was then to be dropped down the barrel, followed by a wad of tow, cloth or paper, and all was to be rammed down with the ramrod. Then the gun was primed by filling the pan with fine powder from still another powder flask, closing the pan cover, and carefully blowing away any stray powder from around it, lest the gun misfire.

Sternly the young nobleman directed his wife to practice this series of operations again, until she could do them without fumbling, and at speed, because, he said, the next operation was more ticklish. But at this point the gun would be loaded.

Later on, when Marguerite was adept at the loading processes, her husband continued his teaching.

To fire the gun, he said, the match had to be returned to the serpentine and adjusted so that its tip would strike the pan holding the powder, and the coal on the end of the match had to be blown on, to make it glow. It was best, then, that the gun should be fired immediately, he told his young wife, or the match might burn back to the jaws of the serpentine, which would put it out. Then there was, of course, the aiming of the gun to be practiced, and then its firing.

One had to close the eyes and turn the face quickly away when the gun was fired. Many arquebusiers had been blinded by the unpredictable explosiveness of the guns, and the flames and smoke they belched out.

Thus to start with Marguerite was taught to use a very light charge, fit, her husband said, only to kill small birds. As it was, the recoil bruised her chest, as the gun flew upward each time it was fired.

Marguerite thought that firing an arquebus was the hardest thing she had ever tried to do. Secretly she thought that it was unlikely that a savage beast would stand before her, motionless, for long enough to let her do all the necessary things to shoot it down.

However the loud explosion and the burst of flame that shot forth when the gun was fired, she hoped, would have its effect in scaring away wild beasts or savages, so she practiced faithfully, and started carrying a loaded arquebus with her when she went any distance from her husband, as he had asked her to do.

After the first try Damienne had refused to fire an arquebus.

She said that, at need, she would load the heavy weapons, which should be almost as much help. So she faithfully helped Marguerite in her weaponry. At the end of one of their lessons, looking at each other with powder-blackened faces, the women suddenly laughed. "To think," said Marguerite, "That my cousin in his care for us left us four arquebuses! He did us great honor to think that we could ferret out the way of firing them for ourselves!"

*

All three of the castaways had now realized that a cabin must be built, and that the work must be hastened. The reality of their situation had been hard to accept, even knowing Roberval as they did, and all had hoped that somehow a vessel would stop to rescue them. It was well known that a ship from the expedition was to be sent back to France for further supplies, and that Jean Alfonce was to make voyages of exploration to map the shorelines. It did not seem possible that no-one would come.

So the daily watch was kept from the summit of the island,

but not even a fishing-boat had been sighted. And now the nights were growing cooler.

Marguerite felt relief when her husband finally spoke of the matter. It was clear to her from his awkward and studied manner that he had planned his speech, and that he weighed his words with care. First he pointed out that there was no harm to be done in his starting a larger shelter, where they could be more comfortable, and where they could store their food and belongings in greater safety. Even in summer the winds were chill when they blew inshore, and now the autumn gales would soon begin, he thought, and their canvas roof might be hard to keep in place.

Food was so easily had, here on their island, he continued, with the abundance of fish and game, that his time was largely free, and so, he said with apparent casualness, he thought he would start a cabin.

What a kind man he is, Marguerite thought. He does not want to alarm us, not realizing that although we are but women, we also have come to realize what it will mean to spend the winter on this island. Love for him warmed her as she thought, half-smilingly, let him believe that we have not given thought for the morrow.

So she laid her arm across his shoulder, as he sat hunched toward the fire. "Our time lies heavy on us, too, my husband," she said. "Now that the garden is growing, but not ready to harvest, we, too, have much time to spare. We will help. It will be a diversion."

Her Lord looked surprised but relieved, she noticed. Building a cabin, all alone, would have been an impossible task, but it was not in his nature to ask women to share such heavy work.

She and Damienne would have to be as tactful as he, thought his wife.

Marguerite noticed, also, that her new husband had evidently searched out a site, chosen some trees, and made some plans. He must have been thinking about the matter for some time, she realized, for the next day he said, "I will not be able to build the cabin in the usual French manner, by sinking logs upright into the ground, in the style called *pieux en terre.* The soil here is not firm enough to hold logs upright."

And he added that the granite was too close to the surface, also, for him to dig deep holes. The cabin would have to be built with the logs lying flat on top of each other. He had noticed such *logettes,* he said, at St. John.

Since he had a broad-axe and could hew the logs flat on two sides, he planned, he would only use the saw to square them at the ends. Deep notches would have to be sawed at the corners, as well, to make the mortise and tenon joinings that would hold the logs together. The young builder had also decided not to erect a square-sided *logette* with a peaked roof, he said, but rather an enlarged dwelling on the pattern of their branch-shelter, where the roof on the windward side would slant all the way to the ground. This would be a better protection from the wind and would not be so likely to blow down.

"Also, he said, "It will be possible to make such a *logette* without quite as much heavy lifting of the logs for the roof, since they can thus be rolled up the slanting sides of the walls."

His wife was secretly astonished to realize how thoroughly he had planned his work while saying nothing to her of what was in his mind. But now that his reserve was broken he disclosed his plans with some assurance.

The site which he had chosen, he said, was not far from their shelter, a bit farther up the valley toward the northwest, on a little knoll where the granite was close to the surface, to afford a solid and dry foundation.

And the *logette* was to be small, he added, for purposes of warmth, not more than seven paces in width and five in depth, for the part where there would be head-room. The back part, close to the ground, would again be used for storage.

The same morning he led his wife to the spot he had chosen, and put stakes in the ground for the corners. He asked Marguerite to help him to square them up by adjusting a string diagonally from corner to corner, and then he went to cut the first trees immediately, in evident haste to get started.

When he had several trees cut down Marguerite called him for the mid-morning meal.

And after they had finished eating she and Damienne followed him, wordlessly, back to the woodland. Damienne had brought the hatchet and Marguerite carried his square two-man saw. Her husband turned when he saw her and laughed nervously. "What is this that you do?" he asked. "You cannot help to saw. It is work for men!"

His wife made no immediate reply but she approached him where he stood behind one of his felled logs and set the big square saw on top of the log, holding the top and bottom handles with both hands. She then pushed the saw toward him so hard that he had to jump backward. "Look to yourself, fellow," she said, "Lest I outdo you in sawing!" In a more sober tone she added, "Well do you know, my husband, that this saw will work faster than the small one."

Her young Lord could not deny the truth of this remark, and he knew but too well that haste was now important. Reluctantly, he let her try to handle one side of the saw as both of them pulled it back in turn, with a constant rhythm. The sawing thus went very well, to his surprise, as though a young boy were to lend a hand; the end of the saw was held down and the coarser blade sawed more rapidly than his finer handsaw. And he had to admit to himself that he needed the help. The trees on this island were of a harder wood than any pine he knew. Perhaps, he thought, they had to be hard in order to live through the winters here.

Damienne, also, now proved to be more helpful than the young couple had dared to hope. She took the discarded handsaw and trimmed the trees which had been cut down, cutting up the branches to be dried for firewood, also, with the hatchet. Her work kept the site clear and saved a great deal of time.

The first four logs were soon laid into place around the staked site, from which the women had dug off all the peaty soil, down to the granite below. And when the actual place where they would live was enclosed, as the corners of the logs were notched and set together, all three exiles suddenly felt a strange sense of home. It was oddly reassuring, they found, to see the actual space of the room which would soon give them warmth and shelter.

So they returned to work with renewed energy. In the next row of logs which they laid in place they left spaces for the door and the chimney, and the logs were broadaxed to lie securely on top of each other. Moss caulking would be forced between them later on.

When evening came all three workers were pleased with their first day's accomplishment, although their hands were again blistered and their muscles sore. And somehow the draughty little canvas shelter seemed more cozy, now that they would soon have a warm, dry *logette*.

*

Now it was an even greater relief to find that they could eat very well without spending much time seeking food, since the work on the cabin filled their days from morn to nightfall. But lobsters and other sea creatures were to be found in the tide-pools, and fish crowded the sea. Ducks and geese of kinds they had never before seen, were plentiful, as well as other sea-birds that walked nearly upright when they came on land.

One day Damienne even cooked a couple of young sea-gulls, which were found to taste rather like chicken. Partridges were also to be had in large numbers, as well as rabbits, and Marguerite had received a husbandly warning to shoot only what was needful for food, since powder must not be wasted.

Seals were also seen in the harbor, but none were killed, since there was goose-fat in plentiful supply for the pan-lamps which would be used in the *logette.*

Marguerite had now taken on the duty of going to the lookout summit, to free her young husband's time for the work on the cabin, and from there she once thought she saw a large herd of grey deer in the marshes of the mainland just north of the island. When she told her husband and Damienne of this they all hoped that the herd might come to the island, since they had heard that the beasts often swam across fairly large bodies of water.

Venison, they thought, would make a fine addition to the winter's meat supply.

—2—

Sometimes during the long, light evenings, when they were weary from their heavy, unaccustomed tasks, the young couple would sit before their fire, under the canopy of boughs and canvas, and play their flute and *citre*. Marguerite's flute was inlaid with ivory and gold, but her husband's *citre* was even more ornate. Its flat, spoon-shaped form was inlaid, front and back, with lighter wood, as well as with ivory, and the pegbox ended in an elaborately carved head with a human face on it.

The young exile treasured his *citre*, tuning its wire strings each time he took it from its case for an evening of music. Its elegance looked strangely out of place in their rustic surroundings, Marguerite thought, like a Countess pretending to be a goose-girl at a Court masquerade.

The young pair played duets with fingers stiffening from less delicate occupations, and sometimes Damienne and her Lord sang to accompany the instruments.

None of them mentioned the thinness of the sound, lost in the vastness around them, nor put into words the lack of the other musicians, now undoubtedly playing their lutes, citterns and viols within the comforts of the colony far upriver.

*

Each of the exiles bore a silent burden of guilt.

Damienne floundered in regret because it had been her duty to be always at the side of her mistress, preventing even the appearance of indiscretions which would undermine the marriageable integrity of a young noblewomen. The old nurse well knew the practicalities of the situation. Just as a man's value lay in the men-at-arms he could muster, and the lands from which he could collect and remit taxes, a woman's value lay in the honor of her person, and her ability to bring forth heirs of unquestionable blood-line for her Lord after her marriage. As Marguerite's nurse, she, Damienne, had failed in this charge.

After what had befallen, Damienne reflected, she would almost rather die in this unhallowed place than to return to France, where the story of her disgrace would have preceded her to the uttermost reaches of the nobility.

And, Damienne also told herself, she should have known the danger of offending Jean-François de la Roque in any way, since a *duègne* survived by avoiding offense to the noble she served, and by complying with his wishes, no matter how outrageous or harsh. She could have served Marguerite best by insuring her compliance with her kinsman's wishes, which permitted her no over-friendly words with men. She, Damienne, had long observed Roberval's strange possessiveness toward Marguerite, and had thought it odd in view of his rather cursory interest in other women.

She and Marguerite had always hoped he would marry.

With Norman shrewdness, Damienne suspected that his failure to wed, and his reluctance to find a husband for Marguerite—or even to let her appear at Court for any length of time—was based on his own financial embarrassment. A betrothed's family would first send its accountants and lawyers to make investigations, and Damienne suspected that Roberval could not afford to have this occur.

As Marguerite approached her majority, Damienne had often wondered what would happen. Now she knew. The problem had been rather neatly solved, and she, Damienne, had let herself be made a pawn in the solution.

*

Marguerite's young Lord felt the guilt of a goodly and responsible man who has failed to protect the welfare of a loved woman.

Bitterly he told himself that he should have understood Jean-François de la Roque better than the women did. Indeed, his own misgivings about the great Sieur de Roberval had caused him to embark on this very voyage—a fact which he had not sought to conceal.

He had known too much about Jean-François to trust him, far away from France, the holder of absolute power in a remote land, accountable to no-one. But Roberval had the reputation, acquired in his military service under la Marck, of being an able fighter, the young nobleman admitted to himself, and Roberval was also an avid huntsman, which ingratiated him with François Premier. But, other than that, few could understand why the King had asked him to head this expedition. He was a profligate, the younger man knew, managing his affairs in such a way that he had squandered most of the inheritance he had received from both his father and his mother.

It was well known that the money had been spent on Court favorites, fine clothing, and horseflesh, as well as maintaining a large retinue. Being ever at the elbow of the King, appropriately garbed and jeweled, and giving lavish gifts—this was the kind of thing a prudent man engaged in only intermittently, the young exile told himself. His own father had early impressed him with the thought that one followed the Court to the least degree made necessary by one's station; wise advice, his son thought sadly, as a pang of remembrance and sickness for his home flooded through his mind.

But his thoughts returned to his enemy, Roberval, who had been trapped in the web against which his own father had warned him. As heavy Court expenses mounted up, holdings melted away, and then one had to stay at Court, seeking preferment, while incurring still more expense, and few escaped, once they were thus involved. Roberval had thus stayed at Court, not daring to absent himself lest another supplant him, but also not daring to let it be known that his resources were wearing thin.

The King may not have known, the young man thought, but Roberval's creditors did. The Canadian venture had been a last desperate roll of the dice, a sort of all-or-nothing attempt to recoup his desperate financial state, that was clear.

Such a man is as dangerous as a trapped wolf, thought the man he had marooned.

Had Roberval allowed me to marry Marguerite before he left for New France, her young husband thought, it would have been the act of an honest and kindly man. I loved her well, as he knew, and he should have known that I would have taken her without question as to her holdings. My family might have thought it proper to look into the state of her inheritance, but if they had found that he had compromised her Seigneuralties, as well as his own, they would have been reasonable. They are decent people, their son thought proudly, as he is not.

It is only I, he reflected bitterly, who have acted the complete fool. My rash behavior sprung the trap on Marguerite, when dimly I knew that we should be wary, that it was a time for self-restraint and caution. But for my foolhardy pursuit of her, my Marguerite, and poor silly Damienne, would be safe upriver at *Sainct Croix.*

*

His Marguerite had her own burdened thoughts. Since childhood she had depended on Damienne only for companionship and love, not in matters of judgment. The marooning is not Damienne's fault, thought Marguerite, since the indiscretions were my own, and I knew the risks very well.

As an orphan from her early years, reflected the young exile, she had had to look to her own affairs as best she might, and had developed a certain ability to do so. In dealing with Roberval she had always had to be wary, and had reduced surface compliance and unobtrusiveness to an art. Far better than most girls of her station, she knew how to stay out of the way of trouble. They could afford to be giddy, Marguerite thought, in their interests in clothes and Courtiers, doing whatever foolish thing came into their heads, because, at the critical moment someone would always rush forward to rescue them from their own indiscretions.

Marguerite, herself, had always known that if she made one mis-step she would enjoy no such protection, and that moreover she had not one living parent or grandparent to be concerned with her security.

Jean-François had everything to gain by having me disappear, she thought. Had we been Catholic, he could have sent me off to a convent.

Her thoughts returned to her first meeting with her cousin, and she recalled the day when she had first looked into his hard, dark eyes, concealing her fear as best she might, in the knowledge that she was now dependent on his good will. Scoundrel that he was, she thought, he had few secrets from me; I knew what he was. I should have had the patience to guard my actions and to play for time, she reflected, and perhaps at my majority I could somehow have gotten away from him, or if I could have married my Lord in France, perhaps we could have persuaded his family to help us. Anguished regret flooded into her mind like a chill tide.

I best knew the danger we both ran, my love and I, thought Marguerite, but like any women in love, discretion forsook me. And in my downfall I brought this exile upon the man I love and my kind old nurse, the two beings who love me.

*

None of the three put their thoughts into words, but translated their feelings of regret into a determination to endure their exile with grace, endeavoring to make the others comfortable, and even happy, so long as this should be possible.

So that after their evening meals the newly-wedded pair played their flute and *citre,* and Damienne sang with them in her rough Norman cadences. Sometimes they even danced.

—3—

After a few courses of logs were laid for the walls, holes had to be bored down through them on both sides of the door and chimney. The freshly-cut pine resisted their awkward spoon-drill, and they found they had to use the smaller, three-pronged drill-bit, and smaller pegs. After that, the work went faster.

But strangely their biggest problem was finding clay for the chimney-mortar and the caulking. "Of all things to be scarce," grumbled Damienne. "This is, indeed a godless land, where the very earth itself lacks good claybanks." She and Marguerite spent a weary day searching the whole island, and they finally found a small bank of clay, covered by sand, in a sheltered cove at the extreme northern part of the island. They mapped out a path by which they could carry heavy loads of it without too much clambering over steep rocks, and Damienne made them a couple of carrying poles by padding short, stiff boughs to be laid across their shoulders. They tied their clay in cloths, to save weight, balancing the loads equally on both sides.

As they trudged back and forth Marguerite said light-heartedly, "My talent as a pack-donkey might please my cousin, Roberval, could he but see it." Damienne sorrowed to see her Lady do such peasants' work, and admitted that she had never thought she would wish for one of the carved carrying-yokes from her family's farm, once she left there to serve a noble house.

But now the two women started to lay the hearth, as the log walls gradually rose in height. They got occasional male help only with the heaviest of the stones. The work was slow, because each layer of clay between the stones had to dry a bit before the next course could be laid on; therefore the chimney rose no faster than the walls.

Grudging the time it would take, the three builders nevertheless decided that a floor would have to be laid in the *logette*. Rain came several times each week, and dampness flowed over the granite within their walls. So, grudging the time, they shaped logs and propped them into place for a floor.

Since the nights were now growing still more chill, all three castaways grew feverishly eager to finish the *logette*. Increasing the pace of their work, they ate hasty meals and little time was spent in talk, with most of the conversation concerned with their work. But it was a strangely satisfying time, as the walls of the cabin became higher each day. Now they were laying logs on only three sides, to allow for the slant of the roof.

—4—

At night husband and wife lay together in such delight as they could well believe to be sin, their tired bodies grateful for the touch and very smell of each other.

They were not oblivious of the privilege they enjoyed in finding their rapture within the very marriage-bed, for marriages among the nobility in France were made more with a view toward joining Seigneuralties than to pleasing the parties involved, and many brides and grooms could not mask the active dislike they held for each other. But children were born, and families went on.

Marguerite hoped to have a child; her husband hoped she would not do so while they were still on the island. The dangers of childbirth were well known to him, since he knew that mothers died during the ordeal, oftentimes, and that only half their children lived past infancy, this in spite of the feverish efforts, in noble houses, of midwives and wet-nurses.

The birth of a child on this island would be a great danger, and the young husband hoped it could be avoided. He even had an embarrassed private discussion with Damienne, with the thought that she might know of herbs or simples which would be useful in protecting her Lady from childbirth here in this savage place.

But Damienne told him, deeply though she regretted it, the potions she had been taught to prepare were meant for the opposite purpose. Many children had to be born so that a few might survive to adulthood, and bearing children was a duty which noblewomen were not permitted to evade.

Even Queen Claude, she said, had borne seven children in nine years, and now lay in her grave, poor lady.

*

Rain and fog were frequent on the island. For the first month the exiles had spent the rainy days under their shelter, propping out the roof-canvas if there was not too much wind, and diverting themselves with games of cards or *tric-trac* or talk. But nowadays they were impatient with the weather. If the rain was light, they went about whatever outdoor tasks they could; if it was heavier they did what work they could do under the shelter.

Damienne found that she could boil kettles of berry preserves under the edge of the canvas; Marguerite started whittling out a carrying-yoke, and her husband worked on the endless shaping of dowels and trunnels and of legs for benches and tables.

But he tried to work outdoors in the woodland on the days of fog, which were frequent, and sometimes so thick that he could not accomplish very much. Once he found himself lost, absurdly, he thought, on this tiny island scarcely eight hundred *arpents* in size. All the trees looked alike, and he could not tell one direction from the other. He felt too much the fool to tell the women about it, and soon he learned to find his way whether the days were foggy or clear.

*

They were all desperately aware that now their tools and implements had to be handled with gingerliness and care, for here on the island there was no friendly iron-worker, traveling from château to château with his forge, anvil and sledges, to stay a week here, a week there, in the places which did not have a *ferronier* of their own. The exiles wistfully remembered the bustle in the courtyards and barns as the broken sickles and knives were taken down from the rafters where they had been laid, and brought out for repair. Here on their island, anything they broke could never be repaired. They did not know how to mend tools, since metal-working was a skilled craft, passed down only from master to apprentice in the *artisinat* of the iron-workers.

Especially before the *logette* was finished, a broken tool would be a disaster, they all knew, and they also understood, they told each other, why the savages were said to be willing to trade a canoe-full of precious furs for an axe-blade. They, the exiles, would have been glad to do the same.

The arquebuses thus also received special care, and they were cleaned, when possible, after each firing, and were laid away, wrapped and tied up tightly in their protective bags of greased leather, in the top of the tool-chest, under the canvas shelter.

*

On one day of heavy rain, as he whittled on the leg for a stool, their young Lord remarked to Marguerite and Damienne that here on their island they were now in effect a separate colony, and that they thus had all best try to remember everything they had heard about matters in the New World. "Before we forget, since we have only each other's knowledge to share," he said reflectively, "We had best make an effort to recall all that we learned of New France before our marooning."

After a moment of thought Marguerite was the first to speak. She said that she had heard her kinsman and Jacques Cartier arguing, on the evening before Cartier stole away to return to France. Both men had been angry, she remembered, and their voices had been raised. She could not avoid hearing them over the sounds of the ship, since her sleeping-place was next to Jean-François' cabin.

"Jacques' remarks had reason, it seemed to me," she said. "He claimed that our part of the expedition had come too late in the year to count on raising crops, and that we would thus be very short of food. He said that even to the south, where Roberval planned to go, the summers are very short, and that crops have to be planted during early June or the frosts catch them in autumn before they ripen."

Marguerite paused. Her listeners did not look very happy, so that as she continued she tried to find more hopeful recollections. "Jacques Cartier said that the soil was very fertile," she added, "And many good plants grow wild in Canada, plums, melons, peas and grapes, for example." None of these things, of course, had been found this far to the north, so she searched her memory for more encouraging information. "There is a sort of wild wheat, with very large heads, barbed like rye," she continued. "The savages call it *kapaige*. It grows wild, and has a grain like oats." Now her listeners were encouraged, she noticed, so she concluded triumphantly, "The savages make a sort of bread of it, and Jacques said, I believe, that it is found along the shores far to the north, here, as well.''

Damienne's interest was aroused. "There is a whole meadow of such a plant growing to the east of us," she said. "It stands in a low, boggy, place, and thus I did not go to look at it, but I remember thinking that it might serve for thatch. I wonder if that is the plant that bears good grain."

They were all heartily wearied of the *pain bisquit,* the hard-tack from the voyage, and their remaining cereal supply was nearly gone. Damienne hoped with all her heart that this grain would be the *kapaige* of which Marguerite had heard.

After a moment's deliberation, Marguerite's husband spoke a few words of warning for both women. "You must not believe, from Jacques Cartier's tales of their husbandry," he said, "And the fact that they eat wild wheat, that the savages in this New World are as you and I. They may bake bread, but they are a strange and uncivilized people."

Nodding his head incredulously at the memory, he added, "Some of the things they do are beyond understanding."

At this the women pressed him to tell them more of the strange ways of the Canadian indigenes, and their savage customs.

"For one thing" he responded, "Jacques Cartier's seamen had some strange tales to tell of a plant called *petun,* or *houan-houan,* which the savages set on fire in pipes, which they hold in their mouths. From these they inhale the smoke into their bodies, a barbaric and peculiar custom, in truth."

But what was more to the point, he continued, the seamen had told him that the tribes waged war on each other constantly, sometimes paddling their *canoes* all the way up past this island to Blanc Sablon to fight the indigenes there, whom they hate. "The northern savages use skin-covered, sharply-pointed craft, with double paddles, as you saw," he gestured down-river, toward Blanc Sablon, "And those indigenes are more peaceful, but the southern savages are very warlike." He paused to let this point be understood. "And they are the ones who come past here when they go northward to make war."

The women showed little concern, their Lord believed, after

assessing their composed expressions. It was as though they were children listening to a tale of wonderment, he thought impatiently; they do not understand that I tell this because of their need to be wary of the passing of the savages from the south. Half-reluctantly, he decided that he must tell of matters he had at first not thought it wise to disclose. "In front of their lodges, these warlike tribes hang the hair of their enemies," he added incredulously, "Stretched on hoops, after it has been cut from their heads, skin and all."

The women now shuddered, but their Lord continued the tale he had begun, determined to make them understand how dangerous were these savage indigenes of Canada, "They are so bloodthirsty that even the seashells they use for money are grown in the dead bodies of their enemies!"

Marguerite cried out, "Ah, I do not believe it!"

"It is true. They cut slices in the thick parts of their enemies' corpses, and then they place these dead bodies under water where they can be found again. After a while these certain white shells grow in the wounds, and the savages seek them out and use them for money." His hearers looked blankly unbelieving.

Although he would have still preferred to spare them such knowledge, not fit for their ears, the young man thought, he wanted to be sure that his women-folk would conceal themselves quickly if savages came past the island. If they landed, of course, he told himself, it would be a lost cause. Perhaps the arquebuses might drive them off for a time, but he had heard that the savages could fire a dozen arrows before an arquebus could be fired once, and this tale he did not for a moment doubt.

A pang of anger and resentment at his predicament slashed through his mind, and he thought of Roberval with fury, sitting in his colony upriver in comfort, with a company of fighting-men to defend him.

But as his composure returned, he thought, far better not to attract the attention of the savages if they pass here on their war-trail to the north, and so he persisted in his efforts to awe his women-folk. "What I have told you is true," he stated firmly. "The shells are called *esurgey* or *esurgney*. I, myself, would prefer to go to my grave with my hair on my head, and my back-side not sliced like a loaf of bread!"

At this juncture, looking rather ill, the women abruptly excused themselves and disappeared in the direction of the place of necessity.

Stretching his cramped legs toward the fire, their young Lord watched them depart. He hoped that he had not been unnecessarily frightening. But it was important that they should always be on guard for the passing of the war-parties.

*

Later the conversation was continued in a more pleasant vein. While Marguerite had heard that the natives had become hostile to Cartier, he had also told of some of the ways in which the indigenes prepared food for winter-storage. "One of their ways," she said, "Damienne and I could also follow. Fish or thinly-sliced meat is simply hung over the lodge-fires, or outdoors in the sun, to dry out."

Such dried flesh, Marguerite added, was said to keep for a long time, and of course she and Damienne would also use salt with it, which the savages were said to shun. She recalled that Jacques Cartier had remarked that herds of a certain grey, humpbacked deer migrated across these northern lands, and that their flesh could also be dried in this way.

"Perhaps," she concluded, "it was such a flock of deer that I saw from the northern summit, and they may come again this way."

Damienne now had a few words to offer. "One of the seamen on the ship was from Normandy," she said, slowly stirring her *ragout*, "And we used to talk together. He knew a man from Captain Cartier's ship, a Breton, who had wintered with him on his other trip to these lands." Her lips tightened at the memory. "They had a terrible time of it, he told me, and many died. A deadly disease took them, such as sailors sometimes get on long voyages."

Her listeners appeared discomposed at this, so she added reassuringly, "The sickness is not a new thing, of this country alone."

Earthsickness was the name of the illness, the old nurse continued, and it loosened teeth and swelled joints as that bad winter ran its course. Finally the natives had told Cartier of a remedy, she had been told, a potion made from the bark and leaves of a certain evergreen tree. It cured the men as if by a miracle, almost overnight.

"It is possible," said Damienne, "That such a tree grows here, and I will see whether I can make such a potion, since as a girl I was taught to brew up such healing sirups."

*

After the others went to sleep, Marguerite lay awake and remembered the arrival of Jacques Cartier at the harbor of St. John, and of her kinsman's shock at seeing Cartier's ships sail out of the narrow entrance into that fine, enclosed harbor, when he, Roberval, had thought them far upriver awaiting his own arrival at St. Croix.

Hardly had they landed when Jean-François had confronted Cartier. He should never have left his post, Roberval had thundered in his most stentorian tones, carrying clearly to the onlookers, although they stood at a discreet distance. It was Cartier's place to stay at *Sainct Croix* planting crops and erecting buildings for the additional colonists, the Viceroy had roared indignantly.

But it was also possible, Marguerite now reflected, that Roberval's anger had been so great not only because of Cartier's disobedience, but because her cousin was fearful of going on into the strange land without the experienced Cartier in the party; else why had Jean-Francois delayed, then, for three more weeks at St. John, after Cartier departed in the night-time for France?

Cartier was a brave man, mused Marguerite, and one who meticulously adhered to the commands given him by his superiors. He did his duty clemently but well. It was therefore an extraordinary thing that he had so disobeyed one who had been given command over him, not only in leaving St. Croix, but in stealing away to return to France. Either Jacques Cartier had no great opinion of her cousin Roberval, or he had been more concerned than he confessed at the conditions upriver, and the hostile behavior of the savages there.

If Cartier could not win their good opinion, Marguerite thought, it is not like that my cousin will do so. But little does he deserve our concern, she told herself rancorously.

Her mind returned to the quarrel. If Jacques Cartier had then decided to return upriver with us, as he was commanded to do, she reflected sadly, shivering in the damp night air which flowed under the canvas roof, perhaps we would not have been set ashore here. Not that Cartier would have dared to interfere. But she remembered how his departure, and his absence afterward, had angered Roberval, and when Roberval was angry or fearful he was wont to lash out at whomever he dared.

Servants were punished when Jean-François was in a pique at the King. Perhaps, Marguerite thought, in the absence of Cartier, her cousin Roberval had struck out at the first defenseless wretches who happened to annoy him, herself and Damienne.

On her own side of the partition Damienne, also, was wakeful. The talk of the savages, and of Jacques Cartier, had gravely disturbed her already-unsettled mind. She, also, wished that her Captain Cartier had rejoined the expedition at St. John. He was a man from her own home province, a kindly man, well-liked by his sailors. She had even heard that he asked their opinions, occasionally, when there were matters of choice to be decided upon, an unheard-of thing for a commander to do. And in his own home village it was known that he had been asked to be a Godfather or a witness in many Christenings, in families not even his own, a great honor, not one to be lightly given.

Shivering in her turn under her clammy bed-clothing, Damienne remembered that Roberval, although he was higher-born than Cartier, and was the Seigneur of many holdings, had been accorded no such honors by his villagers.

—6—

The walls of the *logette* had finally risen high enough so that it now was time to start the roof, and for this purpose taller trees had to be cut, to reach across the long span. The sound of the axe was thus heard from farther up the valley.

On one such day, as Marguerite worked at the branch-shelter, she saw her husband come running down the woodland path in apparent excitement. She rushed anxiously to meet him.

"I have found a cave!" he cried.

Having feared some grave disaster, his young wife received this news rather coolly. "Of what use to us is a cave?" she asked, turning back to her work. "We are building a *logette*."

Picking up the long-handled spoon, she bent over her preserving-kettle, holding her skirt well back from the flames. The strange little red berries had now turned yellow, and Damienne had found that they made very good *confitures*. The old nurse thought that they must be the berries which were called *chicote,* of which she said that she had heard, and both women had been gathering them to preserve or to dry.

So Marguerite was too busy for talk of caves.

But her husband refused to have his spirits dampened. "A cave is a goodly thing," he insisted, "At least for meat-smoking on days of rain." And he added, "Living as we do, far from all settlements, a place of retreat is an important thing. I do not want to frighten you, but *logettes* are said to burn down, many times, in the depth of winter in this northern country. In such an event we do not have any houses nearby to whom we could go, where we would have shelter."

But his wife still did not seem inclined to abandon her cooking-pot.

Finally he insisted in an even more urgent tone that if savages should come a place to hide themselves would be needed, and that thus it might be wise to keep a few supplies hidden in a place of retreat.

At last he had Marguerite's attention. She had been secretly wondering what they could do to save themselves if the savages came. So she called Damienne to watch her preserving kettle and joined her husband for the walk up the woodland path. He led the way proudly, up the log-hauling route and over the rough bridges he had built, past the stumps of trees he had cut, and under the sweeping branches of those still standing.

The cave was a goodly distance up the valley, probably about a half-league westward from the cove, Marguerite found, and it was high on the side of the northern cliff, facing to the southward. She needed her husband's help to climb up the sheer rock wall in her encumbering skirts, and he pulled and pushed at her good-naturedly as she struggled upward.

But Marguerite was openly disappointed when at last she reached the cave-mouth.

It was not what she expected, she said. In the south of France there were many goodly caves, and they had furnished good shelter since olden times, since they went back deeply into the earth, and remained warm in winter. This cave was not at all like the caves of France which she remembered, Marguerite saw to her disappointment. It was only a jumble of fallen boulders under a rock overhang, and the entrance was so low that she could not sit up straight in it without bending her head. When her husband urged her to slide down inside the cave, beside him, she found that the wet granite shelf slanted down fairly sharply, inside, and that the roof domed up somewhat, so that in the very center they could just barely stand upright.

In the dim light Marguerite saw that the wall and floor tapered together at the edges around the back, and that a rough pillar supported the roof on the side toward the valley. Another opening extended out through the rough rocks toward the east, and the enclosed area was cramped and confining, with little headroom and less level floor-space.

Marguerite was disappointed, and she spoke shortly. "Fit only to smoke fish, if that," she said as she clambered up the slippery, wet granite to the ledge outside. Shaking out her dampened skirts, she added, "I wonder at you, *mon mari,* that you took my time to bring me here!"

Her young husband climbed out to stand on the cave-ledge

beside her, arms akimbo, and laughed at her annoyance. "You sound like a bustling wife of fifty years!" he replied, his eyelids crinkling with mirth at her flushed face and disordered mien. "Is not a new sight worth something on this island, that you cannot get your head out of your berry-kettle?"

As he helped his wife down the cliff-wall and down the valley he privately determined that when he had the time he would do a few things to make the cave more habitable. He had heard disquieting tales of this North country from men who had hunted and fished here, having met them while the expedition was delayed in St. John. Wintering here would be a grim affair, he knew, harder than the women could even dream of. And if savages came, or if the *logette* burned down, or if they could not heat it—the intolerable possibilities swarmed in upon him like hornets.

He grasped the elbow of his wife and hastened her back to her *confitures,* and for the rest of the day he worked almost feverishly, his occasional oaths increasing in intensity from his usual *je remie de bottes* to *je remie Dieu,* real blasphemy.

But Marguerite did not hear him, and Damienne said a hasty prayer for his soul.

*

Marguerite felt rather certain that both her husband and Damienne were hoping that she would not have a child while they were in exile here on their island. Both of them had at one time or another, by hint or half-veiled reference, let her understand this.

So she kept her secret, thinking, time enough for them to know of this if I am able to carry the child. She remembered well that at home in France, when it was known that noblewomen were *enciente* with an heir, they were hardly permitted to lift a weighty book, while here on the island, she, Marguerite, was hauling heavy logs and clay, and a large arquebus. It would be a miracle, she thought, if she did not lose her child before its birth-time.

But the others would fret themselves, Marguerite knew, and

would not wish her to work as she still must do, if they knew of the child she now carried. Soon Damienne's wise old eyes would notice, if her husband did not.

Finally she decided that if Damienne questioned her, she would say that she had washed her monthly cloths in secret. And in order to avoid the sin of falsehood, Marguerite solemnly took the squares of linen from their neat folds in the corner of her sea-chest, and washed them in the peaty water from the pond, leaving them somewhat less clean than they had been before.

September, 1542

—1—

The three castaways on the Isle of St. Martha could not help but think enviously, sometimes, of the settlement which must be growing up at *Charlesbourg Royale* or *Sainct Croix.* Surely, so much farther to the south, with fields of fertile soil, the living must be easier. They spoke of the tools and equipment being used, the carts to haul home the grain and hay to stables already built, where cattle and swine must now be cozily munching and reproducing their kind. Butter would be made from the milk, and cheeses.

Enviously, also, they thought of the hundreds of hands to share in work which it was so hard for three unskilled people to do. Upriver were skilled carpenters and joiners, masons and ironworkers, with the materials of their trades, or the knowledge of how to get them. Even a day's help from such men would have meant much to the little outcast colony on the island.

But most of all they thought of the grain-mill which was to have been set up, and the ovens, to bake good, white, crusty French bread. The exiles were now so hungry for bread that they dreamed of it. Sometimes as they sat down to a meal of game stew and hardtack, they could think of little else. In their dreams the odor of baked bread wafted across their consciousness with the very smell of home.

But all three worked as best they could in a determination that steadily increased.

And their garden was doing rather well, a comforting thing, since they would thus have some of the foods they knew. The garlic had rooted and multiplied, rearing its tall, ungainly, onion-like stalks with their clusters of pods of flowerets, at the side of the gardenplot, and Damienne planned to braid strands of it before the deep frosts came, to hang from the rafters. Not a shred of it, she vowed to herself, would be wasted. All winter long it would take away some of the wild taste of the flesh of savage beasts, of which they were so greatly wearied.

And garlic was said to ward off evil, the old nurse told herself apprehensively, dreading the dark winter to come.

*

Now the season for *morue* seemed to have reached its height. The big grey fish, which had given their old name of *baccalaos* to the waters around their island were the staple catch of fishermen who came here from Brittany and Portugal to fill their boats, and sometimes to dry their catch along the shores.

It would now be wise, the exiles decided, to spend a day scooping up enough of the plentiful fish to last for the winter, before the sea-water got too cold for endurance. Since their Lord needed all his time to work on the *logette,* Damienne and Marguerite kilted up their skirts and waded into the shallow water of the cove, carrying baskets which Damienne had woven from shrub willow.

It was quick work to scoop up baskets-full from the teeming waters, but gutting the fish and cutting off their heads was a grisly job for Marguerite, and vomit rose in her throat as she worked. But she did her part, however, smearing her arms to the elbows as she worked, at first awkwardly, then with more skill.

They were going to be short of salt, the women suddenly

realized, as they used the last of their supply to scatter on the flattened, cleaned fish. So in the midst of other tasks, Damienne set up a kettle to boil down sea-water into brine. This would serve to salt down some of the fish, and later she would boil down more, for the salt itself. It would be a long and tedious task, both women knew, since hundreds of gallons would have to be boiled away to get a few pounds of salt.

The fish-curing, however, was more quickly done. After a day in the salt the fish could be laid in the sun to dry. One day's good sun, they had found, was enough to make them fairly safe, and then the half-dried pieces could be taken in to shelter for the night and laid out again on another sunny day, or smoked.

Damienne tended the fish, turning them over when needs be, and driving away the thievish gulls.

Catching and cleaning enough fish for the whole winter's supply had taken less than a day, the women were surprised to realize, and Marguerite promptly returned to work with her husband on the *logette.*

*

While summer storms had been rare and short, the gales of autumn now sent a forewarning, in the form of the strongest wind the exiles had ever felt. Fortunately it came from the northwest, and it had swept over their canvas shelter without damage after they had hastily piled more stones on the bottom edges of the canvas and anchored the top.

But after this warning it was reluctantly decided that the roof of the *logette* would have to be made of solid logs, laid butt to tip, with a covering of bark held down by stones to withstand the heavy winds. This would take more time than they had planned for, the exiles realized with apprehension, and a few vagrant flakes of snow had already fallen as the days grew shorter.

So Marguerite and her husband now worked rapidly, with increasing skill and endurance, to place logs on the roof. Near the top of the *logette,* at the front, they decided to saw out a sort of loop-hole for defense purposes, tapering two logs to a broad chink through which one could look, or even fire an arquebus. In case of attack by wild beasts or savages, they could thus protect the door. But they had made no window, having no way to glaze it, and even the roof would be solid, so that nothing could tear its way in. The cabin would be secure against anything except fire.

*

At court masques, Marguerite knew, the gentlemen and ladies often dressed as woodsmen, shepherdesses and milkmaids, posing gracefully in pastoral scenes. It was the mode. But that was mere play, she suddenly thought one evening, and the reality was not so picturesque, as she gazed at her husband and noticed that he was even more disheveled than she. His hair and beard, so neat when he had forced his way to follow her ashore, now looked wild.

With wifely pride she thought, when he is barbered he is a truly handsome man. So she searched out her sewing-scissors and beckoned him to sit down before her on one of the little stools he had carved during the rainy weather.

He was accustomed to the services of a barber, even on shipboard, Marguerite knew, and had been meticulous in his appearance. Having one's wife trim one's hair was for peasants. She feared this necessity would depress him more than any of his other hardships.

So she ventured to joke about it. "If you wish to follow the fashions of the Court," she said severely, "You must learn not to overdo things. It is *gauche* for you to look like a *real* woodsman!" Snapping her scissors Marguerite trimmed a few of the dark locks over her husband's ears.

"And I will no doubt look worse when you have done with me," he replied ungratefully. "You are carrying things a bit far, yourself, to pass as one of François' goose-girls!"

But Marguerite went serenely along with her task, first hesitatingly, then with greater assurance. He did not look too bad, she thought as she finished, and she handed him her little mirror so that he could reassure himself that he had not been made into a figure of fun.

After he had peered skeptically into it, he arose to his feet and made a mocking flourish toward his wife. In mincing tones he recited:

Aussy bien sont amourettes
Soubz bureau que soubz brunettes!

But his young wife looked beyond his teasing, into his face which now appeared, again, as it had when he left the ship, and she thought, Ah, yes, we do love each other as well, beneath these draggled garments, as we did when we were in our silks and satins.

As she threw her arms about him, grateful again for his unfailing good humor and sturdiness of soul, she noticed that her hands now looked like those of a working-man. Privately she resolved that when they moved into the *logette,* she would rub oil into her hands, and that all of them would resume their old ways of dress and behavior. In the evenings they would don their more formal garments, and again play the flute and *citre.*

It did not do to live as savages, alone though they were on this island, perhaps for all time to come.

—2—

Several rainy days now came in succession, and after trying to smoke fish in the branch-shelter while working there themselves in the blinding smoke, both women saw merit in the thought of doing the smoking in the cave. It was a natural smoking-oven, their Lord complacently agreed, as he had pointed out before. Racks could be set up in the lower part, he said, toward the east, and a fire of damp wood would smoke the fish while allowing the smoke to escape without blowing it into Damienne's eyes while she kept the fire going.

So they all trudged and splashed their way up the hill through the dripping trees, to carry the half-dried fish to the cave, and to set up the smoke-chamber.

Damienne had not yet seen the cave, and as the young pair dragged her up the steep rocks to the entrance, she held back. "Are there beasts in here?" she asked timorously, peering into the gloomy opening in the cliff-side.

"Have no fear," said Marguerite cynically. "It is not fit for beasts."

Her husband did not particularly relish this remark. Awareness had been growing in him that they would be hard put to it to make the *logette* weather-worthy for the severe winter which was to come. At the worst, they might even have to live here, he thought, as hunters sometimes did in the caves of France. So he said placatingly, glancing behind him at the steep cliff below the cave, "At least this place could be easily defended, in time of need."

Marguerite peered back through the cave at the second opening, through the jumbled rocks to the east. "Two arquebuses would do it," she agreed crisply.

Her husband looked down at her shining head, bowing to gaze into the dripping cave-entrance. He felt a chill foreboding, in a wave of sorrow and fear. "One arquebus could defend it, at need, my Marguerite," he said.

*

Work on the cabin roof was now being rushed along. Many of the roof-logs had been worried into place, and the chimney was nearly finished. For it the greatest acquisition had been a long, flat slab of granite, several inches thick and very long. It had taken all three of them a long time to drag it back to the *logette* and to lift it into place over the hearth, but they now had a solid mantel which easily supported the breast of the chimney above it.

And the hearth itself was a matter for pride. Even with no roof above it, already it looked home-like. It would hold a great deal of heat, they assured each other, anticipating its warmth as they worked in the wet and chill.

During these days Damienne was busier than she had ever been in her lifetime, since she had found that the wild grain, did, indeed, have seeds in it like oats. It was a great discovery, and she had cut off all the grain-heads and carried them triumphantly home in a carrying-cloth. On days when the wind was right she took the grain to the top of the cliff, still in the cloth, where the wind would blow off the chaff as she flailed it with a stick to thrash it out.

Afterward, thoughtfully chewing the grains, Damienne tested them for dampness. If they were even slightly damp, she recalled, they might mold. Finally she remembered that grain could be forced to dry, and that bakers often had to dry grain before it could be ground. So she spread it carefully on the shelf of the cave, under the drying fish, and made trips between the cave and her salt-pots on the shore. Over her back she carried bundles of faggots for one fire or the other.

And as she passed the *logette* she was often asked to help with the raising of a roof-log. She had never felt so useful, or so needed, in her life. In the evenings she now fell asleep as soon as she crawled into her damp pallet, too tired to think further of her discomforts, or of the demons which were said to inhabit this place.

Satan's legions could have swooped over her head all night and not disturbed the soundness of her slumber.

*

The foliage of the *chicote* had now turned into variegated colors, and Damienne had hastily gathered one last picking of the ripened berries, spreading them, also, in her drying shelves on the rocks in the cave. She would have liked to make berry wine, but the large kettle was being used to boil down sea-water. Regretfully she decided that they would need salt even more than wine.

And the garden had come along very well, in spite of the strange soil in which it was planted. Earlier the exiles had eaten a few carrots and turnips, almost begrudgingly pulling them from places where the plants were crowded, but now the root vegetables would be stored under the end of the *logette* roof where it met the ground, inside a thick packing of moss. When she had time, Damienne pulled up moss and made a sort of nest ready for the precious foods that would be kept there. It appeared that the turnips, parsnips and carrots would be large enough to harvest, but the cabbage was apparently not going to head. They would have to eat the leaves when the frosts came, for without heads, they knew, the cabbage would not keep.

And unless the autumn days were warm throughout the month, which now seemed unlikely, the barley and millet would not ripen.

*

But they had one great stroke of luck. A huge herd of the grey, humpbacked deer came across to the island. Marguerite was first to sight them, on her daily trip to the summit. Before this, when she had thought she saw such beasts they were too far away for her to be sure. But this time there was no doubt. They were in the water, swimming toward the island.

Stealthily she retreated around a rock outcropping, and stooped as she ran hastily back to tell the others. Fortunately the wind was blowing in her direction—her husband had told her that otherwise wild beasts tended to retreat from the human smell.

Once out of sight of the herd, Marguerite laid down her arquebus, for greater speed, and bounded over the rocks down to the cabin. When she came into earshot at the lower end of the cliff, she shouted to her husband and Damienne, "Come! Bring the guns!" After they answered she stood hunched over, pressing her clenched hands against her chest, trying to catch her breath for the return trip. Damienne and her husband came into sight very promptly, carrying the arquebuses, the powder-horns and the slow-matches, which, from the way they were being carried, apparently had been lighted.

Wordlessly Marguerite pointed in the direction of the herd.

The three of them climbed the hill, first running then slowing down to a more careful gait as they reached the crest and could peer over the hilltop. The herd was in plain sight now, swimming slowly, riding high out of the water, their grey backs sleek. They reached the shore as the hunters slowly worked their way downhill toward them, moving stealthily from one granite outcropping to another. Damienne had been asked to stay somewhat behind the young couple, but she had helped to load the guns. Marguerite carried two arquebuses, her husband three, as she followed him down the slope carrying the guns carefully so that an accidental misfiring would not alarm the herd.

The animals were now in plain view. They were not hurrying, since this must be part of their regular migration route. They were a different kind of deer from those Marguerite and her husband had seen in France—gray, with humped backs, and white necks and tails. At first the herd seemed to be mostly composed of stags, but as they came closer it could be seen that the female animals, also, had large horns. Some of the beasts grazed on the mossy soil; some lay down and chewed their cuds.

Slowly the herd came toward its hunters. As it passed beneath them, both Marguerite and her husband rose to their feet and fired at the nearby animals, hastily picking up second arquebuses and preparing them to fire. But by this time the herd had turned away, running down the hill as fast as horses, their hoofs clicking as they went, making a sort of roar.

Both arquebuses now fired again, each dropping one more deer.

But now the herd had reached the shoreline and was swimming majestically away, bodies high out of the water, heads held erect. One more animal had been hit, and was floundering in the shallows. At last it became still, its body lying in the water, while four other deer lay on the hillside.

Marguerite and her husband looked at each other in unbelief. In a few moments they had acquired a plentiful supply of venison for the winter.

Damienne now came scurrying down the hill, scarcely concealing her eagerness to get this good meat safely home and butchered.

So all three hunters walked hastily down the rocky slope to

look at their kill. They found that all of the animals were fairly young and plump beasts, and must have weighed several hundred pounds apiece. And seen more closely, the animals appeared even more strange to their hunters than they had from afar. Their muzzles had a covering of short fur, and their broad, cloven hooves flared out to a great width, cupped on the underside. Among their pointed antlers there were flat, hand-like sections of horn, and one, a male, gave off a strong, musky smell. Their fur was coarse and long.

Marguerite and her husband waded into the shallow water and dragged the half-floating deer ashore. Then the three hunters clambered back and forth over the slippery granite shore, viewing their kill with satisfaction. Here lay food, leather, tallow, bone, a veritable treasure.

Without further delay, taking his knife from his belt, Marguerite's husband started to gut the animals. He sent the women back to the woodland to cut stout carrying poles and to carry most of the arquebuses back to the branch shelter.

The herd of deer was already disappearing toward the shore of the mainland, the wavelets of their passage dying away.

When the women returned, carrying knives of their own, all the deer had been gutted. Damienne now took her own knife and started to cut away the edible parts from the offal, putting them into kettles which she had brought with her. "I will return for the tripes," she promised greedily, "If there is time to come back for them after we carry away the better meat." Wolves had stalked the herd from down in the wooded area to the east, and these might attack the offal, Damienne knew, as soon as the human hunters disappeared from view.

Marguerite and her husband slit the legs of the animals above the hooves and thrust the carrying poles between the tendons, so that two persons could carry each carcass, and Damienne now offered to help carry, since she could not fire an arquebus to guard the kill.

So she and her Lord carried the deer off, one by one, wending their way up the hill between the rocky outcroppings, and back down into their home valley, where they hung the carcasses beside the branch-shelter. The wolves had already shown themselves on the north slope, but had retreated at a shot from Marguerite's arquebus, one of them yelping as if he had been hit.

Marguerite helped her husband carry the last deer, which was also the largest one. Their wet clothing dried on their slender young bodies as they hurried along, the carrying-pole cutting into their shoulders.

Marguerite had thought that Damienne looked as if she might collapse, and after scrambling up and down the hill bearing one end of a heavy carcass the younger woman could understand why this was so. When they reached the branch-shelter she sat under the edge of the canvas, holding her side and breathing rapidly as her husband started the skinning of the carcasses. "These goodly hides," he said, "Will cover the floor in our *logette,* and mayhap they will even make soles for our shoes," for these, he knew, would have to be replaced before long.

On the backs of the deer were heavy layers of tallow, thickening to almost a hand's span of depth over their rumps. This would have many uses, said Damienne, to preserve leather, and even, possibly for candles.

*

During that night the exiles heard a sound of scratching and snarling from the trees where the deer were hung. Marguerite hastily prodded her tired husband to wakefulness and he hurriedly loaded his arquebus and prepared it to fire. Lifting the overhanging canvas and peering out into the dark branches of the woodland, he saw a huge, clumsy form scrambling upward toward the precious venison. He fired the arquebus, and down through the branches fell a heavy form, landing with a thump, and snapping and snarling until it finally became silent.

At the flame and explosion, a scurrying in the woodland told of the retreat of beasts which had evidently gathered there, perhaps the foxes, perhaps the wolves.

Taking a brand from the fire, the young couple went to look at their kill. A creature that appeared to be something between a bear and a huge, thick-bodied rat lay before them, the ugliest beast that they had ever seen. Marguerite shuddered to find that it had large, curved, bear-like claws and teeth, a sort of bushy tail, and hair even on the soles of its feet.

Two broad bands of paler fur ran from its shoulders to its rump, and it gave forth an offensive odor.

Damienne privately crossed herself as she viewed it. She had heard of a devil which the savages called *Atce'n,* and this climbing beast who came so close to man's dwelling might well be he. But Marguerite and her husband, after some consultation, pronounced the beast to be a *carcajou,* which, from what they told of its habits, was scarcely better than a demon, Damienne thought. It was a beast noted for its destructiveness and ferocity.

The two women slept but little that night, tired as they were, within their frail canvas walls, for fear that the *carcajou* might have a mate nearby.

In the morning there was a spattering of sleet, so that they were now still more eager to get into their strong *logette,* where they could protect both themselves and their food.

—3—

A few flocks of geese were still passing overhead, and Marguerite made a successful foray on them, after loading her arquebus hastily with a handful of pebbles and shooting into a flock that was passing rather closely overhead. Five or six geese fell, and in its confusion the flock wheeled around and came back over the same spot where she was standing, so that she was able to get another shot at them. This time eight more were hit in the closely-spaced flock.

Calling Damienne to come and help, Marguerite then gathered the birds together. First they would pluck them to add to the supply of feathers for mattresses and pallaises, to make the beds warm for winter, and then they would smoke the flesh. The goose-fat would be used in the pan-lamps in the winter to come.

*

Work on the cabin roof was now almost finished. The chimney had been completed and capped with the longest, squarest slabs of granite they could find, fitted across the top to protect the clay mortar underneath. And the chimney was very thick, standing on the solid granite so that it should hold firm against the heavy winds, its builders believed.

Now the roof and walls had to be caulked to keep out the wind and rain. "Moss is a dangerous thatch," said Damienne sagely, "So the dwellers at St. John have found." This axiom the young couple could well believe, since moss caught fire quickly and burned with a smouldering, long-lasting flame. However it must be used to chink the roof and walls. Finally they decided to use it between the roof logs but then to cover the roof with bark, thus protecting it from stray sparks. The bark would be held down by flat stones, so that the winds could not tear it away.

As the work was started they found that it was easy to walk up the slanted roof and spread the bark, and that the work was rather pleasant after finishing the heavy toil of dragging the roof-logs into place. Even hauling up the roof-stones did not seem difficult, since thus they were finishing the heavy work of their house-building.

And the inside of the *logette* now began to look like a cozy, if dark, habitation. The split logs on the floor were light-colored, but the bark walls and ceiling darkened the room, into which light came only from the open door and the loophole in the wall. Even this was to have a plug carefully cut to fit it, or it would let in too much cold.

All three of them now worked at chinking the cabin from the inside with hastily-gathered moss during the days of rain and sleet, pounding it as tightly as they could between the logs and under the eaves by the roof. Over it they finally smeared a plaster of clay mixed with caribou hair, to make it more windproof.

"Hog-bristles are used for this at home," Damienne grumbled, thinking nostalgically of the farm buildings of France.

And mixing the clay for the caulking was a cold, wet job, since the weather had now turned very chill, but even so the inside of the *logette* was soon finished, and the outside caulking was started on the first rainless day.

But toward the latter part of the month the weather became so cold that the women had to take time to bring in their garden crops, pulling the carrots and turnips and carefully storing them in the thick bed of moss at the back of the cabin. They sorted the beans, only part of which had ripened, and cooked the ones that were too unripe to store. As she ate her portion Marguerite remarked wistfully, "Beans are held to be peasants' fare at home in Perigueux, but here on our island I account them to be a rare dish indeed." Her husband, she noticed, was also eating his portion with a relish which he had not shown for a long time.

And now the first really frigid gale of autumn came down on the island. The wind tore off part of the roof covering, which had to be repaired with heavier rocks laid on it to hold it down.

The garden-stuff had been harvested with no time to spare.

*

Now all three worked frantically at their tasks in a race against winter. Sea-water was still being boiled for salt, on the shore, while faggots were being gathered and wood cut for the winter's wood supply. But they feared to start a fire in the fireplace until the clay mortar was thoroughly dry, so that Damienne was constantly in the cave, cutting and smoking the last of the game and fish, and standing guard over it with sword in hand. Marguerite was the woodsman, while her husband worked on the doorframe and the *logette* door.

One afternoon Marguerite straightened her back and swept back her hair from her sweaty face, casting an anxious eye toward the angle of the sun. She had not made the trip to the summit for the daily lookout, and it was getting late in the day for a good view of the distant ships' road. Worriedly she checked the *ragout* kettle, for she was now also the cook, and then she went to the cabin doorway, where her husband was smoothing the doorsill so that a door could be fitted.

"*Mon mari,*" she said, "I have not yet gone to the lookout, and it grows late in the day. Could I ask that you do it, this one time? Damienne is at the cave—"

He laughed. Her face was so serious, and so red. "My legs are longer than yours, and my carpentry is not going too well," he replied jovially. "I will be glad to get away for a time." He vaulted up the path, his wife thought, like a boy.

At the summit the young exile prepared to give one sweeping look around the wide vista, and to rush back to his work. He, too, was pressed with urgency, since the door needs must be done, but he had no idea how to fashion a door. Nothing had ever been seen from the summit, so his inspection, through far-focused, was cursory. He had almost turned away when his eyes were drawn back to two white flecks far to the southwest, along the horizon. Shading his eyes he gazed at them. They might be stray icebergs, he realized, but probably not that far upriver, he thought, at this time of year.

Hope crept into his mind that the white forms might be ships, and he realized how urgent was his longing to return home.

If they were vessels, they were too far to be signalled, but they might come nearer. They must come nearer. His gaze reached toward them as though his very hope could bring them to the island.

France! He thought yearningly. Once again to tread the earth of France!

Frenziedly he threw his arms around the wind-tossed signal pyre and re-stacked it into shape, running farther downhill to bring back more dry branches.

The wind was fair from the southwest, he quickly determined, and he told himself that the ships, if they were ships, could almost as well sail up past his island for the customary night's shelter, rather than to proceed straight out the southern passage.

He started to rush down the hill for Marguerite and Damienne, but suddenly thought better of it, halted, and sat down behind a rock. Better to give this matter some thought, he decided, before arousing the hopes of the women.

Reluctantly he faced the thought that had occurred to him. It was an idea that his mind hardly dared touch upon, but it was possible that the ships, if they were Roberval's, would pass them by.

So he arose to his feet occasionally to watch the distant vessels, and thought of his fellow *compagnons* on the voyage. Which of them would be sent back on this return trip to France to bring back supplies to the colony upriver? Guinecourt and Saineterre, he finally decided, possibly accompanied by Jean Alfonce de Xanctoigne. Which of them, if they were sent past the island, would fail to stop? He did not know.

Jean Alfonce de Xanctoigne was an honest and much-respected pilot, of proven integrity, the young exile remembered, but he now questioned if the man would have the courage to flout the wishes of Roberval as Jacques Cartier had done. Many men, he cynically told himself, bowed before the wrong-doing of those in power over them, and even participated in carrying it out, rather than to bring trouble upon themselves, or deny themselves advancement. What Jean Alfonce would do, he thus did not know.

But among the other men, he believed he had friends. They had played cards and joked together in the crowded quarters allotted them, sleeping spoon fashion, as needs must be, like young brothers in a crowded household.

With a pang of loneliness he thought of the other young noblemen. He had accounted them as comrades, he thought painfully, before the marooning.

With an effort he turned his mind back to the distant ships. There was the dreadful possibility that they might be Spanish, and it would be a great danger, he knew, for French colonists to be discovered by the Spanish on these shores. Such ships might have again been sent to Canada to ferret out French colonies, since Spanish spies had been haunting the harbors of France for information, and, indeed, a Spanish caravelle had been sent to this very sea by Charles Quint just a year ago, to investigate France's activities in the New World. Strangely he even recalled that the spy-ship was said to have sailed from Bayonne, since France, too, had its spies which watched the machinations of Spain.

Better to rot here on this island, the young man warned himself, than to betray himself and his women-folk to the Spaniards! What would follow, at best, would be the burning of the *logette* and a trip home in chains to face the Inquisition. At worst, if the Spaniards realized that the castaways were not Catholic, they would be tortured and killed on the spot.

Before he attracted their attention, he must know whether the ships were Spanish. But they had evidently come from upriver, he thought hopefully, and as he peered at them he thought that they did not seem to be caravelle-rigged as were most Spanish vessels.

While he cautiously waited for the ships to move more clearly into view, he pondered the matter of Spain's enmity, which had come about because an emperor and a king, Charles Quint and François Premier, rivals in so many things, were also rivals in the colonization of the New World. After the Pope had formally given rights in the new lands to Spain, Charles Quint had reveled in his clear right to the new world, and had resented any intrusion into his domain by France. Angered when François Premier had sent Cartier to explore the lands called Canada, Charles Quint had urged that Cartier and all his ships be destroyed, "not saving any one person," to deter further exploration by France.

But François had not been deterred, the young exile recalled, and he had again sent Cartier to explore what he now called New France. And in explaining his action he had wittily remarked that he would like to see the clause in the Will of Adam that divided the New World between Spain and Portugal!

Arising again to his feet, the young nobleman looked out across the gray waters at the *vaisseaux.* Then he turned his head to sweep the horizon with moving eyes, a trick he had learned in falconry, and at last he chose a tall tree on the hillside below, to gauge the movement of the ships. They were indeed moving, downriver, against the tide. Icebergs, with their huge underwater bulks moved only with the tide, he knew. But the movement of the vessels was agonizingly slow.

Bethinking himself of his long absence from the *logette,* which Marguerite or Damienne might by now have noted, their young Lord now made a hasty trip downhill, snatching up a load of firewood on his way. When he arrived there, Marguerite straightened her back and smiled at him vaguely. She seemed to be thinking that the lookout trip had been the usual unrewarding chore. Without a show of haste greater than usual, her husband laid down the wood and returned to the summit. He said nothing, and kept his face turned away, lest some look betray his excitement. As soon as he was out of sight, he broke into a run.

But upon reaching the summit he almost hated to turn his gaze southward, for fear of what he might see. It would be unendurable, he told himself, if he saw only two icebergs. But the white dots were now clearly the blunted triangles of fully set square sails; there was no further doubt of it.

Anxiously the young castaway tried to tell himself that they were narrowing into the rectangular shapes that would tell him of a change of course toward his own island. Surely they were coming closer, he told himself in anguished hope, on a course which would bring them into the good harbor spreading below him, to anchor for the night as was customary.

One of the men on the sounding boat had called this harbor the best on the north shore, he remembered wistfully as the gulls swept over his head and soared out to sea. Surely they would come here. It would be to their own advantage to have safe anchorage over night, and the distance was about right for them to reach harbor before darkness without sacrifice of sailing time.

Although not a man much given to prayer, he prayed. Looking up to the sky, he wondered if the Lord was there, and if he indeed governed what happened in this remote land, so far from France. And he continued his prayer, even as utter despair flooded through him.

The ships were passing by.

Roberval must have given instructions against a stop at this island, he realized, or perhaps, as was also likely, his lieutenants would not care to undertake such an act, which would displease the Viceroy. Nor would they come near enough to have the embarrassment of passing a signal fire.

He could not bear to watch them out of sight as they returned to France.

As he walked back down the hill along the high cliff-side he was struck by a moment's despairing urge to plunge over the edge into the precipice, thus dying quickly now that his hopes for rescue were finished forever.

But a sudden hatred for Jean-François de la Roque gushed through his veins, renewing his will to live, if only to thwart the Viceroy's intent, and some day to gain revenge. Resentment at his enemy's barbarism to two helpless women seared his mind, and his body quivered with such a passionate anger that he was half blinded.

For a moment he stood motionless. Then Marguerite's face, vulnerable in its guilelessness, came into his thoughts, along with the crumpled, aging visage of Damienne. Slowly, resignedly, with a last look at the departing ships, he drew away from the cliff's edge. Like an old man he trudged back to the *logette,* wordlessly resuming his work on the doorsill.

The cabin was now the only remaining hope for them to survive the winter.

*

After the caribou hunt, Marguerite was certain that she would bear her child. If the running and lifting I did then did not cause me to have my flow of blood, she thought, the child will go to his term. The lifting of the logs for the cabin had not wearied her as much as the more stressful work of carrying home the carcass of the deer.

She wondered why Damienne and her husband had asked her no questions. Perhaps Damienne did not wish to know of the matter before she was told, her nurseling thought. Perhaps she did not want to be guilty of failing to warn her Lady against heavy work, thus sharing in the sinful intent to lose a child before it was born.

But there is no way that my hands can be spared, thought Marguerite, for if we do not get the cabin closed in and wood gathered for the winter, none of us will live. I do as I must.

October, 1542

—1—

Before the door of the *logette* was finished and hung the women completed their pounding of moss caulking between the floor logs, and carefully covered it with clay mixed with caribou hair. They even scattered sand across each strip for neatness.

Over the objections of her young Lord, who seemed to lack his usual good spirits, Marguerite had started moving the most perishable of their belongings into the *logette*. Her husband had warned her somewhat gruffly that he would not be accountable for the sawdust and shavings that might get scattered about as he made the door and the furniture. So she tactfully brought in his *citre* and her flute first of all, and then he made no further objection. There was no denying that it was hard to protect the delicate instruments in the canvas shelter as the autumn wind and rain came on.

Marguerite also brought in her precious books, her *Nouveau Testament, Alcuns Pseaulmes et Cantiques, the Book of True and Perfect Prayer,* and the volume published by Queen Marguerite herself, *Le Miroir de l'Ame Pecheresse.* These were carefully ranged on the dried mantle-shelf. The *Miroir* was scarcely larger than Marguerite's hand and not much thicker, and the other books were also small, but somehow with their embossed covers and gilt edges they seemed to give the rude room a remembered touch of civilized France.

*

One day Marguerite and Damienne had a brief argument. It concerned a small pot of *ragout* which Marguerite found simmering over the fire when she returned from a last trip to the clay-bank. She was hungry, and she took the ladle from beside the pot, intending to taste the savory-smelling dish. But Damienne hastily stopped her, saying that she was trying some of the mushrooms, and some of the new herbs of the island to see if they could be eaten without harm.

Marguerite retorted in some alarm that this was dangerous, and not needful, whereupon Damienne replied that in France the women passed down their knowledge of good herbs and simples from mother to daughter and grand-daughter. Old women went through the woods grubbing and digging, and hawked their findings in the streets. They knew what could best be done with each root and leaf. "But the plants here are strange to me," she concluded, "And thus I will have to test them for myself."

Marguerite still objected. "We have our garden plants. Even a bite of an evil mushroom can kill the one who eats it. They are used for poisonings!"

"I have noticed that your Lord no longer relishes his food as he once did," replied Damienne shrewdly. "Although he works harder, he eats less." She peered accusingly into her Lady's face, and added, "Have you not seen the hollows around his neck? We know he longs for the good white bread of France, but I think he is also weary of the flesh of wild beasts. It is our affair to see that he eats well, lest he sicken in this place."

Marguerite looked stricken. Her young husband had been good to Damienne, and it was clear that she loved him now as if he had been her own nurseling. And it was a poor wife, she thought abjectly, whose nurse had to remind her of her duty to a well-loved husband.

In the ensuing silence Damienne went on to say reflectively,

"It may be that our custom of using herbs in food is not only for their taste, but for our well-being. I do not know." She smiled a crumpled smile and added, turning back to her stew-pot, "Let be. I will use great care."

Wordlessly Marguerite gazed at her, and for the first time she thought, in some disquiet, that Damienne now looked akin to her peasant forebears, with her weather-beaten face, deepening lines around her eyes, and her headcovering grimy and pulled awry. A pang of pity and love for this old woman who had been with her all her life, and was now uncomplainingly sharing her exile, forced her contrition. Wordlessly she patted Damienne's arm and picked up her axe for a trip to the woodland.

—2—

Making and fitting a door for the *logette* was a job the untrained carpenter now realized that he plainly did not know how to do. He had thought of many ways to make a door and to improvise hinges for it, but he had neither the tools nor the skill to make the kind of door he thought was needed, or that he remembered from the *châteaux* of France. Having some notion of the severe northern winters, with their fierce winds, and of the night-beasts that prowled, he knew that the door must be both tight and strong.

After several false starts, laboring away with Marguerite's help, he finally sawed planks lengthwise through the largest dried log he had saved aside; then he used the auger to affix crossbars, and finally achieved a sort of thick, rectangular plaque. It was so heavy that all three of the workers had to lift it into place for its repeated fittings into the doorsill.

The hinges were the big problem, but the young carpenter had worked out a way of swinging it on clumsy, makeshift wooden sockets, similar to gate hinges he had seen in France. So that finally, after much measuring, planing, fitting and re-fitting, the door was swung into place.

To the women it had the very look of shelter and safety.

Deer-tallow greased the hinge-sockets, and finally the door

swung heavily and reluctantly into its place, and a strong bar was made to fit it.

A block had been fitted to the loophole, fastened in such a way that it could be quickly removed for purposes of defense, and now the *logette* was complete. Only the furniture needed to be made, and after his troubles with the door, the young carpenter considered that an easy task. So he sawed planks for the table-top and benches, fitted them with the legs he had whittled out on rainy days, and made beds with posts and side-rails of skinned tree-trunks, solid four-posters. Canopies above them were made of split boughs over which a cover could be laid for warmth, and various of their belongings could also be stored there.

Rope was now wrapped crosswise and lengthwise around the frames to strengthen them, and on this net-work would be laid first the straw mattresses, then the feather-beds. The double bed for the married pair was placed with its foot toward the fireplace; the single bed for Damienne in the opposite corner of the room.

The women were pleased to see that their young Lord had even cut slabs of log to make shelves, and they rubbed the furniture smooth with pieces of granite, followed by a tallow-cloth to give it luster.

But while the women occupied themselves with these niceties, the axe was again ringing out with an even more persistent rhythm in the woodland. The winter wood supply was still scanty.

*

The women now reveled in arranging their household. The shavings and sawdust had been swept away with spruce-twig brooms, and they unpacked the trunks, which would thenceforth be *garderobes* instead of sea-chests. These were placed at the foot of the beds, and the clothing they had contained was hung on pegs on the wall to air and be freshened at last. The silks and satins added a strange note of elegance to the rough log walls.

Damienne now took the sickle and went to the field of wild wheat. Since the grain-tops had already been harvested, she was able to hack away at a great rate, bringing home huge bundles of the straw on her head to stuff the mattresses. Thinking of the warm bed in which she would sleep that night, away from the dampness of the branch-shelter, she found it a pleasant task.

And to Marguerite and her husband, standing in their own doorway, watching Damienne come up the path in the thin afternoon sunlight, skirt kilted up, face tanned, and hankerchiefed head carrying the yellow straw, it seemed like a harvest scene in France. Suddenly their island seemed a home, at least to Marguerite.

After the mattresses were stuffed and put on the beds, and the canopies and draperies hung, the room suddenly seemed colorful, especially after the scraped hides were laid on the floor for rugs. And the women now decided that the clay mortar was dry enough that a small fire could be built, adding its welcoming warmth to the room, along with the pan-lamps which were lighted and hung. Fire-tongs and pots were placed on the hearth, and the pot-hook was put into place with its adjustable ratchet to raise and lower the cooking kettles. It was a well-appointed kitchen, the women thought.

On the mantel-shelf their large blue and white glazed plates were ranged, making a brave and homelike show, with the cups and saucers on the shelf nearby, and the table was covered with a cloth on which the candlesticks were set forth. Out of the heavy, round-topped garde-robes came the knives with pearl inlay and the tiny two-tined silver table-forks and spoons which they had not used since leaving France.

Dinner, that first night in the *logette,* was festive. It seemed almost like a return to life. The three exiles did not realize how chilled and weary they had become, huddling in their canvas shelter, until they contrasted it with their snug, new quarters.

So they washed in hot water, with their perfumed soap, and put on clothes they had not worn as yet on the island. The women combed up their hair into stately knots, and their feet felt light in shoes they had not worn since leaving the ship. The young couple eyed each other with rekindled admiration, each thinking that the other again appeared attractive, and young, as neither had seemed during their time of drudgery.

And Damienne had made special efforts with the meal. She

even had prepared a surprise. From the hoofs of the caribou she had used an intricate process to extract a clear jelly, and this had been boiled with berries to give it color and flavor. It glittered with a festive look on its silver plate, between the candles.

Marguerite had shot three partridges, and the small birds had been stuffed with a dressing of wild wheat, herbs and mushrooms. A savory mushroom sauce had also been prepared.

Many a *château* in France, thought Damienne, served no better food.

After the meal they told stories and sang, and even danced to the Court air of *Tant que Vivray,* as their hearth-fire flickered in its comforting gleam, dancing on the colors of their moving silks and satins. *Gayeté d'esprit* had returned to the island.

*

The next morning when Marguerite parted the curtains of her marriage-bed, she found that her husband had already started the fire and had left the *logette.* But before she was fully dressed, he returned, asking for his heavier jacket. "*Une forte gelée blanche,*" he shuddered, using the countryman's term for an early autumn frost. "We got our lodging finished with no time to spare."

So again the three exiles wore their tattered work-clothing, making trips to the cave to carry down the dried and smoked food for storage in the *logette.* Along with the strings of mushrooms and braided *échalotes* and garlic, the smoked venison and fish added their homely odors which mingled with the sharp smell of freshly-cut pine. It seemed to the castaways to be the very breath of security and home.

But much work remained to be done. A greater supply of wood now had to be cut, and without delay. Each of them had been secretly astonished at how rapidly their broad fireplace consumed wood, and they knew that cold, not hunger, would be their cruellest enemy.

The women had already realized that warmer bedding would be needed than was customary in the milder climate of France. They had brought linen ticking to be stuffed, heavy cases for the mattresses and lighter ones for *pallaises* and pillows. These they had already partially filled with goosefeathers, but more fullness would be needed to give the necessary warmth.

More feathers would be needed, for each goose gave only so many feathers, Damienne wryly reminded Marguerite with a droll, country adage. Well they remembered the goose-plucking days in France, which took place about three times a year. The goose-girls thrust the heads of the geese into a long, narrow-necked "goose-basket," and plucked the breast feathers. The screaming and squawking did not go unnoticed in the courtyards of France. The feathers then were put into small cloth bags for easier handling, and these they had brought along. But as Marguerite reminded Damienne, the goose-girls of France did not have to first shoot the geese they plucked.

But she now devoted her time to shooting geese, loading all the arquebuses and carrying them out to the edge of the water where there was a patch of shrubs for cover. Wearing her faded clothing, she lay there, waiting for the last of the migrating flocks to fly over. They could always be heard as they approached, flying in v-shaped formations and baying hoarsely, like hounds in full cry. There were many marshes just north of the island, and the flocks usually had not risen very high when they passed over. Now large numbers were coming, and Marguerite feared that they might be the last that remained to the north.

As the flocks came over she stood and fired, aiming somewhat ahead of them, having loaded the arquebuses with as many small pebbles as she dared. In the one day she killed a great many geese, and her husband came down to the shore to retrieve those that landed in the water, kindling a fire for the plucking, over which he also huddled to dry his clothing.

Marguerite handed him the birds which Damienne plucked, and he rapidly cleaned them, shivering in his damp garments as he did so. Thin as he was, he greatly minded the cold.

*

And every day the winds now grew more chill, with seldom

a warmer day intervening. The leaves of the birch-trees had turned yellow and had quickly been blown away as summer changed into winter with scarcely a breathing-space between.

One day while Damienne was boiling down still more salt, Marguerite attempted to go up the hill for the daily lookout. A gale had been blowing, but she thought it had died down enough for her to keep her footing. But when she got up the hill, above the tree-line, she was nearly blown away, and finally she propped herself into a shelter behind a rock. No ships could move on such a day, she realized. Her trip to the summit was a foolish errand.

The warmth of a thin, autumn sun reached into her sheltered nook, tempting Marguerite to linger there for a time of unaccustomed idleness. Feeling somewhat conscience-stricken as the sound of her husband's axe continued in the woodland, she looked out across the harbor and over the island at the tip of the archipelago. A raging southeasterly surf was piling high against the end of that exposed headland, throwing the spume so high that she could see it over the tops of the stunted trees near the island's crest. Thankfully she understood how much shelter was provided to her own island by the barrier of outer islands surrounding it, some large, some small, placed as if deliberately to break up the surf and to give protection. From no direction could large waves batter their shores, or greatly disturb the waters of their harbor.

As Marguerite rested in her shelter she remembered that Jean-François had wanted to maroon Damienne and her on that outermost island. She searched her memory, remembering the dispute which she had half heard, not understanding it at the time.

Coming down the ships' way from Blanc Sablon, her cousin Roberval had asked the pilot, Jean Alfonce de Xanctoigne, to see his chart, afterward remarking that they were nearing the *Ysles Saincte Martre.* These proved to be just off the starboard bow, far ahead, the identifying sharp bluff showing clearly as it fell sharply into the sea.

The fishermen at Blanc Sablon had told them that behind this tall cliff lay one of the best harbors to be found in the bay. Jean Alfonce had seemed to want to stop and chart it, she now remembered, but Jean-François had said that he was in a hurry. He did not want to go into the harbor, but to press on. They had already been overly delayed, he said, and the business he had in mind was not worth an unnecessary expenditure of time.

Marguerite knew, now, what that business had been. She wondered if Jean Alfonce had known.

Jean Alfonce of Xanctoigne, as master pilot of the expedition, had stated an opposite desire to that of his commander. Good harbors in these latitudes, he said, were worth more than gold. If men knew not where they might safely shelter, in haste, ships would be lost, with all their cargoes. Time must be taken to chart this important habor. Hard-pressed ships could not sail blindly into shelter in the lee of shores which had not been explored, and in case of real trouble, the harbor of Blanc Sablon, itself, was none too well sheltered. Furthermore, he needed to plot and mark the exact latitude and longitude of the harbor for his records and maps. This could only be done accurately from a ship that was stationary, lying at anchor in harbor.

Marguerite remembered that she had been astonished at the unwonted outpouring of words from the usually taciturn Jean-Alfonce.

But Roberval was not a sailor, and none of this reasoning carried import with him. He wanted only to claim lands and to find riches to send back to France. He needed to get his colony established before winter. It might already be too late to plant crops, as Jacques Cartier had informed him so bluntly, but buildings had to be raised. He did not want to stop. It was possible to sail all through the luminous nights at this time of year, and he proposed to do just that, he said, after a quick stop at the outermost island, now coming into view.

For the first time Marguerite realized that her cousin's initial intention had been little short of murder, and her rage, together with an incredulous sense of injury, sharpened her memory to an unwonted clarity. She could almost smell the tarry odors of the ship, and hear the snapping of the rigging printed in her mind on that day, as she had listened to the argument wage on.

Clearly she remembered her surprise at hearing Jean Alfonce

raise his voice. Ordinarily he remembered well that he was under the command of her kinsman. But Jean Alfonce had said firmly, "Our master, the King, has instructed me to plot out exact navigational records for this expedition, including the location and depth of harbors, and the courses for safely entering and leaving them. This information, the King informed me, is as valuable to him as anything else to be gained from this voyage."

Clearly reluctant, but not daring to flout the wishes of François Premier, her cousin had angrily conceded the demands of his defiant pilot. Alfonce gave the necessary orders. The larboard sheets were shortened and those on the starboard were let out. The yards had creaked around, and the large, triangular *artimon* had been hauled almost fore-and-aft. The man at the whipstaff had pulled the heavy rudder over, and the portly ship had swung toward the shore, aimed for a narrow harbor entrance. On the right side a high, sharp bluff, higher by far then their mainmast, dropped its sheer granite wall into the sea. It looked as sharp as the corner of a castle wall, and as high. To the left side of the narrow entrance-way another island, the outermost one to be seen, reached down a more slanting red granite strand. In the offshore breeze only a few ripples could be seen hitting against the water's edge.

Her cousin had walked to the rail and looked at the slanting shoreline of the island on the port side of the ship. She remembered hearing him grumble under his breath, "The ship's boat could just as well have landed there."

Now, as Marguerite stared out across the harbor at the surf battering against that exposed island she wondered, shuddering at the thought, how long the three of them would have lasted if they had been landed there. Even the trees on that wind-whipped outer island looked stunted. The lower part was scoured by the sea, the bare granite top by the wind. Only the birds seemed to find it hospitable, and Marguerite noticed that even the gulls retreated inshore from it in winds like these.

Horror at her kinsman's ruthlessness and perfidy wrenched her with an unaccustomed violence of feeling. Bad enough to maroon two defenseless women for little real reason, she thought, but he really intended to deal with us more cruelly yet than he did. My cousin Roberval is a truly evil man, she thought, a dastard. He dishonors his heritage.

Looking out across the scene of her marooning her gentle young face hardened into stern lines of pride and endurance as she vowed that Roberval should not defeat her. She would live, and she would return to France.

—4—

Later that month, while the women were occupied with their salt-boiling and the arrangement of their household, their *Seigneur* was engaged in an activity which he did not mention to them. As he went about the cutting of logs and turf for winter fuel, he spent some time in walling up the cave.

After much thought, he had remembered the stories of huntsmen as they lounged around the fireside in his boyhood home. Some of them had gone far afield, and had hunted in fairly wild country. They had told of being caught, benighted, in sudden storms or cold. The idea was to find a cave, they had said, driving out what beasts might be there. Caves were cool in summer, true, but in winter they were warmer than one would think. With a fire in a cave, wet clothing could be dried, and the heat of a fire penetrated into the surrounding rock with a comforting warmth that lasted far into the night.

A branch shelter was for summer, they said; a cave was the shelter for winter-time.

But the women had clearly not liked the cave. Marguerite had completely scorned it, with her fastidious disdain, and while Damienne had been willing to work there, she plainly regarded it only as a smoke-house. And as he piled layers of turf on the southern cave-shelf to narrow the opening, he had to admit that it was not an inviting habitation.

Nevertheless he also closed the eastern end with slabs of turf, all but a tiny flue for the smoke to escape. We can tear this down next summer, he thought. But as a man of military training, he knew the value of a place for strategic withdrawal.

When he had finished his task, hands skinned from the rough granite around which he had clambered, he sat for a few moments on the shelf above the precipice, moodily looking out over the valley below. The women are content now, he thought, with a household of sorts around them. But I have almost as much cause for disquiet as before. More, perhaps, since the *logette* now stands large for any enemy to see. And this colony is very short of fighting-men, he thought wryly. We have only strategy to protect us.

The danger of being found by the Spanish, or of attack by the passing savages was greater as all the traces of occupancy became more noticeable to anyone entering the harbor. Then there was the danger of fire, as the *logette* needed to be heated ever more dangerously in its clay-daubed fireplace. The young builder feared that their inexperienced hands might have built a trap for themselves, as still hotter fires had to be built, with sparks flying over the bark-covered roof.

Also there were strange stories of this land, of castaway sailors who went mad from the solitude around them, of earthquakes and strange monsters which were said to seek out and attack men.

There might be a morsel of truth, the young man thought somberly, in some of these strange tales.

With two women to protect, he pondered, best not to take any chances. So along with the piling of turf walls he laid up a scaffolding over the wider opening to the south to be covered with canvas if need be, and he piled some extra turf and a supply of wood close at hand.

Then he continued his carrying of firewood to stack beside the *logette.*

*

That night a gust of snow came down before twilight. And the days were shortening rapidly, it seemed to the exiles. But it was a relief not to have to work so late in the day, since darkness brought an end to the outdoor toil of wood-gathering.

The women had been busy contriving a delicacy of deers' tongues with a savory sauce. They had even pounded some of the wild grain and ground it in the mortar, mixing it with deer-fat and making a sort of flat pastry of it, like a pie-crust. On it were dabs of their berry preserves. And they were wearing more elaborate dresses. When her husband came through the door, Marguerite whirled her skirt coquettishly for his inspection. The pale silk glimmered in the firelight. Her hair had been piled atop her head in a different style, and she was wearing earrings, even a touch of perfume.

"Wash yourself and get dressed," she told her husband. "You are no longer a wood-chopper."

Her weary and begrimed young Lord was glad to obey her. Combing his trimmed beard before his wife's gilded pedestal mirror, he decided to wear his striped hose and an embroidered jacket. Their clothing would not last forever here, he thought with a pang of sadness at their isolation, and as rapidly as the fashions changed in France their fine garments might already be out of style, for all they knew. A pulse of anger and resentment drummed through the young exile's mind, and he bent over to smooth his hose lest his wife notice his mood. She was making a great effort to be gay; no kindness to dampen her effervescence.

That night after dinner they sat around their fire and talked, and for the first time mention was made of the behavior and affairs of Jean-François de la Roque, Seigneur de Roberval. He would be astonished, thought his kinswoman, could he know how seldom we think of him.

But now she mentioned the thoughts that had come to her as she watched the harbor during the gale, and told how she suspected that Roberval had planned to send a longboat to the outer island, sparing no more than a half-hour to set them ashore there. She wondered, she said, whether Jean Alfonce de Xanctoigne had known or suspected what was afoot, since he had insisted on going inside the harbor and anchoring.

"By so doing," she said, "He gave us our chance. That outer island is not fit to live on." Reflectively she added, "My kinsman was not pleased."

A moment's silence passed by as the three of them thought of Roberval, his hard dark eyes, his thin lips, from which a voice issued which either rasped or complained. He could cast a pall on their spirits, the young nobleman thought moodily, even from afar.

None of them but Marguerite had ever heard his manner in the presence of the King, but there, she assured them, he was all affability and charm.

Reflecting a change of mood, Marguerite's eyes now gleamed with an impish light. "Just think," she said to her husband, "If my kinsman had only chained you below-decks while he marooned Damienne and me, you would now be safely in *Charlesbourg Royale,* or even back in France." She looked at him speculatively. "I have often wondered if you sometimes wish that your friends had held you back more firmly!" Between her dark eyelashes her eyes gleamed challengingly.

Her husband did not rise to this wifely jibe. "Had I felt thus," he replied stoutly, stretching his silk-clad legs out toward the hearthfire, "I would not have come on deck with a loaded arquebus to force my way ashore." Mildly he contemplated his young wife's tantalizing remark.

"Reckon to yourself that your kinsman may well have thought to drop me off a few leagues away, on some other island," he added calmly. "Then I would not have had these comforts with which you have surrounded me." He patted the cushion on the stool beside him, which Marguerite had only the evening before stuffed with some extra feathers, gathered from the site of the goose-plucking.

Marguerite and Damienne exchanged glances. Not a word had he uttered to claim credit for the building of the *logette,* which made their comforts possible, and in this effort, they had both noticed, his body had become so lank that his fine garments hung slackly upon him. If women were to be marooned for punishment, their eyes said, it was an oversight to let them be accompanied by such a kindly man. Damienne loves him as she would a son, thought Marguerite. Come what will, I am a fortunate woman. I will be glad to bear his child.

Her husband listened for a moment to the sleet skittering across the bark-covered roof. "I have given much thought to what must have happened at St. John to make Roberval do this thing," he said reflectively, toying with his young wife's fingers as they lay in her silken lap. "It is clear that someone told him of our dalliance, and added to the tale in the telling."

Marguerite blushed indignantly. "I have told Damienne," she flared, "That naught happened to our dishonor!"

Damienne flashed her Lord a rather amused look. He had observed the folded-away sheets from the marriage-bed, and well understood their meaning.

Marguerite added in an insistent tone, "It does not do to wonder who carried the tale. When we return to France, it will be best that we do not know." Thinking of the child which she was now to bear, Marguerite did not want trouble to face them when they returned to France. She feared that her noble young husband would rush about to search out those who had done them this injury, and seek to avenge the dishonor, thereby bringing about his own ruin, since Roberval had more influence at Court than did her husband's family, she well knew. And many of the *compagnons* on the voyage, who had supinely permitted the marooning, had parents in high Court positions. Resentfully she realized that it would still be wise not to embarrass them.

Although she understood her husband's deep anger at Roberval and sympathized with his desire to avenge his honor and her own, Marguerite hoped most heartily that she could persuade him to let matters drop. Well she knew Roberval and his devious ways. She and her husband would have to step carefully, she thought, to avoid further trouble if they got back to France.

*

As the nights lengthened, the exiles spent their time in lighter work than before. When the weather was clear they went about their outdoor duties, Damienne boiling out still more sea-salt and gathering faggots, Marguerite hunting for small game and carrying wood. Her husband continued to chop logs for the winter wood supply, and the women, too, went out with saw and hatchet to cut up the smaller branches. They also cut and carried turf to burn, as well.

The woodland near the *logette* was beginning to be picked as clean as were the copses of France.

During the sleet squalls which now came more frequently, the three exiles worked in the cabin. One of the caribou hides, which had been robbed of its hair for the mortar, was soaking in a soap compound, in the hope that boot-soles could be cut from it. Damienne had been told that the savages cured leather in this way, and shoes were wearing thin.

Marguerite was mending their well-worn clothing, moving unnecessary widths from here and there to eke out the tattered edges. Her husband was carving wooden bowls and storage containers, as well as other tools and utensils, and Damienne was cleaning and oiling all their shoes. She also concocted varied dishes from the foods that would not keep for winter. It was a peaceable time.

The nights were growing still more chill, but in their warm beds, lying on their double mattresses, warmly covered and closed in, they were more comfortable than they had been since leaving France. But they noticed that during the days they had to bundle themselves in their warm clothing, even in the *logette,* if they were not to burn too much of the winter's wood supply.

On clear days all three, now, worked to gather wood, in the knowledge that it burned very fast, especially when the wind pulled the heat up and away, out of their fireplace.

Often in the long evenings, while they still dressed in their more courtly garments, they now wrapped their fur-lined capes about their shoulders as they read to each other, told stories, or played the flute and citre. But when they left the fireside, the *logette* was not warm.

November, 1542

—1—

After one of the cold nights Marguerite found that the fresh-water reservoirs were frozen, so that they would now have to melt their drinking water. She told herself firmly that it was a matter of no great moment, that from the beginning they had been cooking partially in sea-water to save their salt supply. But the freezing of the ponds marked forth another token of the coming of the cold season, and made it clear to her that they would now have to spend the winter in this isolated place.

But on the way back to the *logette* she braced her resolution to use the freezing weather for their benefit. They would freeze fish and game, since already they were weary of the salted foods.

So she walked past the shoreline and found that fish were still to be seen rather near the surface. Hurrying back to the *logette*, she told her husband and Damienne of her plan.

It was too cold to wade into the water with their fish-catching basket, so they rigged it to a pole, and all went down to the edge of the water, where already a thin rime of ice was showing at the edges. Marguerite and her husband lay flat on a steep rock which dropped off into fairly deep water. It would take both of them to pull up the basket, they thought, out on the end of the pole as it was, and with the water pulling it down. They caught several of the familiar *morue* with their make-shift tackle, tossing them back to Damienne for cleaning, and then a fish appeared, lying near the surface like the *morue*, but with a long, flat jaw, like a bill. They caught it, too, and it was large.

Hurrying back to the *logette* several times, as the cold penetrated their clothing, they held hot potions in their hands to warm their stiff fingers, and after a few hours work they had a good supply of fish. They saved aside one of the flat-jawed kind to eat at dinner-time; the rest they hung up to freeze.

Since they now planned to close their fishing-season for the year, they decided to pack the basket with ice and put layers of fish in it, storing them under them under the end of the cabin where it touched the ground, on the opposite side from the vegetables. It would stay frozen there, and with a triangular log door at the end, no beasts could get to it. If they killed any fresh game, they decided, they would keep it there, as well.

It would be a change from the salt meat, of which they had such a great supply.

That evening at dinnertime, Marguerite had planned, she would mention the child which was to be born. Her waistline had thickened. It was time to mention the child, and to her husband first, before Damienne.

She decided to suggest that Damienne find fresh herbs, which were still to be dug from under cover here and there, to prepare a savory stuffing for the fish. Damienne set great store by her fish-roaster, and this would be a good occasion to use it, since this fish would neatly fit into the hinged, fish-shaped holder, crisscrossed by diagonal metal strips which hung on its chain at the side of the fireplace.

When Damienne had bustled away, wearing several layers of clothing and holding a scarf across her face against the evening cold, Marguerite walked over to the hearth into the light of the fire. For a moment she stood there in silence, gazing into the flames. Then she turned and spoke rather formally to her husband. "We are to have a child, *mon mari,*" she said serenely, head held with pride at the announcement, although she suspected that he may long since have known of her state.

He smiled at her in a manner which he hoped was joyous and reassuring, and replied, "Yes, I knew." Then, laying his arms around her still-slender body, he pulled her head against his shoulder. His smile faded abruptly as he looked down at top of her head, and his eyes were bleak. Best to be honest, he finally told himself, since he had never been adept at dissembling his feelings for long periods of time. "*Ma Ame,*" he murmured, "I had truly hoped that you would not be gotten with child until we were safely back in France. There will be much danger for you in bearing your child here." His very being groaned with apprehension for his wife, and he hoped that Marguerite did not sense the full extent of his fear.

Marguerite said nothing in reply, resting against his spare body in utter repose, now that the matter had been brought into the open. But her husband thought she trembled, standing in his arms, although perhaps it was with the cold. He wondered if he had given her proud announcement too chill a welcome. "Dieu!" he blurted repentantly. "I will welcome an heir as much as any man. But I had hoped not to get my children at the expense of my wife." Through his mind went the visions which had come to him many times in the last weeks, women in his own family and neighboring noblewomen, dying in childbed, some within their first year of marriage. Marguerite's own mother had probably died in childbirth, he thought, although she had never mentioned it.

His fears for her had reached the point of anguish now that he was brought to face the thought of the child's actual birth. Somehow he had hoped that by obscure and mysterious means, women's matters, of which men knew not, the problem would somehow vanish. Facing the situation, his response now changed to anger at their needless predicament, at being isolated here at such a time. When I next meet Roberval, he thought, this matter will add heavily into the accounting. I will skewer him to the nearest wall without wasted words.

But the expression on her young husband's face was almost frightening in its fear for her, and its anguish. So Marguerite tried to allay his concern and to show somewhat more of confidence than she was quite sure she felt. She therefore said in her firmest tones, "To bear your child will be a proud thing. If I have not lost him by now, he must be a sturdy babe, and well begot." And silence fell between them as the young pair stood before their lonely hearth fire, still wrapped in each other's arms. What should have been a joyous moment was a pensive one, alone as they were at such a time, an ocean away from family, from France.

But Damienne now bustled into the *logette,* stamping the snow from her feet, face red and breath showing a vapor before her open mouth. But the married pair remained as they were, and finally Marguerite broke the silence. "As I am sure you know, we are to have a child." Her tone was confident, although she well knew that Damienne had probably been hoping that she would lose the child before its loss would be too grievous.

This had indeed been so. Damienne sighed and lowered her head, and for a second her old shoulders drooped. Then she bethought herself. Is my Lady's child a bastard, then, that I give him so cold a welcome? Penitently she laid her few half-frosted herbs on the hearth and approached Marguerite. She made a formal half-curtsey and raised her Lady's hand to her lips. "The coming of your first child, *ma Damoiselle,* is a matter for joy," she said. "May he be like his father!"

Suddenly they were all laughing.

The last bottle wine was promptly opened and a toast was drunk in scanty sips of wine. Damienne hurried about at the hearth, preparing a meal fit to welcome the advent of important news. And they again dressed in their richest clothing, but found that they now had to wear their sleeved, fur-lined capes, even in the *logette,* beside the fire.

—2—

The master of their household had now been sitting at the head of his table, with Marguerite at the foot facing him, as was customary. Damienne sat between them, facing the wall, and serving the food. And before they seated themselves to eat, their young Lord had adopted his family's custom of singing a Grace. Often he chose his boyhood favorite, which began, "*Tes jugementz, Dieu veritable—*" although their three voices sounded thin to him, as they sang it, since in his early years many voices had joined in.

After he had known of the coming of the child he had always added a silent prayer for his wife, for, try as he would, he was still cruelly apprehensive. The child would come in April, she had told him. Thus they had the whole winter to get through beforehand, and already it was bitterly cold. He despaired at the small chance his wife, *enciente* as she was, would have to survive on this desolate and wind-torn island.

And he noticed that Damienne, also, was concerned for her Lady's coming ordeal, and that she was making what preparations she could, so that now no further show of gaiety was attempted in the evenings. In any event, their fingers would have been too cold to play tric-trac, or to attempt tunes on their musical instruments. So they sat before their fire after finishing the evening meal, and talked of matters which were now of even greater import to them, since the coming of their child was acknowledged.

Close to the fire, as needs must be, their long fur capes draped over their backs, they now had more time to talk in one evening than they had had in a week during the building of the *logette.*

Their child would be the heir to two great houses, but the young couple were all too wise in the ways of power in France to think that mere blood right would insure his position. They, themselves, would have to see to that.

It is the place of the husband to arrange such matters, Marguerite thought, so that he must know everything I can remember. We will receive nothing but obstruction from Roberval, of that I am sure.

So with a certain reluctance she introduced the subject of her inheritance one evening as they sat before their fire. It usually belonged to fathers and fathers-in-law to thresh out such matters, but she would have to rely on herself, she thought, if her child was to receive any remnant of his rightful inheritance. Awkwardly she began, "We have not talked of it, *mon mari,* but there is the matter of my properties when we return to France. They should pass to my child, as well. You must help me to think what we can best do to make sure of his inheritance." After a moment she added, "It will not be an easy thing, I fear."

Her husband replied soberly that with Jean-François to deal with, it would be a chancy matter, indeed. "It will probably depend, *certes*, on how much control your fine kinsman had over your own inheritance."

Head bent over her mending, Marguerite admitted that apparently he had entire control, and that this had been given to him when she was very young. "My parents died before I can even remember," she explained, "And my grandfather took me into his home. He was Jean de Sermet, Seigneur de Sauveterre and d'Allas, and he was old and ill." His last illness, she thought, as he must have known, and in his fears for me he did not know where to turn.

"*Grand-père* had heard of Roberval, since he was beginning to make himself known at Court, and he sent for him to come to Sauveterre." Glancing ironically at her husband, she added, "I suppose Jean-François troubled himself to be full of charm when he scented out gain for himself which must have been apparent to him when he knew that an old man was making plans for the wardship of an infant granddaughter." Her voice stilled at the memory.

"I have seen the document my grandfather signed," she finally went on. "It stated that he gave donation on the first of September, 1528, of the rock and noble house of Roquevidal in the parish of Allas, facing the villages of Thomas and Codert to an 'honorable and discreet person.' " She laughed sardonically. "I suppose that is the only time that Roberval has been so described! Only a trusting old man would have been so fooled." Face turned to the fire, she added sadly, "Apparently he turned over my other properties to him as well."

Her husband sat in reflective silence. In the face of such a disastrous mistake, he thought, there was little to be said.

Marguerite chafed her cold hands and said softly, "Poor loving old man—I have never blamed him. He did as he thought he must, as seemed wise to him at the time, impressed as he was at Roberval's splendor, without doubt."

Her husband nodded understandingly, and patted her chilly hand. A worse choice could hardly have been found, in truth, but sometimes strict adherence to the ties of blood brought such things about, he knew.

His wife went on, "I do not know the exact arrangement, and we may never be able to find it out, if Roberval gets back to France before we do."

And that, thought Marguerite, is probably just what will happen. But determinedly she went on, "Jean-François may have been given title only during my minority, or he may have been made guardian until my marriage; I do not know." Significantly she glanced aside at Damienne and continued, "He had already started to sell off property while I was still a very small child, but, of course, he had a great deal of property of his own."

Her husband pulled his warm cape about him and shifted his legs as they stretched toward the fire. "I take it that he must have inherited his own properties when he was very young," he remarked rather indifferently. Continuing the conversation gave him no pleasure, but it would be an offense to his young wife to let her know the full extent of his contempt and disinterest with regard to her kinsman.

"Yes," she replied, "His father was Bernard de la Roque, who died when Jean-François was about fourteen. But he had been *Connetable* of Carcassonne for a while before his death, and I was there for a while, myself, when I was a child. I suppose Jean-François took me there for some reason after his father's death." A dim vision of the towers and battlements of that walled city drifted through her mind. It was all so long ago, and across the ocean-sea, so that it could well have been a dream.

"Roberval inherited his own properties at his majority, before I was born," she responded, bethinking herself of her husband's question. "They may have impressed *grand-père,* because Roberval's inheritance was much greater than mine."

Her husband changed his position, and opened the front of his cape to let in some warmth, rewrapping it around his legs.

"What did he actually inherit?" he asked obligingly, since the whole subject now seemed to be engrossing his wife.

"Oh, our family came from the South of France, you know, and most of his holdings were there, but some were scattered." She glanced up from her mending, but her husband was still maintaining a show of interest. "Roberval, itself, is in Picardy, as you know, but he also got Noë Sainte Remy, Noë Sainte Martin, Racoul and Mauru in the Duchy of Valois, Seuil, Acy les Rethel, Poix and St. Soupplex in the Rethelois, and Arzains and Armenys in the Languedoc."

Chafing her hands toward the fire, she added, "I do not know what came to him from his mother. She was Isabeau de Poitiers, a relative of Diane who is making such a sensation at Court." Marguerite smiled at her husband to apologize for the long family history, and concluded, "Jean-François got Roberval itself from his grandmother, Alix de Popincourt, Dame de Roberval."

"Was he, then, an only child?" he asked.

"Oh, no, he had a sister, Charlotte, and a brother who went into the Church. I do not know what properties were settled on them." It would have been like Roberval, she thought, to assure himself of the largest share. "Charlotte married Guillaume de Magdaillan, the Seigneur de Montataire," she added. "I think you met him when he was helping Jean-François get ready for the voyage."

Her husband remarked that it was a pity that she had lost touch with her mother's family, since they might have been willing to come to their aid.

"Apparently there were none of them left," Marguerite said sadly, "Or at least none came forward. After all, an orphan child whose holdings have been put into other hands is no great bargain." Revealing memories rushed through her mind as she said this. "If my mother's relatives had been interested, I now think that Roberval would have turned them away. He never wanted me to make close attachments."

At her husband's quizzical look, she added, "I used to think it was because we had to travel so much, but I have begun to wonder if there were also other reasons."

Damienne had kept her silence, but she had dark thoughts on the subject which had long been fermenting in her shrewd old mind. And the two young people, as well, fell into a somber mood as they sat gazing into their dying fire. It would be a hard decision for them to make, both were thinking, whether they should attempt to claim Marguerite's inheritance, to be passed on to their child.

—3—

As Marguerite's girth increased, her young husband masked his worry by teasing her. From somewhere in his memory he brought forth a poem, which he claimed to believe Marc-Claude de Buttet had written for Marguerite. Plaintively he recited it, misquoting slightly:

Mais, ah! Margot, tu es plus dure
Que ma cognee á émancher
Que le bois qui ce logette emmure
Et que la coste d'un rocher.

His wife broke into a giggle. She wondered how long it had taken him to dredge up the poem out of his memory, or where, indeed, he had happened to hear it. She doubted that Marc-Claude had written it for her, but, if not, as her husband said, it was indeed a strange accident of words.

Marguerite laughed again, as she looked at her Lord. His courtly gestures had been all the more amusing since he was wearing his shabby work-clothing and gesturing with a chisel. He was hollowing out a large container from a section of log. The work, he said, would keep him warm.

*

One evening that month they had an unpleasant experience. Hideous sounds came through the roof of the *logette.* Something was trying to dig its way in. From the snapping and snarling it might be wolves, or it might be a bear or two which had not yet hibernated.

Damienne cowered, but the young couple jumped to seize the arquebuses. Hastily they each loaded two of them, and readied them to fire.

Hastily they decided to burst out the door and run to a slight distance from the corners of the cabin, in opposite directions, so that they could both get a clear shot, but not be in each other's line of fire. If there were more beasts than they could kill, they would run back into the *logette* to reload. With two guns apiece, they should be able to cover each other's retreat.

The plan was executed in seconds. It would not do to have the roof destroyed.

When the young couple got into their firing positions, they saw two dark shapes on the roof, silhouetted against the darkening sky, heads raised. The arquebuses fired, with their burst of sound and flame. Both beasts fell.

And a crackling through the brush told of the rapid departure of other animals.

While Marguerite held her second arquebus ready to fire, her husband went to look at their kill. Both beasts were thrashing bloodily in the snow, snapping at themselves where they had been hit—wolves, and big ones.

Marguerite and her husband looked at each other. They had seen the wolves stalking the caribou, and frequently had heard their deep sinister howls in the near distance. One of the beasts had had a sort of long, smooth howl; another howled in two notes. But it was one thing to see or hear them at a distance, and another to have them digging their way into the *logette.* Damienne would not find this reassuring.

Marguerite went back into the *logette,* carrying the two discharged arquebuses, which she handed to Damienne. "Clean them, if you will," she said in an off-hand manner. "We have killed two beasts." and without a showing of haste she wrapped some of the kindling moss around the ends of two boughs and sprinkled some oil on them, to make torches. Picking up an extra knife, she lighted the torches and turned to leave the cabin. "We are going to skin them," she added casually.

In the light of the torches, the beasts looked enormous. One, a male, seemed almost as long as her husband was tall, Marguerite thought. Its back was an ugly gray, sprinkled with black, and its legs and underparts a yellowish white. The other animal was somewhat smaller and more reddish in color, a female. Their feet, she noticed, were almost as long as her own.

She was devoutly glad that they were dead.

After a moment of discussion the young pair decided to hang the animals up for skinning, and to throw their carcasses into the sea. Thus other beasts would not be attracted back to devour them beside the *logette,* and the flattened hides would be much less frightening to Damienne.

So Marguerite placed the torches upright in the snow and returned to the cabin to reassure Damienne and to put on more clothing. When she returned the fresh hides were lying in the snow, fur-side-up, and one carcass had already been carried away. She turned the hides over and wiped them off with handfuls of snow. They were already freezing.

On her husband's return she asked him what they could do with the pelts, and they decided to hang them on the *logette* wall, as far as possible from the fireplace. After they had been dried and scraped, and would no longer stain the floor, they could be used for rugs.

"We will put them beside the beds," said Marguerite, "Where they will be warm to step upon, in the cold mornings." This was a greater show of *sang froid* than she felt in her heart, as she still trembled from the night's encounter, but Damienne must be soothed from her deep unease.

As Marguerite gazed at the hides, even the empty eye-holes still seemed fierce and menacing.

—4—

Damienne had found that a savory potion could be made from the leaves of one of the little berry plants, and she had saved and dried a supply. It seemed satisfying after a meal of their roast meat, or their ragout, and they often drank it merely for the comfort of its warmth, cupping their hands around a mug of it to warm their cold fingers.

Their conversation, now, often returned to Jean-François de la Roque, Sieur de Roberval, because he stood at the center of their problems when they returned to France. The women did not doubt that this would come to pass, either during the next summer or a later one, and their young Lord kept his own counsel about the ships which had passed by them, returning to France. There was little likelihood of rescue now, he knew.

When the women spoke of their return home, bitter resignation and angry resentment surged back and forth in his mind so that he could hardly suppress them from reaching expression in his face. Loneliness for the lovely land of France overwhelmed him, at times, so that the tears scalded at the back of his eyeballs like fire, like a very corrosion in his head. But always, with an effort, he avoided betraying his secret, or the bitter hopelessness for which he had clear cause. He, alone, had seen the passing of the ships.

But as sleet glazed the roof, and gusts of snow became more frequent, he governed his mind to talk with the women of their return, and of Roberval.

"My kinsman hoped to recover his fortunes through this expedition," remarked Marguerite one evening. How he persuaded the King to place him in the position of Viceroy of Canada she did not know, she added, since it seemed unfair to many. Jacques Cartier had proposed the voyages to the New World in the first place, all knew, and he had already made two previous voyages there, setting up colonies of sorts. Many thought that he could have handled the colonization, therefore, better than her inexperienced kinsman. "But," she added, "Jean-Francçois has great influence with François Premier, as you know."

With an effort her Lord wrenched his mind away from its dark thoughts. After a pause he said meditatively, "It was, indeed, strange. I have wondered if there was some obligation, perhaps, to be paid off?" Quizzically he glanced toward Marguerite. "It would have been a neat solution. If Jean-François succeeds, he brings in new lands for France; if he fails or does not return, the obligation is paid off."

With a cynical smile, he added, "The King cannot lose, either way."

His wife looked startled. "I'll wager you're right!" she laughed, with a sudden peal of genuine mirth. "How clever! And it is fitting to have such a thing happen to my cousin, since it is the very sort of trick he likes to play on others."

But her voice soon sobered, and she went on to say that she had known that Roberval was very deeply in debt, and that he was trying to conceal it. He had sold most of his holdings, and compromised most of the rest. The King had given a huge sum, 45,000 livres, she believed, to outfit the expedition, but Roberval had still used money of his own.

"He was hoping," she continued thoughtfully, "To recover his investment by selling land-rights to the settlers, and granting landfiefs in seigneurial tenure to the noblemen who came with him on the expedition. Many of them have no lands in France, or not enough to support them."

"Yes," said her husband wryly, "I know."

Land-hungry noblemen were the joke of France, since the inheritance laws which divided estates among children equally, gradually cut up large holdings, generation by generation, into very small and scattered ones. So land was a precious thing, and all desired it almost as much as gold, even to being willing to seek it in New France.

Thinking of this, Marguerite continued, "My cousin had authority to charge annual dues from the settlers, and whatever he gained was to be divided three ways, as you know, one-third to his *compagnons*, one-third to himself, and one-third to the King."

Her husband now folded the inlaid *tric-trac* board and put it away on the mantel-shelf. Their hands were too cold to play, and his wife was thinking of other things.

She gazed into the flames, and spoke slowly and softly. "While François Premier is King, my cousin will be safe. François has used him for many things which Kings wish to have done, but cannot be seen to do for themselves. Thus François cannot afford to lose his allegiance—I will not call it loyalty."

"Making a claim against Roberval will be useless, then," said her husband bluntly, wearying of the whole futile discussion. "Have you any way of proving your inheritance? Proof, that is, that your cousin cannot seek out and destroy?"

Disconcerted at his harsh tone, Marguerite paused to give the matter thought. "The transfer from my grandfather would be recorded. It would be carefully preserved because it would change the responsibility for paying the taxes." She smiled ironically. It mattered little who was disinherited, or even exiled, just so the taxes were duly paid to the King's agents. "The other record of my inheritance would be the pledge of Faith and Homage to the King, which I signed when I was hardly more than a child."

Damienne spoke for the first time. "I well remember that day," she said firmly, her rough Norman accent breaking forth at the memory. "I thought that at last *ma Damoiselle* had come into her own. Still a slip of a thing, and here she was signing her Faith and Homage in as bold a hand as a Queen." She nodded her head proudly, and added, "I can bear witness to that. They read off the titles, too, and I well remember them, as well."

Marguerite smiled. "I had read them off to myself before I signed. Jean-François was none too well-pleased when he saw me do so. It was the first time I had been really sure of what I owned." Wryly she added, "It was not a subject that my cousin encouraged me to discuss."

Damienne leaned forward, elbows on knees, and nearly closed her eyes. "I can see it again now," she said, "The Lords and their Ladies who were also waiting to sign, in their gay-colored silks and satins and brocades. We had all been called to Amboise, and quite a trip it was for us, I can tell you." She clucked to herself at the thought. "What a flurry of dressmaking, before we left! The most splendid clothing that either of us have ever owned, or are like to." A pang of regret for their past glories crossed her furrowed old face. But she went on, "And that stately gentleman before whom you pledged your Faith, what was his name?"

"Raoul de Lestrade, Seigneur de Floriac," answered Marguerite. Turning to her husband, she added, "He is an honest man, and would guard those documents carefully, since they are important to the King. I suppose Raoul de Lestrade could testify to my signing, and show the document." At her husband's dubious look, she added, "He must still be living. That was only six years ago."

"To the month, six years," said Damienne. "It was the seventeenth of November in 1536. I can witness to that."

"Do you suppose we could get Roberval's wardship revoked?" asked Marguerite, looking up at her husband as he leaned against the mantel, his cape held apart to catch the heat. "I am almost of age," she added hopefully.

After a moment's reflection her Lord told her that as he recalled it, marriage rights and wardships were handled by the *baillis* and *séneschals*, and over them were the *enquêteurs*, who were responsible to the King. "As you know," he added, "The Lords were often difficult and unfair when they had the sole right to control marriages." Meditatively he added, "I am not quite sure of where the guardians of minors are accountable now—to the *seneschals*, I suppose, since it is they who apparently award the wardships."

At a sudden memory his wife replied, "It has long been the duty of guardians to seek suitable marriages for their wards, and fifteen years has been the marriageable age for girls in Angoulême." She smiled impishly at her husband. "Do you suppose that my kinsman arranged the matter thus to get me off his hands, so that you could not get away?"

Her Lord pursed his lips judiciously. "He no doubt best knew what would be necessary to find you a husband, my Marguerite. Mayhap he thought to take me ashore trussed like a goose?"

But Damienne made it clear that she did not think these remarks amusing. Marriage and inheritance were serious matters.

—5—

One day while Damienne was pounding grain for flour, sifting it laboriously through her horsehair sieve, and Marguerite was again mending, her husband stole away on an errand of his own.

Taking his axe to explain his departure, he went directly to the cave and built a fire there, using his slow-match to kindle it. Carefully he built his small fire into a moderate blaze, adding a chunk of peat to hold it, and went about his wood-chopping, carrying loads to the *logette* to add to the winter's supply. Wood disappeared with disquieting swiftness, he found.

He had often wondered why woodchoppers worked all summer long, and he now saw that it was to be warm all winter.

At intervals he returned to the cave. As a test, he had closed the door-opening by stacking broad chunks of peat across it. Slowly the cramped space became warmer. The fire seemed to throw more heat in the narrow confines of the cave than it did in the *logette,* and not to use so much wood. Even before the low, vaulting granite was warmed, it seemed to reflect back the heat, albeit the day was very chill. It was a matter for thought.

And every time he returned to the cave, the place was warmer. The rock seemed to hold the heat. So he decided that he would mention the matter to the women, as though he used the cave to save trips to the *logette* to warm himself—a thin pretext, he thought wryly, if they happened to remember how difficult was the climb to reach it, up the cliff-face.

But toward evening he built up a fair blaze there. No danger of catching the roof on fire here, he thought, with a sudden sense of release from care. Starting fires in the *logette* was ever a matter for caution, lest large sparks fly out the chimney and ignite the bark on the roof. Just before he went home for the night, he banked the flames, leaving a few chunks of peat to hold the fire.

The next day was still colder, but very clear. Again the young Lord went out to chop wood, and he immediately returned to the cave. As he took the broad pieces of peat away from the door, he was surprised at the warmth of the interior. Apparently once the rock became warm, it held the heat for a long time, unlike the *logette,* where the warmth held by the stones of the fireplace did not go far to warm the room. Nor did their fires, there, he thought, in all reality. Apparently the hunters' stories at home in France had truth in them, even for such a shallow cave as this one.

From that time on, burdened as he was with his sense of sole responsibility for his women-folk, he carried one load of wood to the *logette* and one to the cave, alternately, following the same plan when he cut and carried peat.

If need be, he thought, it will be here.

*

When their Lord returned home, following this decision, the women showed no curiosity regarding that day's long absence. As he stamped the snow off his feet he saw that they had taken their scanty handfuls of wild-wheat flour, and had mixed it into a sort of dough. They had cleaned and oiled the baking-tongs, and were apparently going to bake the nearest thing they could to bread. Home-like odors filled the rude room.

As he stood at the doorway, removing his snow-caked outer garments, the young exile was assailed with a sudden mixture of contradictory emotions. How gallant his women were, he thought, in their efforts to bring about comfort in this desolate place, and how vile and contemptible were those, now resting in their comforts up-river, who had brought this necessity upon them.

The dancing flames in the fireplace and the homelike smells of herbs and cookery filled the *logette* with a superficial sense of comfort, but away from the hearth the room was very chill, and around them, for hundreds of leagues, was frozen wilderness, untrodden by any man.

December, 1542

—1—

The weather became still more frigid, and daytime now was very brief.

One day a sort of smoke seemed to arise from the sea, in the form of a white haze that lay over the water, drifting with the wind. The exiles noticed this for a few more days, and, after a clear, moonlight night, the sea in the harbor showed no ripples. It seemed to be filled with a thicker liquid than water, which was not yet ice.

The next day a sort of tough, leathery skin of ice lay over the harbor, and within a few days they found that this ice was firm and smooth. After a few cautious ventures they learned that they could safely walk on it, and once they went across and visited the other islands and even the mainland. But the trips only deepened their sense of desolation—the mainland and the outer islands were the same as their own domain, only more barren.

A day or two after these ventures the surface of the harbor ice became slushy, as the salt worked out, and then snow fell, blowing into patterns and ridges on the frozen surface until it was hard to tell where the land left off and the ice began.

Outside the barrier of the outer islands, patches of loose ice floated about, sometimes packed together as far as eye could see.

Sometimes this welter of floating ice-cakes contained icebergs which had apparently come down the northern channel, or down the river.

When the tide moved in and out cracks and lanes opened up in the ice, and sometimes it ground together with a deafening roar. The exiles became accustomed to a sort of ceaseless hum of the ocean, day and night, as the water sounded against the ice. Together with the sound of the wind, which seldom ceased, their very ears seemed to ring with loneliness.

They had discontinued the daily trips to the summit long since. Ships would no longer come, and the fishermen had gone home. Nor would the warparties of savages come down the river to make war farther to the north. Only animals might come across the land-bridge which had now frozen between their island and the mainland.

Across it the exiles now might have left their island, but there was no-where that they could go.

Now they spent most of their time in the *logette,* needing what warmth it gave. The women tried to patch together warmer garments, or cooked, the man carved, or on days of less severe weather, cut wood. And ceaselessly they fed the fire. As their nerves drew ever more tightly-strung, with the effort of staying warm, staying alive, they had much time for talk, and sought subjects which might divert their minds from the foreboding stealing into them when long silences fell.

One evening Marguerite told her husband of the time she and Damienne had spent in Honfleur, before the start of the voyage. Roberval had fitted out his ships there, and had made it a sort of base of his operations in making ready for the expedition. Hunched on her cushioned stool by the hearth-fire, she recalled those days and told of them in a soft, reminiscent tone.

She and Damienne had stayed first in two different inns at the harbor entrance of Honfleur, across from the *Leutnancy,* the harbor headquarters. The names of those inns in faraway France hung lingeringly on her lips—the *Hostellerie des Trois Marchands* and the *Hotel de Cheval Blanc.* Her voice evoked their very existence, facing up the Seine, overlooking the river-harbor. But then Jean François had found them rooms farther up the hill, in the town, in an old house with neat terra-cotta tile floors and a cozy, high fireplace. Easing her heavy body on the stool, Marguerite rubbed her back with one slim hand. Her whole spine had begun to ache, a common thing, Damienne had told her, during pregnancy. And chill air made it ache more penetratingly, so that Marguerite thought of their cozy little room in Honfleur with longing. It had had a steep, spiral wooden staircase, she remembered, with a rope down the middle to aid in ascent, and had faced on a little paved court with a well.

Honfleur itself was a bustling mercantile port, having benefited from the silting-in of Harfleur, just across the Seine, some years before. Both Harfleur and Honfleur were upriver of *Villefrançoise-de-Grace,* now familiarly known as Le Havre, the port which François Premier had so greatly enlarged and improved.

But captains preparing for voyages to the New World still preferred Honfleur as an embarkation port, Marguerite recalled, and many expeditions had left from there to explore or fish, and it was said that a captain from Honfleur, one Denys, had explored the Gulf of *Sainct Laurent* before Jacques Cartier ever went there.

Damienne chuckled to remember that this Denys did not hold his discovery in great store, having referred to his landfall as the "Cabo de Nada"! "From this the name of 'Canada' was taken," she added, with sour satisfaction in her tone, plying her needle with a vengeful air.

"That name may not have helped my cousin Roberval," replied Marguerite reminiscently, "As he sought for colonists to come here. Few were willing to leave France as it was."

She well remembered, she said, how angry Roberval had been at the stubborn reluctance of his countrymen to accommodate him by coming along on the expedition to settle his new land. It had been hoped that many sturdy artisans would see this as an opportunity to gain lands of their own, but no such candidates could be found. After months of effort, the numbers were still few for safety in the savage new land. Even sailors were hard to come by.

So at last, reluctantly, Roberval had returned to Court. Already he had become to some degree a butt of ridicule there, and he was not eager to return without some success to report. His detractors at Court had already dubbed him l'Eslu de Poix, which was a bit pejorative, as though to call him the mere tax-collector of Poix, and even François Premier himself had taken to calling him the Petty King of Vimeux, because of his lordly ways.

But return he had, to request of the King that he might take prisoners from various jails to increase his numbers of settlers. A royal writ was issued empowering him to requisition prisoners from Paris, Toulouse, Bordeaux, Rouen and Dijon, Marguerite remembered.

Her husband replied ironically, chafing his cold hands toward the fire, "So much for the honest Frenchmen who were to Christianize the new land!"

But as a crowning blow it was discovered that even the prisoners were not anxious to leave France. Whereupon, Marguerite remembered, Roberval had pressed into service his brother-in-law, Guillaume de Magdaillan, to find prisoners. To that goodly Lord's dismay, he had been able to find only one, a strangler named Jehan Grevyn.

And one Alonce de Cyville who had also been sent forth to comb the prisons and jails had fared scarcely better. It seemed that few from the prisons and still less from the working classes wanted to go to New France. "Only land-hungry noblemen were interested, and their only skill was in bearing arms," she concluded.

Her husband had to smile at this overly-candid remark as he remembered his struggles during the carpentering of the *logette* door, around which the frigid air was even now creeping into their room.

But Damienne and Marguerite were reminiscing over Roberval's behavior in those days. It seemed that he had been a most unpleasant warder, first, because he was not accustomed to having his wishes thwarted, and secondly because he now had most of his wealth tied up in the boats and supplies for the expedition. It was too late to turn back.

So he had tried to put a bold face on the matter, the women recalled, first by purchasing the *Marye*, a large ship of between eighty and one hundred tons burden. From it he immediately flew the King's standard and the de la Roque crest with its three rocky mounts, as well as the crests of the gentleman-companions which were painted on the *pavese* at the sides of the ship. But the brave show had apparently fooled few of the shrewd French ship-owners. While he had tried to rent two other ships, the *Saincte Anne* of eighty tons and the *Valentyne* of ninety-two, their owners had apparently not trusted his credit, and he had finally been compelled to buy the *Valentyne* outright.

And even the recruiting of seamen had proved difficult as Simon Harel, master of the *Valentyne* and Jehan Mallet of the *Saincte Anne* had had to be paid thirty *eçus soleil* to go recruiting among the ports.

All of this had detained the expedition well into August, the women remembered, and it was then too late to leave for New France. But Roberval had sailed away from Honfleur on August twenty-third, having by that time received the powder, artillery and munitions he had bought in Champagne and Normandy.

And, perhaps more importantly, he had also received a very unpleasant letter, telling him that Chancelier Poyet had informed the Parlement de Rouen that it was strange that the Sieur de Roberval had not yet left on his voyage. This was dangerous news.

"I think Jean-François set forth from Honfleur, after that, only to make a show," said Marguerite reflectively, "And because the King, also, had been pressing him to go." She glanced at Damienne. "After all, this was a full year after he had bought the *Marye,* and he was pledged to meet Jacques Cartier at the settlement in Canada."

After a moment she turned toward her husband and added, "I think that it must have been then that Roberval decided to go forth as a pirate. He needed money, and it was too late in the season to start for New France."

Her husband replied thoughtfully, "Since he had already liquidated most of his estates in the South of France, from what you tell me, and compromised the others, I can see that he was in dire straits."

Damienne and I stayed in Honfleur, as you well know,"

Marguerite continued, "But the sailors had apparently been told that the voyage was under way." As was customary they had made their pilgrimage to the church of Notre-Dame de Grâce in Honfleur, walking there barefoot just before boarding ship, as seamen had been doing for many years. She remembered the old church with its mellow stone walls and round-domed towers, as well as the roadway to it, lined with Breton women in their crossed handkerchiefs and pointed bonnets who had stood to watch the seamen pass by. Well had their lined faces told of knowledge, harshly gained, of what faced seamen who departed on long voyages to strange lands.

For a moment all three exiles were silent, thinking of Honfleur and the comforts there, the inns and houses facing the old port, which was already silting in, the *echoppes* with their cobbled floors, and, above all, of the warmth and coziness there, where the houses and shops had all been built side-by-side, sharing each other's warmth. "Damienne and I were comfortable there," Marguerite concluded. "Those little, low-ceilinged rooms were far more cozy than the drafty castles and *châteaux.*"

And warmer than her lodging here, *enciente* though she is, thought her husband ruefully, adding peat to hold the fire for the nighttime hours. It was more and more difficult to keep the *logette* warm.

A few days later as the women worked inside the cabin the door burst open with a blast of frigid air, and Marguerite raised her head aghast at her husband's state. His mustache was crusted with a solid chunk of ice, and his eyebrows, eyelashes and nostrils were coated with an icy covering. At first he could hardly speak.

"*Il fait un froid de loup,*" he gasped. "I did not know, for a while, if I could get back to the cabin." Shivering, he laid a brace of partridges on the side of the hearth. Their plumage had long since turned white. Then he coughed, and seemed to have trouble in catching his breath.

Marguerite was deeply alarmed. She hastily stripped off her Lord's icy clothing, and wrapped him in a warm bed-robe, rubbing his chilled arms and legs as she did so. Then she put him to bed, asking Damienne to make him some hot barley-broth, while she, herself, gave him a mixture half of wine, half of hot water.

His teeth chattered against the cup as he drank it.

Hurriedly Marguerite rolled wool cloths around the warming-stones from the fireplace to pack around him but still he shivered uncontrollably. But inside the bed-curtains it was warmer, while the room was now chill, and after her husband had eaten a little of his hot barley-broth, Marguerite crawled into bed beside him to add to the warmth.

As her Lord's shivering finally diminished he tried to allay his wife's concern. Through bluish lips he even made a feeble jest about Marguerite's greater resistance to the cold, quoting a popular rhyme:

"Car, comme au froid elle a fait resistance . . ."

But even as he spoke, his lips were stiff with chill. The warmth of the bed did not seem to penetrate his body, and even with Marguerite's arms around him he shuddered with cold from time to time under the thick goose-feather bedding, seeming to gasp for breath.

*

The next day he was no better.

The women took turns nursing him, Damienne preparing whatever tempting foods she could, and even making another trip to the vegetable storage place to get carrots for a *potage.*

When she returned she muttered to her Lady that she had had to dig away the deep snow and ice with a shovel, and for a while, she added, she had thought she would have to use the axe, it was now so bitterly cold.

And the women could not keep the cabin warm. No matter how they laid the fire, the heat seemed to whisk away, up the chimney, and biting cold seeped in through every cranny, especially around the laboriously-built door. The women hung hides over it, and put on all the clothing they could wear, but still they had to warm their hands and feet inches from the fire, at more and more frequent intervals.

So that for several days, even after he said he felt well enough to get up, Marguerite kept her husband in bed, covered with all their bed-clothing, and she included one of the caribou hides on top, furside-down. The cold *logette,* she said, was not a suitable place for a man who was suffering from chill. And strangely languid after his long endeavors, her Lord allowed her to have her way in the matter.

When at last he insisted on getting out of bed, he did not again venture outdoors, but rather, bundled like the women in all his garments, he was grateful for the slight warmth of the fire and for the hot potions that Damienne prepared as sleet lashed across the roof. And the women now were reluctant to open the door even to carry in wood, because of the bitter cold that then swept into the cabin.

But at last the weather became still colder, a cold beyond all experience or imagining, and inside the *logette* food chilled on their plates before it could be eaten.

Finally the sick man raised his pale face to his wife with a look of resignation. "We will have to move to the cave," he said.

At first the women made shocked objections. It was a place hardly fit for animals, Marguerite cried out. How could they carry all the things they needed up there, through the deep snow? The bedding would be ruined, and how could the food be stored?

Cold vapor came from their lips as they stood only a step from the open fire, and at last their words died away. Finally in her despair Damienne sat down on a stool before the fire and covered her face with her hands, rocking her body back and forth, and Marguerite gazed sorrowfully at her husband. The hot potion in his cup, which Damienne had just poured for him, was skimmed with ice.

He spoke just once. "It is our only chance to live through the winter," he said.

And against their own reluctance, the women had to agree that he was right. Thin as he now was, he could not stand the cold, they knew.

*

Sadly they packed to go up to the cave.

As soon as the decision was made the women climbed the hill to make the fire there, beating a path as they went. Their Lord had nearly wept at his own helplessness when they would not permit him to join them, but his step was still infirm.

On succeeding trips they carried up the food supplies, after deciding to take just one pot, for a sort of permanent *ragout.* They did not think they would care to eat much.

Reluctantly the young pair decided to cut their canvas in two, since it was needed both to shed water out of the south side of the cave, and to drape over the double bed to protect their belongings, since they already had evidence that the roof would leak at every thaw.

And the container of oil was finally taken to the cave, together with the pan-lamps, since they all believed that the confinement there would be unendurable if they did not at least have light.

Finally the women dug out the stored vegetables, planning to keep them under the very bed-covers at the cave, if necessary; they also took the hides, since these could be laid all across the deep saucerlike bottom of the cave, to give it some feeling of warmth.

At last all was bundled to go. Their silks and satins were stored away under the canopy, and their fur-lined capes were their only remaining garments which hinted of past luxury. It was a strange procession, led by one torch, encumbered with bundles and unsuitably dressed, which left the *logette.*

As they closed the door, the cabin again looked bare. Only the blue and white plates still stood above the mantel.

*

They had replaced the ladder under the mouth of the cave, and Damienne had to be pushed and pulled up, encumbered with layers of clothing as she was, and Marguerite, heavy with child, could climb scarcely better. Her Lord made a brave show of nimbleness, but his breath wheezed in his throat as he reached the cave-shelf.

As the young couple helped her slide down into the cave, under the broad over-hang, Damienne moaned at the darkness within, at the thought that this miserable jumble of rocks was to be their home. Hastily she groped for a pan-lamp, filled it, and lighted it from the fire. The others had slid into the cave and had relaid the turf across the entrance. Marguerite was starting to arrange their supplies out of the way around the edges of the cave, near the ceiling, while her husband hung one of the hides over the chunks of turf at the entrance-way. Enough air would get in, he said, through the openings in the stones at the other side.

And the women were surprised at the warmth of the cave. As a hunter their Lord had learned a valuable thing. The cave was not inviting but it was snug. In shape it was similar to the space that would be made by two cupped hands, held side-wise. But the center portion was barely large enough for the three of them to stand upright at once, and when they did, their heads came close to the ceiling.

From this central area the floor sloped upward toward the edges in a deep saucer shape, and the ceiling sloped down to meet the floor at the sides in a somewhat similar curve. They had to make their bed on the slanted stone, across from the fireplace, which was built on a sort of natural shelf. The smoke escaped through the north opening, which was partly closed with clods of peat. There was even a sort of place of necessity, in the form of an opening which dropped away between the rocks at the north end. And they would not need to leave the cave during the worst weather, even for water, since an icicle had formed at the cave mouth within easy reach for melting.

So the straw tick from the double bed was laid down, with the feather mattress over it, then the woolen sheets and *pallaise.* Hides had already been laid underneath, to protect the bedding as much as possible from the damp and stain of the granite floor.

They would all three sleep together, they decided resignedly, needing each other's warmth as they did. And there was really no space for a separate bed for Damienne.

And for their food they had brought along only the metal

plates they had used on the voyage, and their spoons. The knives from their belts would serve to cut meat. The elegant use of forks would have seemed incongruous in these surroundings.

The pot was already bubbling over the fire, sitting on two stones, and Damienne had started things off with a potful of savory *ragout,* well laced with herbs. They ate. The cave was snug. It did not seem as dismal as they had feared, with the lamps burning and their comfortable bed laid out behind them. Damienne sat on the one small stool they had brought; the young couple reclined on the furs. And the small fire heated the cave better than a far larger fire had heated the *logette.*

They talked. Marguerite even made a small joke as she finished her inelegant meal. ''Prisoners are often starved, in France, in order that they should die,'' she said jauntily, ''But at least that is not happening to us here, imprisoned as we are beneath rock on this island!''

The others obligingly laughed. It was necessary to put as good a face on the matter as possible.

*

Privately both women though of the move to the cave as a sort of defeat; the man, having military training, tried to think of it as a strategic withdrawal to save one's forces.

No mention was made of Christmas, however, as the season came and passed. While they all tried to keep up every possible semblance of good cheer, their cramped cave did not seem like quite the place for a festive celebration of *Noël.* But while none of them mentioned the season, Marguerite still marked her calendar as the year drew to its close.

There were only a few hours of daylight now, but inside the cave as they were, it did not matter to them as they cowered together in their shelter under the granite shelf across which swept the raging winds and sleet.

The days passed in lamplight, firelight or darkness, and all three slept as much as they could, huddled together, with Marguerite between her husband and her old nurse.

And the child within her grew ever larger, and moved sluggishly about.

January, 1543

—1—

The heavy snows which had fallen since late December now covered the ground, drifting to great depths as they moved with the wind. The snow was powdery and dry, like light sand, and the drifts moved in various directions from day to day. Beneath the cave entrance a deep drift slanted gradually away, down into the valley below. When the wind blew, the loose surface snow rose in the air like a heavy smoke, sometimes reducing to a few feet the distance one could see.

Only the dark treetops and the rock faces blew clear of snow; the rest was whiteness. And the snow crystals were frozen so hard that they felt like tiny stones as they blew against one's face. So that for the most part the three were content to stay in their cave; indeed they were forced to do so. They could not descend to the valley by their accustomed path, and a trip up over the crest of the cliff, by the other path, was too dangerous to attempt. If there was wind, they could be swept off their footing, and the dry, crystalline cold could frostbite the face in a very few moments.

And there was almost always a biting wind, usually from the north or northwest.

They had heard that when the snow packed journeys could

be made over it, on a heavy crust. The snow on this island did not pack in this way, and they wondered if it would ever do so.

But on one sunny day, when the wind had died down, Marguerite and her husband finally ventured outside the cave. The confinement within had finally become too nerve-wracking to be borne. They had to climb up to the clifftop by the western path, feeling their way carefully to seek secure footing under the drifted snow.

With her increasingly cumbersome body, Marguerite felt handicapped, as did her husband with his lessened strength. They were aided, however, by the fact that the snow had blown off the vertical parts of the cliff-face, so that they could get hand-holds, but it was drifted on any flat areas.

In a way it seemed good to be outside the crowded confines of the cave, although the landscape was desolate, and it had become frighteningly unfamiliar and featureless. The ice and snow stretched in all directions, and landmarks were covered or disguised. Even outside the harbor, the sea was covered with floating ice which seemed to have packed solidly together.

The young pair saw a few tracks of birds and animals, grouse or partridges, they thought, and rabbits. Since a goodly supply of meat hung in the cave, they did not really need to hunt, as, indeed, they doubted they could do. Movement was hazardous. They knew that deep clefts in the rock were now covered by snow, and an occasional slip of the foot warned them again of this danger as they attempted to walk across the drifted patches of snow on the summit. A fall into a deep crevice could be deadly, they realized, and it would be foolish for either of them to go far outside the cave alone.

Across the bay, in the low marshes, the herd of caribou could be seen, since apparently the animals could find food there. And it was a comfort, somehow, to see them, the only living things in view except the birds which soared over the barren wastes.

Since the ice was now frozen solidly between their island and the mainland, the beasts could have been hunted had their flesh been needed. But as she looked at the forbidding rough and crevassed ice between their summit and the marshes of the mainland, Marguerite was glad that they did not need to cross the frozen passage and hunt. Her husband had not regained his strength and agility since his illness, and in her pregnancy she was no more able-bodied than he.

On the way back to the cave a few partridges flew out of the scrubby bushes near the summit, and the firing of the two arquebuses brought down four birds. Fresh roasted partridge would be a great treat, after the endless *ragout,* so the two hunters floundered and crawled back to the cave with some sense of triumph, having acquitted themselves rather well, they thought, in this strange country.

*

That night Marguerite found herself short of breath, and she decided to climb outside the cave again, for a moment. So she took away the peat chunks which covered the opening, but let the hide fall back into place so that too much of the bitterly cold night air would not sweep into the cave.

As she stood on the narrow shelf, the sky above her was clear and chill. Then, suddenly, it was alight with radiating, jagged beams, flaring upward from the north. The lights flickered over the snow and reflected from the white drifts in an eerie, unearthly cadence. Confusedly Marguerite passed her hand across her eyes, then looked again.

But still the strange lights rose and fell, rising from the cliff overhead, to the north. They resembled nothing that Marguerite had ever seen or imagined, and they seemed demoniacal, unearthly.

Firmly she tried to tell herself that women heavy with child were prey to strange fancies. They had odd whims, she had been told. Perhaps this was such a matter, although mostly such notions, from what she had heard, ran to cravings for delicacies or fretfulness with one's husband. Baffled, she stood staring at the lights.

At last the bitter cold stung her face; her nostrils prickled, and her fingers started to throb. So Marguerite slipped awkwardly back into the cave and replaced the layer of turf across the opening.

And keeping her silence about the strange vision she slid down into the floor of the cave to warm her hands at the fire.

—2—

Marguerite had now begun to worry about her husband's failure to regain his health and his strength. When she had seen him in the daylight, outside the ruddy firelight of the cave, his face had been thin and drawn, with a sort of yellowish color, like that of a man much older than he. And as she lay beside him in their slanting, rock-encased bed, she found that his body had become as gaunt as his face.

If she could, she resolved to try to raise his spirits, and thus to improve his appetite for food. He had eaten the partridges, she reflected, with some relish, so she murmured to Damienne that they must somehow contrive changes in the food. Also, she decided, she must endeavor to be more entertaining. He was a man who was accustomed to much activity. Perhaps they were all sleeping too much.

So that night Marguerite dug out from her small jewel casket her packet of playing cards, and after the evening meal she hung the lamps where they could see their cards, dealing out three hands. Her effort was successful. At least her husband picked up his cards and looked at them with a show of interest. "We used to do this during hunts," he said reminiscently, "When we were weathered in."

More and more, his wife noticed, his thoughts returned to France.

But she attempted another of her small jokes. "Playing cards were invented, it is said, to entertain an insane king when he was no longer fit to decide on affairs of state," she said wryly. "Perhaps they will keep us sane, as well." But neither her husband nor Damienne showed the slightest amusement, and as she glanced at them Marguerite thought suddenly that one could go mad in this place—it had been a sorry jest.

But after that they played cards, now and then, to divert

their minds from the cramped quarters, the monotonous food, and the desolation all about them. And Marguerite firmly deterred her husband from going outside. If the sights she had seen were not a delusion of her own, she thought, it would be well if the others did not know of them. Her husband and Damienne were in no state of mind, she thought, to be subjected to further unsettling experiences in this forlorn place.

As it was, the sounds were terrible enough. Fierce crushing noises came from the sea as the ice ground back and forth and the wind howled. Sometimes the noises resembled human cries, as though a thousand men howled aloud at the same time; sometimes they resembled heavy firing by cannons or lighter artillery.

Even surrounded as the exiles were by rock and piled turf in their cave, the sounds could constantly be heard. They seemed to travel through the very earth, carrying a sense of desolation, even of fear.

—3—

Marguerite and Damienne now talked of every subject which came into their minds which they hoped might be entertaining to a man, or might arouse their Lord from his speechless lethargy. He had never been as talkative as were many of their countrymen; now he seldom spoke at all, except to answer a question.

So one night when she was desperate for a topic which might truly interest him, Marguerite asked her Lord about developments in weaponry. The five arquebuses they had brought ashore were their most valuable possessions, but, she asked, were they the best guns to be had? The process of firing was so complicated, she complained, and the slightest fumbling or miscalculation resulted in a dangerous predicament for the hunter.

Her husband stirred from his reclining position on the slanting bed. "Yes," he replied, "What you say is true. And not only in hunting but in warfare, the problem of unreadiness to fire brings danger." He slowly raised his body upward, and clasped his hands about his knees. "We were told," he added, "That the savages could fire a great many arrows before an arquebus could be discharged one time, and I am sure that is true.'' Sighing, he stared into the fire, not wishing to pursue that uncomforting subject further, nor to express his thoughts that the wild beasts, too, had readier weapons than did the user of an arquebus.

''But are there no better firearms?'' Marguerite persisted. ''I thought that I had heard that the King's Italian master, old Leonardo, or some German arms-maker had found a way to improve arquebuses.''

Her husband smiled thinly. ''Yes, Leonardo did leave some drawings in his sketchbook, his *Codice Atlantico,* showing what has been called a wheel-lock, and then others claim that one Johann Kiefuss of Nurnberg invented them before Leonardo did. I do not know the truth of that dispute.'' He paused reflectively. ''Such weapons are gifts for emperors, not the province of ordinary men, since but a few of them have been made. Charles Quint has several, I have heard, but the Emperor Maximilian is said to have thought them so dangerous, and so likely to lead to violent crimes, that he forbade their use in his dominions.'' He glanced across their bed at his wife with a livelier show of interest than she had seen in many days.

Marguerite was reassured at his air of interest, following as it did, long days of depression. Ah, *mon amour,* she thought, at home in France you would be accounted still almost a *garçon,* but here on this island you have borne the cares of a man. Her eyes filled with tears as she realized anew how devotedly he had worked to insure her safety, even her comfort, in this desolate place, and how he had spent his own strength in the endeavor. But since her talk of weaponry had aroused his interest, of weaponry she would talk. ''Has nothing more been done to improve the guns?'' she asked.

''Oh, the powder is a problem as you know. Even when using the two different kinds of powder, as we now do, it cakes into lumps and packs in the barrels in such a way that it will not explode, but simply burns away.'' He glanced at their powder-cask, stored in a dry corner away from the fire. ''It leaves sticky remains in the barrel, too, which must be cleaned out after every few shots, as you well know." Smilingly he added, "Some shooters have been trying to mix or sift the powder so that it will work better."

Again he shifted his position on his lean back, and coughed slightly. "The balls for firing are a subject of constant dispute, as well. Stones and lead pellets are used by some; others swear by brass, iron, copper or tin, and in every shape you can think of. Some even use little arrows instead of bullets." He smiled sardonically and added that the arguments in these matters of weaponry waxed as hot as those on religion, which was saying a great deal, in faith-beleaguered France.

But after a pause he added soberly, "I, myself, do not think to be an expert, and since arquebuses are so little to be depended upon, I am glad that you are my man-at-arms, as well as my love. Thus we can protect each other, even as soldiers do, my Marguerite," he added with a shy and rarely-spoken affection.

Smiling, his thin face looking even more boyish than it had, he dozed off into sleep.

His young wife sat watching him for a long time. He repined deeply for France, she knew, and for the acres and château where he had been born. Heartsick at the thought of the cold months still ahead, she asked herself if she could somehow arouse him from his despair, his intermittent depressions, his lethargy. Ah, *mon homme,* she thought, somehow you must again walk the soil of France!

Damienne, too, watched her young Lord as he slept. When he awakened, she planned, she would give him a hot potion which she had made from her garlic, since the colds and infections of winter-time had long been dosed with such drinks. Fortunately she had brought her string of it along to the cave and kept it warmly wrapped from the cold that sometimes crept into their shelter, toward morning, when the fire smouldered down.

And grimly cold it was, indeed. All three exiles knew that clearly they would by now have died of it in the *logette.*

*

After her success in her talk of weaponry, Marguerite bestirred her thoughts each evening for subjects which would enliven the dreary, wind-lashed existence in the narrow confines of their cave, and which would arouse the flagging spirits of her Lord.

One night, rather reluctantly, she turned their talk to her cousin Roberval. Her husband held him in a rare contempt, she knew, but his very anger, which he believed he concealed from her, might arouse him more than gentler topics, she thought.

So she shifted her cumbersome body to a less cramped position on the end of the bed, and spoke of their last days in France, when she had thought to be parted from her love, perhaps forever. Jean-François had been vicious-tempered in those days, like a cornered weasel, having spent his inheritance and needing yet more money to start the voyage whereby he hoped to regain his fortune. For the first time she mentioned her cousin's venture into piracy.

"Pierre de Bidoux, Seigneur de Lartigue, joined forces with him," Marguerite said scornfully, "That renegade Lord! They were two of a kind, both thinking piracy a quick way to ready money."

Her husband curled his lip at the memory of Roberval, but did not speak. It was Damienne who entered the conversation, as though she understood what her Lady intended, although Marguerite had not discussed her misgivings, nor her plan.

From her stool by the fireplace the old nurse interjected vengefully, "For myself I then thought your kinsman had landed himself into real trouble with the King. Banding with a villainous pirate, *alors*, to rob the ships of a monarch François had been cozening!"

Marguerite laughed. "Yes, our long-nosed King had truly been a-wooing Henry of England, the Eighth of his Name. What folly for Roberval and Lartigue to attack an English ship!"

Damienne grumbled, "Crony of the King's or no, your fine cousin could have paid with his head for that affair."

Marguerite turned toward her husband, trying to draw him into their discussion as best she might. "My kinsman had to hide himself for a while, in truth," she admitted. "Last October he did not even dare to land at St. Malo for provisions, but only to send some seamen ashore for flour and bread." Bowing her head she added, "He had robbed Frenchmen, too, you know."

Her husband patted her arm. Roberval had brought shame upon his family, but little could be said of it that would bring comfort, her Lord thought, since if he lived to return to France he would no doubt carry forward still further shameful enterprises.

Shuddering, Marguerite added that the affair had attained real notoriety at Court, when the English Ambassador, one Paget, had demanded an audience with the King, and had presented a complaint. It was in the form of a letter from the French Ambassador in England, Lord Marillac, complaining that certain English merchants had been robbed of six hundred quintals of iron and four hundred morocco skins by Jean-François de la Roque. He had done so on the pretext that these supplies were put on board the English ship in Spain, and that they hence belonged to Spaniards, an unfriendly nation.

Her husband now chuckled at his wife's indignation, and at her kinsman's unabashed villainy. "Pirate's logic, in truth," he commented. "And what did our François, the First of his Name, say to that?"

"He was either very angry or pretended to be," Marguerite replied. "I do not know whether his rage was real or a mere pretense to make a show for the English Ambassador." She looked intently at her husband and added, "As you know full well, our King is a man who shifts and changes. But he is scrupulously loyal to his friends, and I suppose he thinks of Roberval as his friend. At any rate he said that he would do all he could to catch my cousin, who had deceived him like a false traitor thief. And he said that he, the King, had given my cousin money and supplies to conquer the land of Canada, even giving him prisoners for the peopling of these countries, but that now Roberval leaves this enterprise and lies upon the coast of Brittany robbing Englishmen and Frenchmen, and all that come in his way, but, the King said, 'He shall be hanged by the neck if I catch him!' "

Her husband smiled sourly. "That was indeed quite an outburst from our François, always so ready with his words. Whether he meant one *parole* of it is another matter entirely."

Indignantly Marguerite went on, "That he could so disgrace our name, that knavish cousin of mine! And to think that he had the *effronterie* to proclaim that my behavior had dishonored *him*!"

Her husband smiled grimly. "I agree. He does not want for audacity when he can spit in the eye of two kings," and, he thought bitterly, can maroon his own cousin in this dreadful land, a *damoiselle* of the blood of noble houses though she may be.

But Roberval had then left France with well-judged alacrity, Marguerite recalled. She and Damienne had been waiting in Honfleur when a messenger came to tell them to come with all haste to New Rochelle. "I never will forget that ride!" she said. "Roberval had thought to pick us up in Honfleur with the *Marye*, but he was in too much haste for that. I suppose that the King sent him a peremptory demand to leave, forthwith, for New France."

Marguerite went on to say that Roberval had been in a sour mood when they reached him, but now, as she remembered all that had happened, she thought that perhaps he was also frightened. He dared not offend the King beyond a certain degree, and to damage the relations with England, which Francis had so laboriously built up, was a serious matter.

"François Premier is not easily angered with his friends," she went on in a reflective tone of voice, "But, once angered, sometimes of late his friends find it hard to regain his good graces." Again she paused and glanced significantly at her husband. "It may be happenstance," she added, "But as I recall it we hastily embarked in the middle of April, and the English King made his complaint to François only in the middle of that same March."

After a moment of unexpressed resentment, Damienne burst forth to add tartly that for many years she had doubted that Roberval meant Marguerite well, that this marooning had proven that she had good reason for her misgivings, and that indeed she and her Lady were well rid of him. "Even Jacques Cartier did not relish having Roberval made Viceroy over him," she added, and garrulously went on to say that there were few that had managed to quarrel with the genial Malouin.

Hunched around their scanty fire, victims of Roberval's spite, the castaways let their thoughts drift to that cataclysmic quarrel between Cartier and Roberval whose aftermath had led to their own disaster.

Damienne asked her mistress with probing curiosity how much of the argument she had actually heard, before Jacques Cartier stole away by night to return to France.

Marguerite reflected for a moment, glancing at her husband to assess his weariness. "Yes, I heard most of what they said," she replied crisply, "And I have since tried to remember it. Jacques was angry because we had been so long in coming. He not only said we were too late to plant crops, but that we had brought too few supplies to feed ourselves and his people. He said that even the savages must be fed during the winter, if they were to remain friendly."

Her husband's look was suddenly alert. The mention of savages had aroused him, his wife realized, because always he feared their coming.

But Damienne interjected the question, "These savages, can they not, then, feed themselves?"

"Sometimes they do not keep enough food for winter," her mistress replied. "Their ways of providing for themselves are as those of children." She returned to her story of the quarrel, recalling her kinsman's anger at Cartier for leaving the colony up-river. He was afraid that the buildings there would be burned or torn down by the time we reached there, she said, especially since Cartier had admitted that the savages had grown unfriendly.

"Every day," he had said, "They went about to make annoyances," and he had believed that he had left with no time to spare before real trouble started.

Her husband smiled grimly. "An encouraging outlook, indeed, for our Roberval. He was probably fearful, as well as angry with Jacques Cartier!"

Marguerite again eased her swollen body on the thinly-cushioned granite cave-floor. "Toward the latter part of the argument my kinsman made an attempt to explain his delay in arrival, mentioned his troubles in getting seamen and credit, and told of the problems in gathering *forçats* from the prisons, but

Jacques Cartier was not persuaded. He said that he, Cartier, had had to wait too long in Charlesbourg Royale for us to come, so that his men did not wish to return there."

Again she sought a more comfortable position. Her husband seemed wrapped in memories of his own, but she added that their delay in St. John after Cartier had stolen away was in order for Roberval to judge upon a dispute between Portuguese and French fishermen, which she suspected her kinsman had relished greatly, since it was his first act as Viceroy of Canada.

Her husband replied rather vaguely, "Yes, I had wondered why he took so long about that matter when we should have hastened on our way. Such a large company as ours ate up a great many of the provisions during our needless stay there." He added critically that a military man should have thought of that factor, and acted accordingly.

His wife nodded in agreement. "I sometimes think of the rest of our ship's company, L'Espiney, my cousin's ensign, Guinecourt, Noir Fontaine, Frete, La Brosse, De Mire and La Salle" sonorously the names rolled from her tongue, but she added cynically, "And I think they will have their fill of Jean-François before they again see France."

Pausing, she looked toward Damienne. "I wish that I could know how they are faring, upriver. If my cousin could so severely punish one of his own blood, he will not withhold his hand from any of them, should occasion arise while he has sole rule in Canada."

Her husband stretched his arms about his head and looked above him at the low, smoky ceiling of the cave. "The very thought of their predicament makes this seem a pleasant place," he said with a flash of his genial spirit and good humor. For the moment his long depression was forgotten, together with his despair after the passing of the *vaisseaux*.

*

By now the constantly replenished pot of *ragout* became such a monotonous diet that none of the three could eat more than few spoonsful of it, at increasingly longer intervals.

At last Damienne bestirred herself to open the hoarded barley-sack, and to rob it of a few handsful of next year's seed, since, fortunately, barley expanded to four times its volume when cooked. She sautéed it first, in oil, with herbs and garlic, then added water to cook the grain.

From it she made barley cakes, and with the remainder she started a fresh *ragout* with dried fish in it, along with fresh green herbs grubbed from under the snow at the cave's mouth. The dish tasted rather strange, with its unheard-of leafy flavors, but the change seemed satisfying, somehow, as if some deep, inchoate need of their bodies had thus been met.

During their weeks in the cave Marguerite had been steadily growing heavier and more awkward in her movements, and now even Damienne could get about in their cramped quarters more easily than her Lady. Thus Marguerite ceased going outside the cave.

But once on a sunny day Damienne ventured outside to see if she could dig a few more fresh herbs from the cliffside. The glare of the sun quickly drove her back into the cave, red-eyed and blinking. She brought only a small handful of greens.

"If I had stayed longer, I fear I would have been blinded," she admitted. "The sun on the snow hit into my eyes like fire. We must beware of this danger also." Wetting a cloth in water she held it to her stinging eyes, but they were sore and red for several days afterward.

Thus they learned to squint their eyes nearly shut if they looked outside the cave on a sunny day.

—4—

But when the exiles did occasionally peer out of their dark shelter on the infrequent clear days, the vista from their cliffside perch had a savage splendor. Seals come to the harbor from time to time on the drifting ice, their puppy-like barks faintly to be heard when the wind blew inshore. But there was no need to hunt them; the oil container was nearly full.

Seabirds flew across the icy wastes, back and forth to the open water, although it did not seem possible that birds could live among the reaches of barren ice, in bitter winds. And the watchers thought that it was strange of the birds, who could fly away to kinder climates, not to do so.

Most of the time the three in the cave tried to sleep, like the hibernating animals, as long as they could, and they ate but little. For liquid they melted the icicles outside, and used the corner of the cave as their place of necessity. It was too cold to go outside, most of the time, even for that private purpose, so they threw a few spadesful of snow into the opening at intervals, with an occasional pot of snow-water to wash it down.

Their existence now was almost animal-like.

They could hardly stand erect in the cave at the same time, since the higher part, at the center, was so small. Therefore, without discussion, they formed the habit of taking turns at stretching their legs or sitting on the stool. They lounged on the bed, or on the furs alongside it, where the floor slanted upward toward the low roof.

But sometimes, still, they made an effort to talk of matters in France. In a strange way it seemed comforting to remember that affairs were going forward there as before; people were walking in the streets and going about their dealings as though New France did not exist. For well did the exiles know that most of their countrymen, and even the King, who had financed the expedition, had only a remote and minor interest in this new land.

But they did not discuss Roberval's settlement up the river at Charlesbourg Royal, except in an occasional passing mention. Somehow it was more discomforting to the women to think of that colony, nearer to them though it was, than to think of France. And it was also a bit frightening to speculate on what might have happened to that expedition without the experienced Cartier in the group, with his ships and hardened veterans.

Their young Lord, moreover, having seen the departure of the *vaisseaux,* believed that Charlesbourg Royal was probably deserted, a still more disquieting belief than those being entertained by the women.

Damienne spoke of the earth-sickness which had afflicted the previous settlement before the indigenes had helped them to find a cure. Roberval, she said, was not likely to ingratiate himself with a savage people who had even come to odds with the easy-natured Cartier.

For her countryman, Cartier, was known to get along well with his men, Damienne added, and at first he had even managed to win the friendship of the savages, so that two of them had come back to France with him on his first expedition, and had learned enough French there to act as interpreters on his second voyage.

But even so, she continued gloomily, the ten savages he brought back on his next trip had all died in France, with the exception of one ten-year-old girl. Perhaps it had angered the savages when he did not bring back their friends and relatives this time. Perhaps they had not believed Jacques' story that they were alive and well, and happily married in France. At any rate they had already showed hostility to Cartier himself, and that was why he had left, he said.

Now Roberval was presumably wintering among these same natives, with no experience in dealing with them, and he ruled, the women knew, with force, not persuasion. Matters, therefore, must be precarious indeed upriver, if, for that matter Roberval had not already removed himself by sailing back to France.

The women rambled on with their conjectures. Perhaps the upriver colony had been killed by attacks of the savages, or illness, or even the severe cold, if their countrymen had tried to live in dwellings such as those used in France. The subject was uncomfortable for the women to contemplate, but to their Lord it was agonizing, certain as he was that his trusted companions had abandoned him and his women-folk to their fate in this desolate land.

February, 1543

—1—

The winter weather now became still more cold, a dry and crystalline cold beyond anything dreamed of or imagined. Even the hauling in of the day's wood supply now allowed too much frigid air to enter the cave, and its chilled inhabitants decided to bring in a larger supply, all at one time. Plans were made to do this in as hasty a manner as possible.

Marguerite took the stacked turf from the door-opening and propped the hide covering to one side with her body, while her husband crawled out onto the ledge. Knifelike cold then swept into the cave. The trees were cracking like gunfire in the icy wind.

So that working as rapidly as they could the two of them passed the logs and turf inside the entrance to Damienne, who scrambled up to the far edges of the cave to push or stack the fuel there, thus saving their scanty living-space.

The blown snow numbed their eyelids and made a crust over their faces.

And Marguerite was now too heavy in body for such exertions, so she lay near the door opening, passing along the heavy sections of log and the clumsy chunks of frozen turf across her body, not attempting to take them farther toward Damienne than she could reach. The old nurse was now more able to move around hastily than was her mistress.

The hands of the workers rapidly became numb, but they did not stop carrying in fuel until a large supply was stacked in every available space at the sides of the cave and back along the shelf where they built their cooking-fire. But it was fortunate that fuel lasted as long as it did in the cave, the women sturdily assured each other.

At last her husband dragged himself wearily back through the cave opening and Marguerite hastily stacked it shut. Then she held his cold hands against her face as Damienne built up the fire. He was shaking with cold, but he spoke with attempted cheer. "The wood supply is lasting well, I find, and we will have enough for the rest of the winter *certainement.*" He had intended to reassure the womenfolk, but his voice quavered as he spoke.

Alarmed at his state Damienne hastily laid yet more wood on the fire and set the kettle across it, while Marguerite gathered the warming-stones from beside the hearth and wrapped them in cloth, placing them under the chilled bedding. The two women pulled off their Lord's boots and opened the bed.

Even under the heavy coverings and lying between the warming-stones, he shivered uncontrollably. For a man already weakened, he had stayed too long in the cold.

Marguerite hurriedly crawled under the coverings beside him and held him in her arms, and when Damienne brought him her hot potion, his young wife held it to his lips. Her Lord drank it gratefully, his teeth chattering against the drinking-mug as he did so.

His face had lost all color, and his skin glistened with a tallowy clamminess, alarming both to his wife and to her old nurse.

After placing warmer stones around her Lord's legs, Damienne now also crawled into the bed at his side, and both women pressed their bodies against him. His only warmth seemed now to come from them and from the warming-stones, but he finally drifted off into a fitful sleep. Outside their shelter the wind shrilled and screamed past the cliff-face, and the incessant growling of the ice resounded through the granite around them.

And the women lay awake, in silence, each a prey to her own fears. They were glad they could not see each other's faces.

*

In no château in France, its Seigneur having fallen ill, could there have been greater effort made to return him to health. For there was now no doubt in the minds of the two women that their Lord was gravely ill. He was hot and cold by turns. Awake or asleep, he was restless. Marguerite and Damienne lay beside him, in turn, keeping him from throwing back the coverings as he tossed his thin body from side to side, disturbed by the roaring of the gale outside and the sea-sounds.

He could eat but little, but the women held up his head and gave him a few sips of liquid whenever he aroused himself. Potions of water and vinegar were heated for him, and herb poultices were applied. Night and day became as one to the two women. While they did not even look outside, except to break off icicles to melt for water, they realized that a vast depth of snow had now fallen, filling the valley so that only the tops of the trees rose above it.

Eating little themselves they tried everything they knew to get the sick man to eat and drink—a few spoonsful of mashed carrots or turnips, barley broth flavored with venison—he ate little and seldom spoke. His breath wheezed, and he coughed with a deep rattling sound which echoed harshly on the rocky ceiling of the cave.

Dreams strayed vagrantly through his mind, taking him back to the warm meadows of his childhood as his pain seemed to leave him and he was no longer conscious of his labored breathing. At last all care seemed to leave him and when he dimly remembered his wife it was without the anxiety of their dire circumstances. *Ma chèrie,* he thought, *ma chèrie*—and then his mind drifted inexorably away from all human remembrance or care.

Sitting at his side Marguerite felt such agony of spirit that she feared madness. "Help him. Help him," she moaned, but whether she spoke to Damienne or in prayer she did not know, and dazedly she readjusted the bedding around his body to retain some semblance of contact with her love. *Mon amour, mon amour,* she murmured wordlessly, as though she could throw a net of her love about him, through which his spirit could not slip away. But at last he seemed to drift away from all consciousness of her nearness, and finally he seemed so far removed that for a nightmare instant she had the sense of his being a stranger, someone she had never known.

For an insane moment she almost hated him, obdurate as he seemed to be in his intent to leave her behind.

*

At last the sick man seemed able to swallow only liquids, and hardly enough of those to moisten his rasping throat. Damienne frenziedly prepared every potion she knew, or had heard mentioned. The last of the honey was mixed with warm water and a few spoonsful were swallowed. Broths of herbs and of vegetables were prepared. The women even tried a brew made of the dried berries.

And days and nights followed each other in an anxious, wakeful succession. Sometimes both women awoke with a guilty start to find that they had dozed into needed sleep as they sat beside the sickbed.

At last their Lord could hardly swallow at all; the carefully-prepared broths dribbled down his chin or choked him. Desperately Damienne poured wine from their last carefully-hoarded bottle and mixed it with heated water. It was the last thing he swallowed.

Before morning his breath moved in and out of his chest with a strange, irregular rhythm. His face, having been so pale, now had a purplish flush, and his eyes gleamed through half-closed lids. After a few delayed and hesitating breaths, he raised his head slightly and opened his eyes. He seemed to be seeing the face of his young wife for the first time in many days, and his lips formed an inaudible word or two.

Then his breathing ceased.

Marguerite threw a stunned glance toward Damienne, but Damienne had dropped her eyes. Seizing her young husband's face between her hands, Marguerite pushed his head from side to side almost roughly. His eyes were half open, and his lips bore a slight, fixed smile.

With an animal-like outcry Marguerite threw herself across his body, holding him against her.

*

For a long time both women wept.

At last Damienne bethought herself of her Lady's state, and she reached out a quivering hand to pull Marguerite back, away from the body of her dead husband. "Come, my Lady," she said, from the depths of her own sorrow, "You will do yourself harm. It is not well for you to lie with the dead at a time like this."

Marguerite looked at her in dazed silence.

"We must prepare him to go to his grave," said Damienne.

A groan burst from Marguerite's lips. "I cannot endure it!" she cried. "I cannot believe that he is dead." Again she threw herself down beside her husband's body. His face already felt like damp leather.

Damienne reached under the bedcoverings and straightened his limbs. Then she went to the other side of the bed and pulled the covers around Marguerite, lying down beside her.

Best that we both sleep, she thought wearily. We can go about the burial in the morning.

—2—

Strangely, both women slept through the night and far into the next day. Exhaustion protected them from their first frantic despair. And beside Marguerite her husband's body stiffened.

At last the women awoke. Both were dazed.

They could not think what to do with the body. Nothing in their experience of death was relevant to the situation which faced them. They wanted to give this loved young man the dignity that was due him, but they had no way of performing the accustomed rites.

Damienne had composed his body. Now she took one of the blankets from the bed and wrapped it about him. Marguerite sat with bowed head. At last Damienne said, hesitantly, "My Lady, we will have to take him outside."

Marguerite raised her head. "Outside?" she asked dully.

Damienne answered with Norman bluntness. "The cave is warm. He will not keep."

Marguerite shuddered. Unbearable to think of him lying outside, in the cold, in only the blanket. Finally the women decided to sew him into a caribou hide, but they found that this was not easily to be done. The hides were stiff, but Damienne finally managed to soften one with hot water, and to cut enough holes around the edges to lash it around her young master's body. She made the thongs for the lashings out of the leather itself.

While Damienne went about this task, Marguerite sat with bowed head, staring straight down at her clasped hands. At last Damienne said quietly, "My Lady, you must help me. It is not seemly that our poor Lord's body should be dragged about."

She took the clods of peat out of the cave opening and crawled outside. There she crouched on the ledge, reaching inside for the body, which was within arm's length. Marguerite roused herself and bent over at her husband's feet. She lifted him. Together, gently but awkwardly, the two women carried the body outside the cave, onto the ledge.

They were shocked at its lack of weight. He was far more gaunt than they had realized. It was as though they carried a tall child.

Damienne pulled up the canvas which shielded the cave-shelf, shaking off its burden of ice and snow, exposing the turf wall and scaffold which he had so carefully built to protect them, only a few short months before. There she laid his hide-wrapped body, packing it with ice and snow. Then the two women pulled the canvas into place over him, packing it again with stones and ice to hold it in place against the winds which came down over the cliff-face. It was a desolate and make-shift resting-place, but for the moment they could do no better. Silently they stood beside the newly-buried corpse of their Lord, still not realizing their final loss of him, and finally, for the first time, they thought to pray for the repose of his soul. "*Nostre Pere estant lassus es cieulx,*" they murmured numbly.

The problem of burial must somehow be solved, but neither spoke of it. They crawled clumsily back into the cave and closed the entrance. After a few mouthsful of food from the pot, they again went silently to sleep in the bed, the two of them lying stiffly side by side where their Lord's body had lain the night before.

*

In the morning a semblance of life returned to them. Damienne built up the fire, and they washed, combing and pinning up their disordered and neglected hair. They did so almost without thought, as a needed act.

Their first real thought was for the child. Marguerite believed that if she had not lost him by now, she never would. And Damienne said, "You must not think of our Lord. You will do the child a harm. If we were at home in France you would not have been permitted to attend a death-bed."

Marguerite stared at her in silence. During her husband's illness and death, she had almost forgotten about the child. Now her arms grasped her swollen belly, and the child moved sluggishly, as if to remind her of his existence. All I have left from my Lord, she thought numbly.

Her silence alarmed Damienne. Noble ladies, about to bear an heir, were sheltered from all possible shocks and unpleasantness. How much of this was custom, and how much necessity, Damienne did not know, and as she though of it, it seemed a miracle that her Lady had lived through the events which had taken place on this island, *enciente* as she was with her first child. Best to take no more chances.

"My Lady," she said firmly, "We have done all we needs must. We can do no other, now, than to think of you and the child." In the face of Marguerite's continued silence, she grew garrulous. "I remember of a certain Countess," she said, "Who was not told of her own father's death until months afterward, when her child had been safely born."

Marguerite's eyes turned toward her old nurse. "If we are to abide by French Court etiquette, perhaps I should remain in this cave for a year, since it is here that I first heard of my husband's death." Her weary young voice was ironic, and gesturing imperiously to Damienne not to follow her, she crawled awkwardly out of the cave.

As she reached the cliff-edge and attempted to stand upright, she came near to toppling forward into the valley, overbalanced as she was by the burden within her. But grasping the cliff-face she regained her footing and stood erect, looking down at the snow which had already drifted across the fading canvas.

Alone, she looked down at the place where her dead Lord lay, chilled by the realization that she would never see his face again. His voice would not reach her, except perhaps in dreams, and the ringing of his axe-blows would be followed by a silence in the woodlands.

At last sleet began to blow down against her face from the edge of the cliff. Heart leaden within her, she murmured aloud, "*Répose-toi doucement, amour perdu.*"

—3—

An icy wind now howled past the smoke vent, and from the sea came the crackling and grumbling of ice-floes in movement. And sitting helplessly in the cave, captives of the arctic cold, the two women had their first angry argument.

It was with regard to their Lord's final burial.

The snow in the valley was now freezing to a hard crust, and Damienne suggested that some day soon she should slide the body down the hill and take it to the first crevice in the ice of the harbor. There she could drop it into the water.

Marguerite screamed at her in angry refusal.

But Damienne insisted stoutly that it was no worse than burial at sea, and that, further, she had heard that bodies were so buried in this country, in winter, when interment in the deeply-frozen earth was impossible. Jacques Cartier, himself, had so buried some of his men, she said defensively. He had even covered them up only with snow, when all the colony was weakened by the earth-sickness.

Marguerite again screamed a violent refusal. "He was my Lord and my husband!" she cried in anguish. "Alive I loved him, and dead I love him still!" She shouted at Damienne again, a fierce, wordless wail through whitening lips drawn back from her teeth. The older woman was alarmed. She had never seen her self-contained Lady in such a wild state, since from childhood the girl had always been one to keep her feelings to herself.

At last Marguerite lowered her voice and said in a steadier tone, "He deserves better from us than to be thrown into the sea, like a dead animal. But for us, he would not have come here; he would not be dead."

The older woman was silenced. Sadly she thought of the blithe young lordling who had stepped aboard the ship in France, carrying his treasured *citre* across his chest. Such a short time ago it had been, far less than a year. And, again, she thought of him as he had forced his way ashore to care for his Lady, and of her thankfulness then.

Truly he deserved to be decently buried, and long mourned.

*

But on the ice-locked, barren island he was not yet to have peace. A hungry night-beast scented him out, and the two women heard the scratch and scramble of something coming down the ledge to eat of the body, since prey was no doubt scarce by now.

Marguerite snatched up an arquebus and prepared it to fire, fumbling to load it in the low confines of the cave, and to light the slow-match at the fire. She clambered awkwardly to the cave-entrance and clawed aside the turf; laying her body half-way outside, she fired blindly at the dark shape looming beside her. The creature howled and scrambled away.

The next morning the two women saw a trail of blood and the tracks of the wolves. They had dragged away their pack-mate, to satisfy their winter-hunger.

And now the women searched their minds desperately for a way to protect their Lord's body from the beasts. Finally they chilled a pot of their melted water and poured an icy covering over the snow and ice which covered him, and they repeated this until he was thickly encased in ice.

At least, they vowed to themselves, the beasts should not have him.

March, 1543

—1—

Without their young Lord, and their need to care for him, the cave seemed to the two women to be even more dreary and confining than it had been before. And since sunny days were now more frequent, Marguerite wanted to leave the cave, even though the weather was still bitterly cold, and heavy though she now found her body to be.

But the sun still seemed to give little warmth, bright as it was, so both women bundled themselves heavily in all their warm garments. While Damienne had deep misgivings, she did not dare object to her mistress' wish to do this dangerous thing, since the girl had been so long distraught at the loss of her husband, and he lay unburied at her very door.

The snow had now formed a thick crust, as they had heard it would do, and had now become as hard as paving, even under the trees. The women found that it supported them easily, on a surface which was glazed like ice. But it was slippery. Damienne feared for her Lady, and grasped her firmly by the arm, forcing her to walk slowly, and with care.

Airing the bedding and furs was their first venture. They had found that the stone of the cave retained its warmth and was quickly reheated, even after cold air had been let in, so they took out their belongings and freshened them in the clear, cold air.

On succeeding days they went farther afield, Marguerite carrying an arquebus and Damienne carrying her Lord's sword, arms about each other, lest either should slip and fall. They soon learned to step in such a way that they could walk more surefootedly on the glazed snow, and they learned, also, to wrap something over their eyes, or to partly close them, thus avoiding the burning glare of sunshine on snow. And during the time that the sun was at its brightest they stayed outside only for very short periods of time, but still their faces took on a yellowish color which ladies of fashion in France, they knew, would have found a disfigurement.

At last they boldly decided to visit the *logette.* If they went down in the morning a fire could be started and they could check through their belongings in reasonable comfort, they thought, returning to the cave before the cutting cold of night came down. Damienne would have feared for her Damoiselle, heavy with child, to take such a slippery and toilsome journey, but, she thought, it might be best that Marguerite's mind be diverted. Not unnaturally, her Lady seemed to be brooding on the presence of her Lord's unburied body on the cave-shelf. So Damienne agreed that they would make the trip.

Marguerite carried the arquebus and the spade, and Damienne the axe as well as the sword. It would not be easy to dig down through the drifted snow to the doorway of the *logette.*

So that after breaking through the heavy crust of ice with the axe, both women dug and pawed snow away from the door, finally using their hands to clear it. Fortunately the door opened inward. They thus were able to pry and push it open, and a small supply of dry wood and turf lay beside the hearth. Using the slow-match, they soon had a fire started.

Although neither mentioned it, both women were shocked at the chill, icy cold in the *logette.* Even the walls were covered with ice, and there was ice on the floor. Their fire hardly melted it, even near the hearth.

Since they had left no food there, the rodents had not been attracted, and their belongings had been protected, under the canvas as they were, from the dampness which must have dripped through the roof. But even stripped of all comforts as it was, the *logette* made them feel less animal-like than did the rude warmth of the cave. Both women longed to return to it, but they saw that it was still too cold for them to hope to heat it as they could the cave.

But before they started back Marguerite gathered her books, a change of clothing and the *tric-trac* board. Now that they knew that the cave was well dried out, these things would come to no harm. And Damienne found her knitting frames and some wool. She also decided to take back with her another stool, so that they would have two.

The two saddened women now tried to live in a more accustomed way, washing, cooking and dressing themselves as though they lived in an ordinary household. As though by common consent they forced themselves to rise about their squalid, cave-dwelling habits, finding the absence of their Lord as much as could be borne, without living in a sordid way, as well.

So as the days brightened and grew longer, they talked of the garden, and of moving back to the *logette*. Damienne cooked a variety of foods, insofar as this could be done, and served the meals on their plates, as though they were going to eat at table, instead of sitting knee-to-knee beside their fire. She now feared that her Lady might sink into despair in the loss of her *mari*, as noble ladies were prone to do, and, Damienne thought, surely her mistress had good cause.

So that she decided to keep more of the pan-lamps lighted, since they now knew that the wood and oil supply was ample, and the cave was brighter and more homelike. Marguerite read aloud to Damienne from the books she had brought back, and Damienne did her knitting.

Both women refrained from mentioning their young Lord's absence, lest it remind them of his ice-encased body outside the doorway. But as Marguerite's shock wore away, she felt his absence daily, in a depth of sorrow hardly to be borne.

But she disciplined herself sternly, mind and body, for the sake of the child which was to be born. As a living memento of her husband, she cherished the thought of his secret existence within her body, moving about, as his father could no longer do.

So for his sake Marguerite mastered her despair and sought quiet occupations to calm her mind. While she had never cared for the thought of knitting, she now said to Damienne, "You brought back two knitting frames. Do you suppose you could teach me to knit?"

In some surprise Damienne replied, "*Ma Damoiselle,* it were a goodly thing for you to learn. As you know, we sorely need warm undergarments and hose." She went on to explain that she would spin out thread, ekeing it out by spinning fur from the hides into it. The knitting frames were fitted with bone pegs equally spaced all around the frame, and Damienne explained the thinner the pegs were, and the closer they were together, the finer the knit.

She showed Marguerite how to cast on the stitches, tying the yarn to the first peg, and then winding it around each peg until each was looped around with yarn. Then a second set was cast on and drawn over the first with a hooked knitting needle, a process repeated over and over to form the knitted fabric.

It was simple, mindless work. Damienne could knit without looking at her hands, and Marguerite remembered old women in Nontron walking down the street knitting and chatting with their friends, as though their hands did their work of themselves. So she sat peaceably knitting with Damienne in the evenings, working by the light of the pan-lamps and the fire, her mind strangely at ease.

The scene was commonplace, almost homely.

But her young Lord's body lying outside the cave-entrance, still unburied, was a constant reproach in the hidden reaches of Marguerite's consciousness, and Damienne, too, gave the matter great thought, She did not know how he could be buried in the ground, as her mistress insisted must be done. The earth was frozen, covered with deep snow. And yet if they waited until the ground thawed, the body would no longer be preserved by the cold.

All this would be bad enough, but for a gently-reared women, ready to bear her first child, to be exposed to such a matter, was beyond anything in Damienne's experience, or in her remembrance of overheard lore. The old nurse hardly dared to think of the possible results to mother and child of this grisly affair which had come about. She did not know what to say or to do, and so she therefore kept her silence.

And as the month drew near its close, daytime thaws occasionally took place. The water dripped from the face of the cliff, and ran down the canvas covering over the south entrance of the cave. A few birds came back to the trees, among them some gaily colored ones with blue and white wings and a raucous cry.

The seals were bearing their young, and thin barks joined the deeper ones arising from the colony out on the ice.

One morning Marguerite arose early, and dressed in several layers of her heaviest work clothing, arranging them as best she was able to do about her greatly increased girth. Saying nothing to Damienne, she opened the cave-entrance. The sun poured in. Marguerite picked up the axe, the shovel and her arquebus and laid them outside on the ledge. Then, awkwardly, she pulled her swollen body upward and out the doorway.

"What is it that you do?" Danienne called anxiously after her.

Reluctantly the younger woman answered, as from a depth of sadness too painful to be exposed, "It is time that my Lord was buried. Soon I will be too near my time to do such work."

Scowling out into the sun's glare, the older women made frenzied objections. The danger to Marguerite was extreme, she called after her, but apparently her Lady no longer cared. She slid and scrambled down the hill toward the *logette,* with Damienne following not far behind, hastily fastening her own outdoor clothing about her.

The site at which Marguerite started to dig away the snow was close to the *logette,* and not far from the garden. Damienne realized from her decisiveness that the younger woman must have been giving the matter much thought, for this was probably the best place which could be found on an island where the bedrock was too near the surface for a grave to be dug in many places.

Damienne remembered that there was a mound or slight hillock here, beside the tiny rill that came down through the valley. The soil would be deep enough for a decent grave, probably, and high enough to be dry. But, thought Damienne, all this is covered by a layer of crusted snow, deeper snow than I have ever seen.

But Marguerite had already started to dig. She was using the axe, and was wise enough, Damienne noticed, not to start digging as narrow an opening in the snow as would be dug in the earth. She started a wide distance around the site she had chosen, so that the hole in the snow would slant down toward it, allowing footing on the earth to dig the grave itself.

So, perforce, in the face of her Lady's determination, Damienne helped dig. It was slow work. Even getting the snow away was a heavy task, requiring the chopping away of blocks of the crusted snow with the axe before the spade could be used. And the women had to stop at intervals. After a winter of relative inactivity the heavy work did not come easily to them, the one being old, and the other large with child.

At last they decided to return to the cave for a hot meal and dry clothing. It would then be better, they also thought, to bring some fuel and food down to the *logette,* so that they could rest and warm themselves there. It had already become clear to them that the grave-hole would not be dug in one day, perhaps not in two. With hours of work they had not yet even removed the snow.

And it was possible, both women knew, that another fall of drifting snow would erase all the work they had done.

They had only one shovel. Therefore they worked as rapidly as they could, floundering heavily back to the *logette* to warm themselves, by turns, one warming and resting herself, the other digging. By the end of the day they had reached the surface of the ground beneath the snow.

That night, as they crouched wearily by their fire in the warm cave, Damienne almost hoped that another snow would come, making it impossible for her Lady to go further with this tragic effort. But she knew her ward too well to interpose additional objections. Only an act of nature could stop Marguerite. The determination of the de la Roques was well known, and Damienne thought that under her gentle manner Marguerite had inherited her full share of it.

The next morning dawned clear, and the women again returned to the grave-site. Frozen clay would have been like stone after a freezing night; the root-enlaced, turfy soil was not much better, having frozen deeply during the night after its covering of snow was removed. They had to use the axe to cut around the edge of the grave, and to cut away chunks of turf in sizes they could pry away and remove. The same means had to be used a second time, since the ground was frozen deeply, but level by level they deepened the grave, their hands blistering and bleeding from the continued use of the axe and spade.

The intervals spent in the *logette* became longer as both women became almost too weary to drag themselves back to their task. The grave was now so deep that they had to chop a sort of step in the side, and pull each other out of the deepening hole.

At last, when the grave was almost shoulder-deep, they reached the granite bed-rock. And although this was a shallower depth than was customary, both women were relieved. No deeper grave could be dug here than they had made for their Lord.

Carefully they cleared away the turf, down to the rock, gratified to notice that it slanted slightly downward toward the streamlet. Thus the grave would drain.

Marguerite pulled Damienne upward out of the burial-hole and both women looked at their work with a certain satisfaction. Lined with fir boughs, it would be as fitting a resting-place, Marguerite thought, as could be made.

But haste would be necessary now, if they were to do this thing in a fitting way. Laying their tools ready to hand, they quickly returned to the cave. There they dropped the hide over the entrance, built up the fire, and washed themselves, putting on warm but decent garments, and arranging their hair in seemly fashion.

Marguerite took her Bible and Book of Psalms and the women put on their fur-lined capes.

Under the canvas outside the cave enough of the ice had melted away so that the body was not difficult to loosen from the rock shelf where it lay. After a moment's hesitation they placed it on the crusted snow to slide it down the hill; the footing was too slippery for them to have carried it, they realized.

At the side of the grave they stood for a moment, deciding how to lower the body gently, and with what seemliness they could. At last they knelt at the head and foot of the grave and lifted the body downward on the fir boughs, covering it with the rest of the branches they had gathered.

Then they stood motionless for a moment, and for the first time they allowed themselves to think of their young Lord who lay here, never to return to France. Burial away from home was a misfortune almost as serious as death itself.

Both women wept.

Then with shaking hands Marguerite finally took her Testament and her Book of Psalms from the sleeve of her cape and opened them to the marked passages. "*Dieu tout pouissant,*" she read, "*Que es la source de tout biẽ, nous te priõs très humblement de benir . . .*"

The birds chattered in the trees and swooped over their heads. Damienne's lips were moving, too, along with the remembered words which were a comfort somehow, in this savage wilderness, the very words of burials at home.

"*E les conduis à tõ Royaume éternel, par Iesus-Christ notre Seigneur,*" Marguerite concluded her reading.

Then, together, the two women recited the familiar psalm:

Le Seigneur est mõ pasteur
Ie nauray faute de riẽ
Il me faict reposer es pasquiers herbeux . . .

The sun had dropped below the horizon, and the bitter cold was again sweeping across the glazed snow. They concluded their prayer,

E habiteray lõgtemps en la maison du Seigneur.

Their voices stilled. Each took a handful of turf and dropped it into the grave, and then they walked up the hill, staidly arm in arm, red-eyed but no longer weeping.

Entering the cave they changed back to their work-stained clothing without even closing the entrance, and hastened back to the grave.

Carefully but quickly they packed the turf down as tightly as they could over the pine boughs covering their Lord's body. Then, Marguerite insisted, they must carry rocks from the cave to cover him, lest the beasts dig up his body. No other rocks could be gotten; all were deeply covered with snow. So the two women plodded wearily up and down, making many trips, to carry down the warming-stones and some of the larger boulders which were loose at the edges of the smoke-vent. More stones would later be piled into a cairn, but these should serve until the spring thaw. They piled snow back over the grave, to freeze over it for still further protection.

Again disheveled and bitterly cold, the two women finally hauled their weary bodies back up the darkening hill. What needed to be done, they had done.

April, 1543

—1—

The marks on the calendar now told the two women that April had begun, but to Marguerite and Damienne few indications of spring were evident. The soft, long springtime of France had not prepared them for the late and begrudging advent of that season on their island. True, the days were longer, and the sun was now hot in the afternoons. But the nights were still cold enough to freeze a hard crust over the snow, which did not thaw until nearly noon. Then water flowed down over the surface the rest of the day.

In the harbor the ice nearest the shore melted, and a widening area of open water surrounded each island. And in this channel the returning waterfowl were already paddling and diving, their harsh, hound-like cries heard overhead all day as the flocks returned to the marshes still farther to the north. One day Marguerite crawled out onto the ledge and shot down a goose from a flock which was flying overhead. When Damienne retrieved it from the brush where it had fallen it was found to contain several fully formed eggs which the women ate with hungry relish.

At last the ice in the river broke up and came down to sea with catacylsmic crashings and shatterings. It sounded as if the very rocks were breaking apart and moving, in the earth-tremblings that were said sometimes to afflict this land.

Marguerite and Damienne thus decided that they must now resume the trips to the hilltop to watch for ships. But there was no question of Marguerite's going until after the child was born. She was too near to her time to clamber up the hill over the narrow path and the ledges of rock. So Damienne made the trips, carrying the sword, and watching warily for the approach of beasts from the edges of the woodland.

In her viewings she saw nothing except the increasing areas of open water, but the summit was now clear of snow, except in the shade of the taller rocks, and Damienne took the water-kettle with her to bring back water, since the rock reservoirs had now begun to thaw around their edges in the middle of the day.

There were still intervals of sleet and rain, however, which kept the women from going outside at all; the footing on the narrow ledge outside the cave then became dangerous, and their long skirts quickly grew draggled with ice or wet, taking hours to dry.

In the obliviousness of approaching motherhood Marguerite now waited out her time, thinking sometimes of her departed love, sometimes of France, and sometimes of nothing at all. As the child within her dominated the functions of her body a strange and unwarranted peace of mind descended upon her, erasing the sharpest edges of her sorrow and despair.

*

Both women now longed to return to the *logette.* With the advent of the warmer days they believed they could warm it sufficiently even for the birth of the child. But the move was a serious one, they knew, and they discussed it in all its hazardous aspects.

"Sometime soon," Marguerite pointed out urgently, "We will be trapped here when the crust over the snow melts for then we cannot walk over it." A vision of Damienne disappearing into a soft, bottomless depth of wet snow crossed her mind, a picture too real to be disregarded lightly.

Damienne pondered. "Much deep snow remains to be melted," she finally replied, "And there is no knowing how long it will take. Even the stream may run deeply for a while then."

If they did not leave promptly the birth would take place in the cave, and both women dreaded the advent of the child in such a cramped and savage place. Thus they finally decided to make the move to the *logette* as soon as they could, but to do this by careful stages.

The icy crust over the snow was still firm in the mornings, they found, before the heat of the sun softened it so that it would not hold Damienne's weight. So she first coasted a supply of dried wood down the hill during the morning when the crust was firm and stacked it beside the cabin. She also carried a good supply inside, and built a fire to dry out the walls and floor, and to thaw the snow from the roof. During the heat of the day she left the door open.

The supplies and most of the arquebuses were then carried down, when the cabin was dried out; the bedding had to be left until last, when they would no longer sleep in the cave. And as Damienne returned their belongings to the *logette,* she arranged them as they had been, after determining the location of the leaks in the roof.

At last it was time to move Marguerite from the cave, and this was not easily done. Her awkward girth now hampered her in getting up the incline to the mouth of the cave, and in standing upright on the ledge outside, as well as in climbing down the ladder which now emerged from the snowdrift which had covered it. Damienne stayed a step below her on the ladder, and the two women walked down the hill with slow and careful steps, their arms about each other for safety on the slanted, slippery ice.

Once her Lady was safely in the *logette,* Damienne made several quick trips to bring down the bedding and the remaining supplies. She even bundled the furs and the canvas, dragging them down the hill behind her; the heavy bundle moved along easily, she found, sliding downhill on the ice.

After taking the other belongings into the cabin Damienne climbed the roof and spread the canvas over the places which leaked, and she moved the bark and the stones in such a way that the large piece of canvas would be held in place.

At last the *logette* once again looked homelike. The beds with their draperies, the furs on the floor, the table with its cloth, the cushions, all seemed luxuries long lost and regained. But for a moment, surrounded by the house their young Lord had labored so hard to build for them, both women missed him with a sharp renewal of grief which brought tears to their eyes. The reminder which neither could pretend to ignore was the *citre.* As Marguerite took it from its place on the bed and laid it on the table, neither woman could speak.

If only he could have lived until now, they thought, the warming days might have healed him.

And to his young wife, about to bear his first child, the presence of her lost husband seemed to permeate the room, not as he was in his illness, but during his days of gaiety and strength.

And as though in further reminder of him, that evening they heard a rattling among the grave-stones. Beasts were digging at the grave.

Marguerite quickly loaded and primed the arquebus and opened the door. A dark hulk was outlined against the snow, head down, snuffing and pawing at the grave-mound. She fired the heavy gun, staggering as the hard recoil threw her unwieldy body off balance. The beast screamed. Marguerite closed the door and carefully reloaded the arquebus. Time enough in the morning to see what beast had been there.

In the morning, when Damienne looked for it, the body of the animal had been torn up and eaten. But from the odor she believed it had been another *carcajou,* and if this was so, they were especially well rid of it, both women agreed, considering that the other such beast, last year, had tried to steal the meat out of the very tree in their dooryard.

—2—

Late in the month Damienne rushed into the *logette* in great excitement after making her daily trip to the lookout on the island's summit. "Two ships, sailing upriver, far out at sea," she gasped. She had watched them long enough, she said, to be sure that they were, indeed, ships, and not icebergs.

The women quickly decided that Damienne should light the beacon, but they thought that the ships were probably too far away to see such a signal through the morning mists that would drift along on the wind and mingle with the smoke. But Damienne hurriedly scooped up a potful of coals and rushed back uphill to light the beacon, wetting it down to darken the smoke. But by then she could hardly see the ships, she told Marguerite disconsolately afterward, and so they quite evidently could not see her signal fire.

But Marguerite found herself less disturbed by the ships' passing than she could ever have believed. In the serenity of her imminent motherhood, the matter seemed almost unimportant, far removed from her atavistic concerns.

And that evening both women bravely said to each other that they would as soon stay on their island as to go upriver to the colony there. With Marguerite so near her time the child might well be born on shipboard, and that would not be well. Both women were too familiar with the pitching and rolling of ships, the battering during storms, and the cramped, odorous quarters, to think such a lying-in chamber preferable to their sturdy cabin.

Also, Jean-François would be unlikely to be overjoyed to see them, the women agreed, particularly with a babe whose advent he would not welcome. Signed marriage contract or not, he would consider the union unauthorized and illegitimate, and the child a bastard, or worse yet, an additional heir to menace his questionable stewardship.

If ships went upriver, they would come back down, the two women told each other with sturdy hopefulness.

*

Grouse were now heard in the woodland, and a few of the ducks and geese were already starting to nest. Damienne found a nest with two fresh eggs in it, and she made an omelette with a handful of shallot-tops which were already peeking through the ground in their sheltered bed.

And sitting at the table, lamps alight and silverware gleaming, the women bowed their heads for the accustomed Grace with their minds at peace. Thus far they had managed rather well, they thought, even without the aid of their young Lord. Sharply though she felt his loss, Marguerite felt a renewal of spirits at the child so soon to be born. If she had not lost it ere now, she thought again, surely it was a sturdy babe, who would live to give his father an heir, and to give her a child to love as she had loved his father.

Both women knew that the birth was not like to be an easy one. Marguerite was worn from the long winter, and from the loss of her husband. Damienne feared for her. In Damienne's experience, gently-born women died in childbirth even oftener than did their humbler sisters; this in spite of the best care that could be given them while they carried the child, and the attendance of skilled midwives at the birthing. Even Queen Anne had lost all but two of the eight children she bore.

Marguerite had been spared nothing during the months she had carried this child, thought Damienne, and she, herself, had never assisted at an *accouchement*. She knew only vaguely what needed to be done.

But both women now sewed busily on the needful baby garments and swaddlings, making some from one of Marguerite's full petticoats, some from Damienne's. It had been impossible to cut or sew a layette in the cave; now they even made baby bonnets, working feverishly far into the night, as though proper garments for the babe would insure a fortunate birthing.

And during the endless days of waiting, the two women chatted ceaselessly, as they again sat in decent state before their hearth, of earlier days, days in France, before their since-dead Lord had come upon the scene.

One evening Marguerite spoke of her child's inheritance, her tone calm and impartial, almost desultory, as though the matter were of only slight concern.

Since Roberval had been involved in much litigation, Marguerite was no stranger to the Courts of France. And as her child's legal rights might well have to be sought there, she explained their workings to Damienne. "François has extended the duties of the *Grand Conseil* in lawmaking," she remarked, almost disinterestedly, "And he has also set up a *Conseil des Affaires,* reserved to his intimates, which many think to be of preponderant standing." Perhaps, she said, they could bring their appeal there, because while the recent Villers-Cotterets ordinance had put a limit to lawsuits, and had separated the powers of the civil and the church courts, it had also reduced the number of lawyers, and had changed procedures somewhat.

She could almost picture the scene, she told Damienne dreamily, the Judge in his robes, sitting under his canopy of state, on his pedestal in the center of the room, the advocates and their clients on either side of the bar, the notary in the middle with his seal, together with the clerks, keeping a record of the proceedings.

"I wonder," she said, "If the necessary papers can ever be found. Well I know that strict proof will be required." Her voice was cool, as if she analyzed a problem far removed from her affairs, or from those of her child.

Damienne was appalled at her Lady's unconcern. *Enciente* or not, such matters were not to be taken lightly.

Tartly she responded that her notion of the law in France was based on a saying of Philip le Bel: "*Si veut le roi, si veut la loi!*" and she believed that the will of the King would rule over the law in their case, where Roberval, moreover, had the ear of the King.

Both women pondered the matter, the one indignantly, the other at a strange remove. For the King's Machiavellian cynicism was well known, and his wishes might now dominate the Court. It might have been easier, Marguerite said ruminatively, in the days of the seigneurial assizes, which were held in different localities. The Court traveled around the country and came into each district at intervals, dispensing justice to all, whether they were clerks, chevaliers or free men. But in those assizes one was judged by his peers. Such Courts, Marguerite seemed to recall, were still held in Languedoc and Normandy, where the old ways were kept, but elsewhere they were now supplanted by the King's tribunal, which was a fixed and permanent Court, sitting at one place, at which a public magistrate, who was a public official, presided.

He was assisted by a counsel composed of agents of the King, and it was therefore quite unlikely, Marguerite said unconcernedly, that they would not be influenced by the known wishes of the King.

"And is it true, *Ma Damoiselle,*" Damienne asked, "That the positions of Magistrate and Judge are often sold, and are purchased for gain?" Some of the judges were corrupt, she had heard, and one Leonard Baleston, the judge at Nontron, had been so accused in 1509, a most scandalous affair, Damienne concluded, clucking in dismay.

Her Lady responded, after a pause at the memory, that unfortunately Damienne spoke the truth. Good Queen Marguerite was one of the few rulers who refused to sell the judicial charges in her principality, although her revenues were now very small, it was said. The Queen had even departed from her usual tact to state publicly that "the sordid commerce of magistracy causes corruption, dishonor, and all the vices which undermine and destroy commonwealths"—strong words, indeed, from the King's own sister!

For a moment the two women considered the matter in silence. Queen Marguerite was known and venerated for her readiness to help those in trouble, and she might well be their only source of aid when they returned to France. But her namesake said nothing of the thorny matter of their return, remarking only that Queen Marguerite was a wise and good woman, just in her views and fair in all her dealings.

*

But even in her newly-won tranquility there was one deep concern which Marguerite could not relegate to the furthermost reaches of her mind. The sighting of the ships had reminded her that they might soon be able to return to France, and there she had cause for qualms regarding her status even if she were to refrain from appearing as a litigant in François' courts.

As a member of the new religion she had never felt endangered, because Roberval, while he was also of this faith, was also a useful crony of the King's. Indeed, the de la Roque family had been of the New Religion for generations, as far back as the affair of the Albigensians in southern France, more than two hundred years before. There, also, the King had needed the services of one whom he had then promptly given a royal pardon for his religious indiscretion—no less a person than Roberval's own father. Before the King gave him his appointment, it was necessary that he be pardoned, and, Marguerite thought cynically, since he was useful the King had forthwith done so. And at need, she thought, history was likely to be repeated in the case of his son, but hardly for an obscure orphan cousin. If the religious winds blew from a different quarter now, in France, as had been rumored even before the expedition departed, the rift with Roberval would deprive them of his protected position.

And there was no knowing, Marguerite thought, what François would do, least of all in matters of religion. While he had at first shown great religious tolerance, early in his reign, it was rather obvious that he did not really care about religious faith, one way or the other. Of course it was understandable that he would not frown too harshly on the Sacramentarians, as they were often called, since his own mother and sister were said to favor them.

But after he had become King he had had to placate the Pope, and of course numerous incidents had occurred to irritate him, as monarch, Marguerite remembered. Some members of the new faith had used very poor judgment in promoting their goals. Once they had even nailed up a placard criticizing the Mass on his very door.

At this the King had been angered, and had turned against the New Religion, since he felt that the group had committed an offense against his sovereignty—a more serious matter than heresy, to him!

The affair of the placards, as it was afterward called, had marked a sort of turning-point with François Premier. He had become severe thereafter to those of her faith, Marguerite had been told, and even his well-loved sister, Queen Marguerite, had had to tread carefully in sheltering its proponents. Rumor was, her namesake remembered, that the Queen had even had to make a tactful withdrawal from Court because of her involvement.

And if the King's own sister did not dare show open approval of the New Faith, thought Marguerite, its members had best look to themselves in dealing with their monarch.

Arousing herself from her reverie she now spoke to Damienne of her misgivings, adding morosely, "It is hard to know how the wind blows just now in the matter."

"Between placating the Pope on one hand and wooing the German protestants on the other," she went on, "François Premier is caught between two stones. Just before we left, I understand, he forbade further persecutions and tortures of those of our faith." She paused at the remembrance, her sewing-needle motionless above the white linen in her lap. "And he sent out letters of pardon," she added hopefully, "And even gave his own niece, Jeanne d'Albret in marriage to one of our noblemen."

"That was not for the sake of his Faith," Damienne responded grimly. "I heard that he sorely needed the German princes and those of Sweden and Denmark, with their men-at-arms and their fleets!"

"Of course," said Marguerite, "We do not know which foot he is on now. As you remember, only the year before last, François and Charles Quint had their grand reconciliation, and the Emperor Charles is firm in the Old Religion. Our faith was clearly out of fashion during that affair!"

But as she said this a wistful expression came into her eyes, and she added, "How well I remember the festivities then!" and her old nurse suddenly remembered her Lady as the gay young noblewoman she had been in those days.

But her mistress was speaking once more, softly, as if only to herself. "It were folly," she murmured, "To pin faith on the constancy of François."

*

When Marguerite's pains began the women prepared as best they knew for the ordeal to come. Damienne tied a long linen sling over the head of the bed and scurried to bring in more wood than they ordinarily used during the night. Even now the nights were still very cold. More of the pan-lamps were filled and lighted, and soft linens were boiled and folded.

Damienne helped Marguerite to walk back and forth, holding her as the pains gripped her. Marguerite did not want to lie down, somehow, until her time was upon her. Little was said.

Through Marguerite's mind went the hope that she would not die in childbirth as her mother had done. On this island, alone as they were, she must live to nurse her child, she reminded herself, otherwise it, too, would die. Somehow she felt, however, that in these wild surroundings, like the animals, she could nurture her own young, although Damienne had pointed out to her that for many generations the women of her family had not nursed their own babies.

Indeed all the families of the nobility had wet-nurses on call when the birth of an heir was expected, for sometimes the lady-mother died, as had her own, and at other times it was simply easier to leave the babe with its nurse than to drag it from place to place in the constant journeyings of the seigneuralty back and forth across France.

Marguerite remembered, through increasing mists of pain as she at last lay in the bed, her own childhood, and the years during which she had slowly begun to know what it meant not to have a mother. Other children, even those whose mothers were often away, could always depend, at the last resort, on motherly support in the small crises of childhood.

Mothers, it seemed, were always on the side of their own children, against the world, if need be.

But Marguerite, herself, had often felt like an orphan lamb if she approached the mother of one of her few childhood playmates, for it seemed, sometimes, that she was not welcomed. Because a lady was a mother, Marguerite had early found, it did not follow that she felt motherliness toward any children but her own. Mother sheep butted away the tiny intruders who came to their sides in the pastures; lady mothers were not so rude, but they could somehow convey almost the same effect.

Eyes swimming with pain, Marguerite looked up into Damienne's worried old face, her memory returning to the early years of her childhood. Damienne had done for her all that she could, but while in some houses even great ladies bore but little influence, in all of them the wishes of a nurse bore none at all. With a strange and timely clarity, Marguerite remembered this. A mother was a necessary person, she thought hazily, and therefore she, Marguerite de la Roque, must live to act as mother to her child.

In an interval between the onslaughts of unbearable pain, she therefore said, with effort, and rather formally, "Damienne, I want you to know what you have been to me. You have been as a mother, and I thank you for it. But it will take both of us to care for this child." She subsided into another long spasm of pain.

Fear not, my Lady, thought Damienne. If you die I shall take the child and jump from the cliff. But she tightened her lips and remained silent.

*

The long ordeal stretched out through the night and into the next day. Damienne was as covered with sweat as was Marguerite, when, clumsily helping in the task she had never done, the old nurse drew the child from its welter and gore and held him up like a skinned hare in the flickering light of the lamp-flames.

Marguerite stirred and opened her eyes, raising herself slightly on her elbow. She looked straight at Damienne. "Give me the child," she said.

Damienne started. She had almost hoped that the child would not be born alive, but he was alive. He moved and gave a choking cry. Damienne knew the anguish of losing a child one had grown to love, and there was no hope, she thought, that this child could live long, at the best. His mother could never nurse him, and he would surely sicken. Damienne had almost hoped to be able to lay the child quietly aside, not shaking him into life, and later to be able to tell her Lady that he had been born dead. Easier for her, and kinder, if she never saw the child.

But Marguerite spoke again. "Give him to me," she said.

So Damienne quickly wiped the puny, red, wrinkled rawness of the babe with warm oil, wrapped him in soft woollen swaddling cloths, and handed him to his mother. She caught her breath at the look of weary love on Marguerite's face.

"We will name him for his father," said her Lady. A sudden flow of energy seemed to return to Marguerite's young body. "I must baptize him as soon as I can." She inched herself upward farther in the bed, while Damienne cleaned and tended her and restored some order to the bedding.

And after her face and hands had been wiped off, and her hair combed back, Marguerite sipped a hot potion from a cup held in one hand, while she still kept the baby in her other arm. And soon she fell asleep with him still in her arm, her fingers curved around his tiny swathed body under the coverlets.

Damienne sat and watched them for a long time before she finally went to her own bed to sleep.

*

The next day Marguerite asked Damienne to warm a little water and to put it into one of the silver bowls. She baptized her son, naming him for his father, and scattering a few drops of water on his red and wrinkled head as she asked the Lord's blessing on him in the words of the new faith. After the rite was performed, she smiled radiantly up at Damienne.

In spite of herself, the old nurse was flooded with a sense of love and loyalty to this new being, her new little Lord. "May he be a joy and honor to his house," she said.

*

A lying-in for a lady of gentle birth back home in France was a ceremonious affair, and as Marguerite lay in the canopied bed, recovering her strength, the women talked of the lyings-in of which they had heard. There were many regulations. Only Queens and Princesses were allowed "*la chambre verde*"; even Countesses could not drape their chambers in green, whereas but a few years before, the proper color for lying-in chambers had been white.

Damienne even chuckled a little at one thought which came to her. It was customary that the blinds be kept closed during the lying-in, and the room then had to be lighted by candles. So she brought out their few remaining tapers and ceremoniously lighted them in the windowless room. Their young Lord should have all the dignities they could afford him, she said jovially, bustling about the hearth to prepare a festive *pièce tourtière* seasoned with herbs for the new mother.

And to Damienne's amazement and relief, it now seemed that Marguerite would be able to nurse her own child. A miracle, the old nurse privately considered it. But she preserved a calm air, and bustled about the room as though a staff of servants were outside the door, within beck and call. For it was well known that new mothers were skittish creatures and prone to be easily disturbed. Damienne went about her duties with renewed confidence now that the baby was safely in the world, and the mother gaining in strength every day.

Her secret misgivings about the birthing had not been warranted, thought the old nurse, and even the first few painful nursings had not gone too badly.

Although the father had not been present to receive the child in his arms and to acknowledge it before witnesses as his own, at least he had signed the marriage contract, and it was dated, showing a seemly time before the birthing. The honor of the families had been preserved, under even these difficult straits, and it now looked to Damienne as if this heir might live to return to France and claim his birthright.

She, herself, Damienne, would be his witness, she vowed to herself. And for a second she turned and faced upriver, toward *Charlesbourg Royal* and the Sieur de Roberval, her lips pursed, an impish look of triumph in her faded eyes.

May, 1543

—1—

Channels of water had now begun to form in the ice between the islands, widening with the ebb and flow of the tides. As these spread and finally merged, the ice in the harbor broke into chunks which floated and ground against each other. Over it the gulls and the other returning sea-birds soared and swooped, sometimes riding on the frigid surface hunting for food. But only Damienne now viewed them.

A tiny babe was a creature of wonder to Marguerite, and she lay indoors watching him as he slept, hardly seeming to breathe, or awoke, opening the swollen slits of his eyelids, revealing fogged, unfocused eyes.

He seemed mysterious and remote from his mother, as though he had never curled himself within her body.

But the duties of caring for the baby fell equally on the two women. Marguerite still felt clumsy and insecure in handling the tiny, fragile body, fearing that he would fall apart in her very hands like a badly-stuffed doll, so that Damienne cleaned and changed him. His mother nursed him when he awoke and seemed to need food. After nursing he again relaxed and slept, and Marguerite did not believe he knew his mother from her old nurse.

But daily she examined her son's face, and even his hands

and feet, searching for resemblances to his father, for her deepest hope now was that in her son his father would live again.

*

Marguerite's strength returned swiftly, and she wanted to be up and about long before the prescribed lying-in period had run its course. For when the door of the *logette* was opened from time to time, sunshine flooded through it, and the cries of the birds could be heard. While the babe was an engrossing wonder, Marguerite still wanted to get out of the cabin. Much was now to be done outdoors.

Soon Damienne brought her a cluster of the first tiny wildflowers, which had been found in a sheltered corner, and reported that the wildfowl were all nesting, and that the snow had melted away from all but the very deepest drifts. Streamlets and little rills were running down every valley and hollow. The days were again long. Damienne had brought back with her also two more wild goose eggs which were so large that the two made an omelette. With a few herbs and a dash of their dwindling supply of sea-salt, it made a dish which had the very taste of home.

But both women were beginning to worry about gardening in the short summer ahead.

Damienne had taken a shriveled carrot and a turnip, along with a garlic bud, and had soaked them in warmed water until they showed signs of returning life. Then she had planted them in little containers made of bark, in the best soil she could contrive. With such an early start indoors, she thought, these roots might be brought to ripen their seed, but short as the summers were on this northern island, she did not believe they would bear good seed without her contriving an early start. And the hoarded supply of seed would be gone after the garden was planted this spring, but the nights were still freezing. It was a matter for grave concern.

So Damienne set her rootlets in their rough containers outside, against the south wall of the *logette,* during the warmth of the day, and then brought them indoors at night, hastily rescuing them, also, from the occasional snow showers and the frigid breezes from seaward which were still frequent.

One day early in the month, when Damienne returned from an errand, Marguerite had arisen and was dressed in her working garments. Around her waist she had buckled her husband's belt, and from it dangled his powder flask, bullet-pouch and dagger. "There is much to be done," she said blithely. "While the child sleeps I must be about those things you cannot do alone."

Damienne was shocked. The length of a lying-in was not to be so lightly abridged. How much of the custom was a matter of formal etiquette, and how much a necessity to protect the mother, she did not know. They had been luckier than Marguerite knew, Damienne remonstrated, with the birthing. Best not to tempt fate at this point for the lack of a few more days in bed.

But Marguerite laughed. She felt that her full strength had returned. "If the ladies from the neighboring houses come to pay their calls," she said mockingly, "I will not disgrace you! I will hasten back to my chamber and you may light the tapers!"

Even while Damienne had to laugh at her lady's absurd fancies, a picture came into her mind, unbidden, of her young mistress lying in wait for the visitors, at home in France, as the ladies from nearby seigneuralties came to see the new babe, heir to their neighboring holdings. Marguerite would have lain in her linens and laces, under the embroidered canopy, with soft chairs at hand, and the tapers burning. She, Damienne, in her best cap and kirtle would have been summoned forth with the newly-born son to be shown in his lace-bedecked garments, and the ladies would have exclaimed over his likeness to this relative or that one.

They would have eaten the dainties served them and would have taken their departure with satisfactory feelings all around. And then as the babe grew up to be a lordling with adjacent holdings, the ladies would tell him that they had first seen him in his nurse's arms—particularly, Damienne thought, the ladies with daughters.

How much her Lady thought of these things, Damienne did not know. She hoped that such vain images in the mind were the province only of the old. Did Marguerite miss the excitement and the praise that would have been showered on a lady who had borne a lusty son as her firstborn, a fit heir to her own estates and her Lord's?

Damienne did not know. Best, then, she thought, if no mention be made of the ways of home, lest they remind her Lady of all that was lacking here. So she made no more objection to the shortening of the days of lying-in.

*

The two women decided that one or the other of them would always plan to be within hearing of the child's cry, and that they would bar the door from the outside whenever they had to leave him alone within. He would make a tender morsel for the beasts, they both knew, and the beasts seemed to be pressing in more boldly since there was now no man on the island. Marguerite was already wondering secretly how they would defend themselves when the powder supply was gone.

Surely they would be rescued before that came about! But in the meantime, she decided, she would shoot an arquebus only at easy targets, for needed food, or when great danger threatened.

They had no other weapon except the sword. Her husband had mentioned that a crossbow would have been a good thing for them to have, she remembered, but he had not owned one. Now Marguerite wondered if he, too, had been concerned about their dependence on the powder supply.

But even without shooting, she thought hopefully, much good food could be gotten. The *perroquets,* so named because of their gaudy hooked bills, were tasty, and could actually be caught by hand. The plump little birds made their nests in burrows, laying just one egg, and they were easily caught when they emerged from their holes. Colonies of them sat on the rocks of the shore, upright and solemn with their dark backs, white breasts and bright red feet. When in the water they floated like ducks, but on land they ran along nimbly on their toes. There were so many of them, Marguerite thought, that they would be an endless supply of food which could be gotten without the use of an arquebus.

And with her son to fend for, now, she told herself, plans

must be made so that his childhood would be both safe and well-nurtured. Here in this savage place she must somehow shelter him from the beasts and yet not keep him too often shut away in the *logette.* When he began to toddle about this would be a hard problem to solve, thought his young mother, but with Damienne to help her they would somehow keep their young lordling warm, and well-fed, and safe from harm.

*

Marguerite's first outdoor task had been to find larger stones to pile in a cairn over her husband's grave. The mound was now shoulder-high, and extended outward over the edges of the burial-hole for a safe distance. Marguerite had even placed sod over it, so that it did not seem such a harsh resting-place. And deeply as she mourned her Lord's loss, it was comforting that he lay in a decent grave, albeit not in the earth of France.

On the first warm noontide she carried her son out to his father's grave, and stood there with him in her arms. He must know of his father from the very beginning, she told herself sadly, and before carrying the babe back to the *logette* she murmured the prayer, "*Qui-conque espère au Dieu vivant jamais périra.*" If her husband, indeed, had not perished, but lived in another world, he must be rejoiced to know that he left behind him a fine son, born of his love, to a woman who had loved him dearly.

Each day Marguerite paused to leave a nosegay of flowers on the grave, and to murmur a prayer for the repose of her Lord's soul. While his body was buried on this island, so distant from France, she told herself that at least he lay close to his wife and son, and to the servant who had loved him; close, also, to the home he had built for them, and the garden he had helped to make. The pathway between the garden and the *logette* passed near by his grave.

And as soon as she was able, Marguerite asked Damienne's help to saw a flat piece of wood for a grave marker. In the evenings as she tended the baby, she shaped it with a rounded part on top, and on it she carved her husband's name and titles. After the two women had set it deeply into place at the head of the grave, there was an odd comfort in seeing it as they passed.

Their young Lord did not lie, at least, in an unmarked and untended grave.

*

The days had grown longer, and the two women now decided to turn the soil for the garden, so that they could plant it very quickly when the nights were no longer freezing. So they spaded and turned the peaty chunks, chopping them up into something more resembling a loamy condition, and, as they had hoped during the summer before, the second turning of the soil was easier than the first.

Marguerite's energy had now fully returned, and she made trip after trip to the north end of the island, bringing back two heavy bundles of sand each time, dangling from the carrying-yoke. This she stored in a careful hoard to cover the seeds when they were planted.

As she performed this rather strange task she smilingly said to Damienne, "Jacques Cartier said that there was not one good cartload of earth on this whole north shore." And sardonically she added, "He was not far wrong; there may be two or three cartloads."

—3—

At this time a large caribou herd came across the island, on what was apparently their accustomed migration route to northern pastures. Their approach was not known in advance because it was a day of deep fog. The melting snows and warming temperatures had brought with them frequent fogs, which sometimes lasted all day, and on such days the women did not make the trip to the lookout on the summit.

So that it was through one of these fogs that the herd came snuffling their way down the valley, hooves and horns clicking.

They came past the *logette,* looming out of the fog like a herd of inquisitive cattle. Marguerite and Damienne had been working near the door, and had been able to take quick refuge in the cabin. The forest of legs had hooves which looked sharp, as did the horns in their massed array.

Marguerite decided that it would do no harm to kill one more of the beasts for its flesh and hide. Although they still had dried and smoked venison, there was no knowing how often the herds would pass this way. So she loaded two arquebuses and followed the animals as they went northward toward the marshes of the mainland. They were not moving rapidly. Even in the fog she had no difficulty in killing a young buck which was straggling behind the herd.

At the sound of the gun the herd moved rapidly away, and Damienne came bearing the knives, two kettles and the carrying-pole. She gutted the animal, so that they could more easily carry it, and butchered out the edible parts, which she placed in her kettles. Then the two women awkwardly stumbled back to the *logette* with the gutted carcass. There they hung it from a bough for skinning and let it cool, keeping a watchful eye for beasts who again might try to steal their kill.

And that evening they quartered and sectioned the meat on their chopping-block and brought it into the *logette* for the night. The liver, tongue and heart were soaked in salt water for evening meals on the succeeding nights. Even the hooves were saved for jelly.

And as Marguerite sat nursing her son after her successful hunt she felt a renewed hope that she could do those things that needs must be done for him, here on this island, as his father would have done.

The following day Damienne went out with the shovel and a large basket and picked up all the caribou dung she could find. There was a great deal of it, since the herd had been large.

"We have no beasts wherewith to manure the fields," she said to Marguerite, "And it is a necessary thing." Using the entrails of the slaughtered beast to start with, she made a large pile of the caribou dung beside the garden.

But it was fortunate, both women realized, that the herd had passed by before the garden was planted. Their hooves would have trodden young plants deep into the sod. Marguerite and Damienne hoped that the migration times were always before planting and after harvest, as they had thus far seemed to be. But, as time permitted, they decided, it might be best to lay up a little wall around the garden with the rocks that came to hand. It might keep the beasts out, they thought, at least when it became fairly high. And it would give a look of cared-for property, they decided, almost like a wall in a village, where one might walk past it to see other houses.

*

The babe was now thriving and both women delighted in his presence.

It was as though, tiny and unknowing though he was, he gave them another person on the island for whom they could plan, and arrange, and consider. Although still closed away and quiescent, except when hunger awakened him, he nursed strongly, seeming to take all the milk his mother's young breasts could give him. Then, replete, face whitened and no longer ruddy, he would drift back again to sleep.

Both women attended to his needs, Marguerite learning how to do what needed to be done, and Damienne remembering when she had done the same things for his mother. Somehow thus the days did not seem so lonely as had the time when only the two women had survived their young Lord, before the child's birth.

The babe's occasional cries were the sound of another human voice on the island, however inarticulate.

*

Damienne decided to smoke the caribou meat in the cave before the duties of gardening would take her time. At Marguerite's suggestion she oiled the hunting boots which had been laid away among her dead Lord's clothing, for she would need to wade through the streamlets and marshy areas on the way to the cave. Many trips would have to be made to carry the fuel and the meat up there. So she kilted up her skirts and strode contentedly up the hill, carrying his sword, also, with her as she went.

And Marguerite decided that she would now try to cut down some small trees and lay them down to make bridges and walks across the low places where they both had to pass to and fro. The boots would not last forever. Their feet were always wet, and none of their shoes would last much longer if they had to wade through water wherever they went.

And now both women were fiercely impatient to plant the garden. At home in France it would by this time have been both planted and well sprouted up, they told each other uneasily. But ice still drifted back and forth in the harbor, and even large icebergs occasionally drifted by in the packed ice when the wind blew from seaward, grinding and churning to and fro with the changes of tide and current.

Seals were still present, and Marguerite decided to kill one or two for their oil and skin. There was no knowing when they, too, might go away on some seasonal wanderings of their kind. So she loaded the arquebuses and went down to the shore, hating to kill the soft-eyed creatures which showed so little fear of her. But, she reminded herself, she had a soft-eyed creature of her own to nurture. She shot two of the beasts, and Damienne came to gut and skin them and chop them up so that their oil could be rendered out.

Containers for storage had become a problem, and the women spent a day during intervals of boiling out the oil, in making baskets of pine boughs tied together and woven into shape with willow shoots. These they lined with pieces of one of the fresh sealskins while it was still pliable, and these containers, they found, held all the oil which they got from the two seals. It would give them a full winter's supply of oil for the pan-lamps, and, they thought, there were probably other uses for the oil which they would learn.

Also having thought for the long months of darkness, Damienne had saved all the tallow from the caribou. From it she thought she could probably dip a supply of tapers which would cast an even brighter light than did the flat little lamps.

—4—

Flocks of crows had now returned to the island, along with other small birds which sang and nested in the woodlands. Their trillings and flutterings made the island seem more habitable and less strange. And late in the month violets and other wildflowers began to bloom, even though the ice still lay in shaded places on the shores of the harbor and where the deepest snowdrifts had been. Marguerite gathered clusters of the flowers, short-stemmed though they were, to place on her husband's grave and to put in water in a little mug on the table, near where her baby son lay.

And already the foxes had had their young, for Marguerite saw a pair of the puppy-like creatures frolicking outside of what was apparently their den when she made the trip to the lookout on the summit by a route which took her farther west on the island.

Sea-birds were nesting on the islands, in a profusion and variety undreamed of, some with markings which Marguerite had never seen in the wildfowl of France, although most of them seemed to be colored only black and white. She and her husband had noticed this in the summer before, but in their haste to finish the cabin they had noticed little more. Now, Marguerite thought, I have time to take a more careful look.

Many of the birds seemed to be different varieties of geese and ducks, some similar to those of France, some very different. Some of them, when they came ashore, stood nearly upright and walked like toddling infants. One of this sort, which she supposed to be *Le Grand Pingouin,* which she had heard mentioned, had a black back and wings, with an oval white spot before its eyes. The birds were so slow and clumsy that she had heard they could be killed with a blow from a stick, and she was sure that she could have caught them in her arms if she had tried. Their wings were too small for flying, and were only used in the water, as the birds swam.

Others seemed to be those birds, larger than geese, which Jacques Cartier had called "*margaulx,*" and which, he said, bit like dogs. There were also the *perroquets* with their triangular red and yellow bills, broad when seen from the side and very narrow and knife-like from the front.

As she got to the summit of the hill for her watch-keeping, she saw several white bears outside the chain of outer islands, on the floating ice. They were moving northward, sometimes climbing over ice cakes, sometimes swimming slowly toward the north. Apparently they were following the receding ice, she decided, strange creatures that they were.

When my babe is older, Marguerite thought, what marvels I can show him.

*

At the end of the month the garden still lay unplanted. Every night Damienne made trips to the door of the *logette* to see if the night air was below freezing, and too frequently, so it still was.

And impatient as the women were to start the garden, knowing the shortness of summer in this latitude, they did not dare risk their few, precious remaining seeds before they would be safe from destruction. So they waited in increasing apprehension as the plants in their bark containers grew a bit higher each day, and they took them into the *logette* at night to keep them safe to bear their seed in the autumn, before the early frosts.

June, 1543

—1—

At last the nights became warm enough so that Damienne believed that it was safe to plant the seeds, and this must now be done, both women knew, without delay. After the seemingly unending winter in this land, they well knew how short the summer would be.

But when at last they went out to plant their garden, Damienne stood for a moment and again viewed the strange, root-enmeshed soil in puzzlement. As she had thought before, there was no earth such as this in France. It seemed to be earth without any earth in it—brown, thready peat entangled with rootlets, and sometimes a granite chip or two. Having the texture of shreds of sponge, it did not even sift through her fingers in the usual way when she made the immemorial gesture of gardeners testing the tilth of their soil. It floated to the ground like wet feathers.

She was glad for the sand Marguerite had carried for later use. Ashes and burned bones had also been saved outside the *logette,* and were now spaded into the ground as was the practice in France, along with all the crushed small bones and shells which she had gathered from time to time.

The clusters of shallots and the parsnips which had been left in the ground all winter had sprouted, and Damienne separated the shallots and spaced them out in an orderly row down the side of the garden to multiply. It seemed a miracle that they had survived the hard winter under the snow. If shallots and parsnips did not freeze, she had forgotten it, having had duties far removed from gardening for most of her years in France.

A thin thread of hope now grew in Damienne that somehow they could grow the plants of home, here in this savage climate, as they gained the knowledge of how to go about it. She did not believe that either she or her Lady could endure to eat only the flesh of savage beasts.

Marguerite helped plant the garden and even carried more sand in which to embed the seeds. But she also was preoccupied with other concerns. As she helped Damienne plant the rows of lettuce, cabbage, turnips, parsnips and carrots, she again held back the merest pinch of each kind of seed. In this harsh climate there was no knowing what might happen to destroy their last remaining seeds. Like Damienne, she did not believe she could endure to eat meal after meal only of the flesh of beasts, and wildfowl and fish. It was strange to hunger so avidly for the homely vegetables and grains which, in France, were not considered lordly fare, but so it was. She did not know if this craving was mere homesickness or some deeper need. So she was as much concerned about the garden as was Damienne, especially since she knew that when her babe was a weanling, he would need broths of grain and garden-foods.

At last the two women had the seeds planted, carefully doling them out almost one by one, scantily covering them with sand, and gently pressing them down. Damienne planned to hover vigilantly over the garden, spattering water over the rows whenever the sand showed signs of drying out, and chasing away the birds.

When she suggested to Marguerite that they put up a withe fence, Marguerite agreed readily. She, too, had been worrying that rabbits, whose tracks she had so often seen in the snow, would now eat off the tender plants. Last summer it seemed that they had been more timid. And more likely than the return of the caribou, Marguerite thought, would be destruction by the rabbits.

So taking turns the women chopped thick boughs to make the posts, pounding them into the ground to make a solid row all the way around the garden plot. At the corners, and at intervals in between, they set heavier posts deeply into the soil, and pressed large stones around them. Then Damienne immediately started the weaving of the withes from limber branches, going all the way around the plot each time, so that by the time the seedlings broke through the ground, they would be protected in the enclosure.

Marguerite devised a gate also made of branches and hinged with caribou-hide thongs, which she managed to fit closely between the gateposts. Inside the fence of withes she laid up a low wall of stones to strengthen it against the winds. With enough of a stone wall, she thought, even the caribou herd might be turned to one side.

And by the time the seedlings were grown, Damienne had woven the fence as high as her chin, nearly to the top of the posts. Besides protecting the garden, the women thought, it was a sightly thing. Many a garden at home was enclosed within just such a fence.

*

Knowing that the garden was planted, and nearly a month earlier than it had been the year before, Marguerite was considering another matter.

She did not want to go back to the cave for the winter. It was a matter she hesitated to mention to Damienne, because she thought that the older woman was pinning her hopes on their rescue by some passing ship. She, herself, thought that there was little hope that her kinsman would permit such a thing, or, indeed, that those under him would flout his wishes by stopping at the island. Their own slim hope, she thought, lay in the fishermen, and it seemed that they did not come this far except by accident.

But something in Damienne's face, when she looked up expectantly on Marguerite's returns from the summit, told the younger woman of her hopes for rescue.

They had best not depend on an early rescue, thought Marguerite, nor fail to prepare for a long stay on the island. She was glad, therefore, that Damienne was so vigilant over the garden. This was a needful thing, but she, Marguerite, was giving thought to the *logette.* While often when she looked at it she thought of her young husband's desperate work of building, work which gave them their shelter, none of them had conceived, even dimly, of the deadly cold of the winters on this island. As the *logette* stood, it would serve only for a summer shelter. But Marguerite did not think that she could endure to move back into the cave, to take her little son there to live like an animal, nor to face its memories of her husband's illness and their desperate, unavailing efforts to save him.

So that as she went about her duties and cared for her baby son, Marguerite gave thought to ways of making the *logette* warm enough for the three of them to live in all winter long. It came down to two matters, she thought, an enormous wood and peat supply, and a thickening of the walls and roof. Wind must not suck away the heat from their fire through tiny chinks or around the door.

Carrying the baby as she considered the matter, she walked around the cabin and gave the matter thought. The roof was heavy, being made of solid logs. It would bear more weight. She knew that her husband had been worried about fire because they had all known that cabins often burned down, but, Marguerite thought, even if the *logette* should burn, we could always return to the cave.

—2—

For several days, while Damienne was busy in the garden, Marguerite considered and planned, pacing around the *logette* with her sleeping son in her arms.

If she took off the bark from the roof and covered the logs with a thick layer of sod, she thought, it would keep out the cold. Then the bark could be laid back, so that the rain would run down it, and so that sparks could not embed themselves in the sod to smoulder there. More bark would then have to be laid on, because even now the roof had leaked.

But, she realized, in the winter very hot fires would have to be kept burning. Reluctantly she admitted to herself that the danger of fire must be thought upon.

Marguerite searched her memory. Roofs of thatch, roofs of carefully laid slate, in France—here on the island materials for them were lacking, as were the skilled artisans to lay them securely in place. At last she brought to the surface of her mind a dim remembrance of a hut-village in Allas, one of her holdings in the Dordogne. A little group of round huts had been laid up with flat stones, and the roofs had been of flat stones, too, laid upon each other like fishscales, rounded scales, not cut square like slates. Those roofs had lasted for generations, and such a roof would doubtless serve well here. Surely if she and Damienne searched, they could find enough flat stones to cover the roof of the *logette.*

When the garden was well started Marguerite decided that she would tell Damienne of her plan. In the meantime, on her trips to the northern end of the island for sand, she also brought clay to chink a layer of stone up over the log wall beside the hearth, and to narrow the chimney.

With a young babe in the house, she told herself with some misgiving, they would have to use much care to be sure the room would be warm enough for him, tender as he still was. It was therefore a great risk to think of staying in the *logette* all winter, and Marguerite decided that she would have to rely on Damienne's judgment on this.

As she pondered her little son lifted his head and looked up into her face, seeming to see her for the first time. A spasm of protective love wrenched through his mother, almost physical in its impact. At all costs this tender being, a part of her husband remaining to her, must be preserved. She held the baby to her, laying his head in the curve of her neck, and stared past him at the dark woodland behind the *logette.*

*

On her daily trips to the summit, Marguerite noticed that blocks of ice still floated in the sea, occasionally coming into the harbor on the tide. Sometimes large icebergs came down from the north melted into strange shapes by the sun, and once she saw such an iceberg turn over, clashing its icy prongs down into the water like devouring jaws. If a ship had been nearby, she thought, it would have been crushed.

There were stories of monsters which devoured ships in these Northern waters, and Marguerite wondered if such a sight as this, half-seen by some sailor through the sea-mists when a vessel disappeared from view, had given rise to these legends.

The water was still so cold that the women decided not to go into it to fish with their baskets, but to weave a net from rope for this purpose; also, they told each other, this would save their shoes, which were nearly worn out. Damienne oiled hers and put them away, wearing only her sabots over her heavy, knit hose, since the summer was damp and chill.

And the two women now tore down the branch shelter, from which the canvas had been stripped so long before, marveling that they had lived in it without discomfort, open as it was to the rain and cold.

July, 1543

—1—

Marguerite learned to enjoy watching the birds and wildfowl, some of which were peculiar to the New World, she thought, such as the pairs of ducks, one bluish-grey, one gaudily splotched with black and white. Others seemed also to be ducks, but had reversed colors, being black underneath, with white backs.

But the beasts were becoming more bold, as if they scented out weakness and desired to dispute possession of the island. Perhaps, Marguerite thought, it was because she fired the arquebus so sparingly these days, or perhaps the animals had become accustomed to the scent of man, and thought of Damienne and herself only as other creatures to be stalked and killed.

Once a *carcajou* carried away an arquebus from its place by the cabin door, and Marguerite found the gun after a day of searching far up in the woodland, its stock badly chewed. Damienne could not believe that an animal would have carried away the heavy weapon, saying again that the creature must be a species of demon.

And both women were horrified to think that the foul creature had been bold enough to come to the *logette* door, in broad daylight, so near to the sleeping child. It had even left claw-marks on the wall, tearing the bark away near the door.

It was terrifying to realize that all this had been done while both of them had been fairly close nearby, Damienne at the shore and Marguerite in the garden.

And had the beast somehow managed to tear the bolt from the door, he could have entered the cabin where the baby lay asleep, a tender and defenseless morsel for those fangs and claws whose ferocity they well remembered.

After the finding of the damaged arquebus the women were more frightened than they had ever been before. Somehow, they knew, they must find ways to defend themselves and the child, ways of securing the *logette.*

Sitting at their table, the door well barred, the women confessed their fears to each other. "We must build an outer wall around the front of the *logette,*" said Marguerite, "A bailey for defense, a courtyard, to which we can retreat, at need." This would give them the needed time for the complicated firing procedures, she added, if beasts attacked them. "We could retreat there, shut the gate, and have a better means of defense," she concluded.

Shuddering, Damienne agreed.

Marguerite now wished, more than ever, that her old nurse would learn to fire an arquebus, but the older woman was in no state to consider another fearful matter. It would have to rest until a later time. So Marguerite held her voice to a tone of firmness and stated that she had already been planning to thicken the roof and walls of the cabin, to make it ready for winter. They might well build the outer wall at the same time, she suggested.

"Think you that we could make the *logette* warm enough so that the babe would come to no harm here," she now asked rather hesitantly, "Cold as the winters are hereabouts?"

Somewhat to Marguerite's surprise she found that Damienne was even more eager than was her mistress to make the cabin fit for the winter. Damienne, it seemed, had hated living in the earth, like a beast, and she never wanted to return to the cave, she now admitted. She reminded Marguerite that children lived through the winters in the chill castles of France. Surely, between them, they could make the *logette* warm enough for the child.

With a last uneasy recollection of her husband's reliance on the cave's security and ease of defense, Marguerite decided that they would spend their time working on the *logette,* so that they would not need to return to the cave when winter came.

—2—

The women considered many kinds of barriers for the courtyard. The beasts would climb over a stone wall, and would tear down a wall of withes, Marguerite believed. It would be necessary, she finally decided, to set pointed logs into the ground, upright, hard though this task would be. When Damienne demurred at the thought of the brutally heavy dragging and lifting of the logs, her mistress asked, with some asperity, "Do you fear only the small beasts? We need a wall, I trow, to keep out the *carcajou* and the wolves, not the foxes and the rabbits!"

So the women did not delay. They started digging the trench for the logs on the very next day. With the axe and the spade they dug the sides as sheer as they could, to hold the heavy logs upright, and slow work it was, in the fibrous soil. They had marked out a large semicircular curve ending against the front corners of the *logette,* which enclosed an area as large as the cabin itself. It would be just as well if their winter's wood supply could be stacked within the enclosure, they had decided.

Again their backs ached and their hands bled.

And at night as she lay with her baby son at her side, waiting for sleep to come, Marguerite remembered all the enclosures she had seen in France, walled towns, castles, and even fenced farmyards. The new style in houses there did not include walls and moats; houses were now being built with more thought to comfort than to safety. But Marguerite well realized, now, the feeling of security that must have come to the earlier builders as their walls rose higher and higher, timeless and unscalable.

In childhood she had seen the vast, encircling walls and towers of Carcassonne, arising in the far distance across the plains of Languedoc. Even the lower town there had been walled, she remembered, with less dramatic but equally securing effect. What a comfort those walls must have been to the people sheltering within them, she thought, in troubled times. The walls of Carcassonne were laid with cut stone and good mortar, and would last forever, she reflected, but there was no way of making mortar on this island. Perhaps the buttressing she had seen at Carcassonne, however, could be mimicked in sod and wood.

Marguerite thought, too, of the towers and walls of Pierrefonds, overlooking its village and lake at the edge of the Forest of Compiègne, not far from Roberval. The long, spiralling climb to that ancient stronghold led one past walls of a height to discourage all hope of intrusion, although she remembered that the château had been surrendered to the King of England a hundred years before, wall or no wall.

So the walls were but one thing, she thought meditatively; the spirit to defend them was another matter. And perhaps, of the two, it was the spirit that would be the more difficult to maintain as time went on.

But I have a helpless baby son to defend, thought Marguerite, cupping his warm head in her hand, and an old woman who has shown great spirit for one of her years. With a good wall, and the arquebuses, surely I can defend them, she told herself uneasily, even as my husband would have done.

And against the side of his young mother her child murmured and nuzzled sleepily, unmindful of how fragile a cocoon of safety lay about him.

—3—

With an almost feverish determination the two women now cut and hauled the logs for the wall, copying what their young Lord had done during the summer before. Marguerite missed him poignantly as she now worked across from her old nurse instead of her young husband who had paired so gaily with her during the building of the *logette.*

But she had sharpened the square saw and tightened the rope at the top of the handles to increase the tension on the blade, as she had seen him do so many times. And now with a set face and no visible showing of her sorrow and loneliness she worked across from Damienne, sawing the bottoms of the logs flat across while preparing them to stand firmly on the granite bedrock. The tops were chopped into sharp points. And the women even scaled off the bark to make the standing logs more difficult to climb, after which they held them upright in the trench, ramming rocks and soil around them to hold them up.

A low stone wall was laid on the outside and a higher one inside, to hold the logs more firmly in place in the peaty soil.

Between gardening, nursing the baby, and food-gathering, it took the two women the better part of the month to erect the wall, advancing it a few feet every rainless day. But at last all the logs were set in place, allowing only a narrow opening for the gate, and for it they made a solid door, with bars, patterned on that of the *logette.*

At least, they told each other, when both of them were needed to do some task, the babe could be safely locked away behind two sturdy doors, and they, themselves, would have a secure dooryard into which to retreat.

*

During her hasty trips to the summit Marguerite now gathered aprons-full of mushrooms or berries, which were again dried in the sun along with the *morue* and some wildfowl which were also being smoked. And the oil and venison for the winter were already safely stored.

But the frigid cold of the coming winter would be their harshest trial, both women now knew, so they set to work on the cabin immediately after finishing their work on the wall. The labor now went forward almost uninterruptedly from dawn to dusk in the long days, with short intervals for Marguerite to tend the baby and to feed him, greedy as he had now become.

His tender, baby softness now deepened his mother's uneasiness at the thought of the winter to come. How dreadful it would be if the cold of winter were to strike him down, as it had his father, she thought, and she told herself drearily that another sad and defeated procession might wend its way back to the cave, once winter came down on them.

But now Damienne was determined that this should not be.

So they thickened the roof with turf and bark, laying flat stones over it so that the winter gales might not tear it away, nor sparks set it aflame.

And while Marguerite ranged afar, searching for flat stones, Damienne was stacking a thick outer covering of turf against the walls of the cabin. After some deliberation the two women had decided to close in the ends of the *logette* where the roof touched the ground, sawing a hole in the back wall to give them access to the storage-place without going out-of-doors. This space would stay cold enough to store food, even so, of that they now had no doubt as they remembered the harsh cold of the winter just past.

"We now have lived here for just over a year," Marguerite told Damienne as she marked her calendar, her feelings a strange blend of sadness and gratitude at their accomplishment. Sorely though she missed her love, she thought, matters seemed to be fairly well in hand; the warm summer days were passing by, and her nurseling had grown too large for his first garments.

Flowers again bloomed, first bluebells, then *fleurs de lys,* and daily Marguerite laid clusters of them on her husband's grave, murmuring her prayers for him as she did so. During the warm days of the short summer in the year before, he had been with her, gay and reassuring, and as the same birds called their nostalgic cries, reminders of him were constant. Everywhere his young widow cast her eyes she saw a plant or a wildfowl they had remarked on, together, at this same season. Even the eyes of her little son were beginning to resemble those of his father.

August, 1543

—1—

The wild berries were now ripe in the hillside meadows, and the two women spent a few hours each day gathering them. "I plan to try making wine," Damienne said complacently, "And if only vinegar results, that, too, is needed." Marguerite only smiled at the crusty remark.

Huge flocks of birds came to feast on the berries, feeding mostly on the outer islands. They were slim-legged wading birds with pointed wings, and they uttered plaintive two-note cries as they swept overhead or ran daintily along the water's edge among the larger waterfowl there.

The young geese were already beginning to fly, but icebergs still were occasionally to be seen, floating down from the northern channel, melting into sharp points and pinnacles as they came farther south.

This is a land where there is no true summer, Marguerite thought. All the ice will scarcely be melted before the early snows come upon us. No wonder the berries ripen all at once! They have so little time.

*

One question still remained as to the *logette*'s fitness to withstand the northern winter—the problem of the cold that had come in at the doorway during the winter before. While Marguerite and Damienne had searched their memories for all they had heard regarding survival in New France, they now realized that these advisements had come from those who had wintered far to the south of their island, where the winters were not so severe. Marguerite remembered ruefully that all her countrymen had agreed that Canadian winters were far colder than those of France, but those on this northern island were far colder still. So that bitter as the winters had been considered at Stadacona and Hochelaga, this island of theirs was far more chill, far nearer to the arctic pole.

Thus Marguerite tried to remember all she had heard or seen at St. John and Blanc Sablon, and urgently she prodded at Damienne, "Try to remember! How did they build their dwellings there?"

But Damienne remembered little. "I saw a sort of rain-jacket," she finally said, irrelevantly enough. "A native woman had made it by sewing together the intestines of a seal." It was somewhat transparent, she added, and it crackled when the woman moved. "I wish I had traded for it," she added, "Since there is more rain than sun in this place."

So that between them the women could remember but little that had been learned of the ways of the northern indigenes, and how they survived the winters farther north. Marguerite and Damienne both had seen their skin-covered boats, covered at both ends, with which they paddled out to sea with double-ended paddles to hunt seals.

But such methods of hunting were not needed here on their island, where game was plentiful.

One usage of those savages, however, might sometime be of help on the island, the women agreed, and that was their way of walking on snow. They made paddles of bent wood, crisscrossed with leather thongs, which they tied on their feet to walk over the snow without sinking into it when it was soft.

But their own problem was one of warm housing, and of

this they had heard little, having passed there in the summer. At last Marguerite dimly remembered a jocular remark by one of the fisherfolk, about climbing on hands and knees down tunnels into the winter-dwellings of the natives, which he strangely believed to be made of solid blocks of snow. "That tunnel!" she blurted to Damienne. "It was their way of keeping out the cold! Like a deep cave, such an entrance would keep the warmth inside." She went on to explain that something like a hallway or a closed entrance-way, with a door on it, would probably serve them in the same way. Also, this inner door could be closed before the outer door was opened, when they went out to get wood and fuel. For an agonized moment she remembered that his efforts at carrying in a supply of fuel may well have caused the death of her husband, weakened as he had then been.

With an effort she averted away the torturing memory, and returned to her description of the hallway, remarking that such an entry-way could be made large enough to store a temporary supply of wood, so that it would only need to be replaced at intervals, when the weather was favorable.

Fortunately Damienne understood the plan at once. "Some farm-houses at home have such a covered entrance-way," she agreed with brusque approval. The usages of her native province must be provident and wisely done, she believed, although she added that she had never understood that such hallways were to save heat, believing that they were only meant for the men to leave their stable sabots outside the house, thus keeping manure out of the kitchen.

*

As they started building the structure, Marguerite noticed that Damienne had only laid turf to the top of the *logette* door, since she had had no way of supporting the turf above it. "We can make the roof of our entrance-way strong enough to hold up the turf covering above it," she cried. "If we cover its walls and roof with turf it will make our logette as warm as the cave!" Relief flooded her heart. She had felt half-guilty at her desire not to return to the cave, since little would her baby son know of its squalor, and he might well need its warmth. Now, she thought, there is no question but that we can make the *logette* warm enough for him, as warm as the cave.

With renewed vigor she tore away the turf from around the door, measuring a space for the entrance-way.

Again the women took the axe and the two-handled square saw and went to the woodland. This last task was almost a light one, Marguerite assured Damienne buoyantly, since the logs would be so short. The new structure was to be small, only about three full paces in each dimension, and the work of cutting and hauling the logs would thus be easier, almost a diversion.

They set a base of rocks across the area to pave it and to act as a foundation for the vestibule, which was laid up directly on it. A niche was chopped in the logs of the *logette,* into which the bottom logs of the addition were fitted, to hold them closely in place, and the corners were cut to interlock with each other, as the women had learned from their Lord's ways of carpentering with logs. So that again, feeling very confident, they bored holes and used dowels to hold the sides of the doorway together.

"The roof should slant away from the *logette,*" Marguerite said firmly, thinking of the water which had run into the room, and the ice which had formed on the walls. So they tapered the tops of the logs, sawing indentations to hold the cross-logs for the roof. Like the roof of the *logette,* they extended the roof into broad eaves, to cover the thick layer of turf which Damienne planned to lay up around it.

As she did this final task, Marguerite worked on the door, tending the baby at intervals and carrying him with her as she planned it. After discussion she decided to make it from a light frame of boughs, covered with caribou-hide. "It will have to open inward," she said meditatively, "On account of the snow that will pile up against it, but there is danger that a solid door might freeze shut so firmly that we could not open it. Thus we would be trapped." Damienne shuddered. A fortunate thing it was, she told herself, that her young mistress had such an old head on her shoulders, alone as they now were in this place.

So she helped to soak the hides to soften them so that they could be lashed into place around the frame. At last the door was finished and it hung on its wide leather hinges with a thong at the other side to secure it. In the summertime and early fall it would be left open, and wood would be stacked there to dry.

And as she turfed the wall above the entrance-way Marguerite covered the loophole, thinking of her husband's pride as he had planned and carved it out. How innocent we were, she thought, of the real enemy which would beset us here—fiercer by far than the wild beasts—the cold, she thought, the deadly, murderous cold.

—2—

During the mild weather Marguerite often brought her little son outside and laid him in the shaded corners of the courtyard where the sun would not shine into his eyes. He was too young to watch his mother as she worked, except to look up when she came near him, but he seemed to be pacified at her nearness. It was not well for him to be too much alone, both women knew, but during these summer days they could not remain forever at his side. Much had been done, but now the winter wood supply would have to be gotten in, and a vast amount of it would be needed. They planned to lay it several rows deep, around the entire inside of their stockade, from which it would be moved first into the hallway to dry out, then into the pile on the hearth.

Since the beasts were now so bold, the women decided not to work separately in the woodland, cutting or chopping wood into fireplace lengths there, but to drag all the deadfalls they could find down near to the courtyard, into a pile, and to do all their cutting and sawing there. Thus they would be safer, and they could hear the child if he cried, or, on the warm days, could have him with them in greater safety. And they found that they could even saw firewood inside their hallway on the days of rain, so that work-time did not need to be lost.

*

Life had now assumed a sort of placid routine. With their walls and their fences Marguerite felt a certain sense of home, of security. She hoped that Damienne did, as well.

The older woman, she feared, pinned too much hope on their rescue, and as the days began to shorten they were again approaching the season when no ships could be expected to pass. The northern strait iced in very early, Marguerite knew, and she supposed that ships would start back to France before there was danger of being caught in the ice.

So she tried to interest Damienne in the marvels of the island. One afternoon she called to her to listen to a rippling bird-song, new to the island; another time she pointed out how the gulls carried sea-creatures high over the rocks of the summit and dropped them there to crack their shells. But Damienne seemed to make some show of interest only as a matter of courtesy to her mistress.

And some of the sights, Marguerite thought, were truly to be wondered at. Once the water seemed to glow, and as the ripples came to the shore they splashed into little moons, luminous beads, which looked as if they had a cool light within them. But this sight, and the lights which flickered up from the horizon to the north of them, did not please Damienne as they now did Marguerite. Damienne believed that they were unholy, the result of some sorcery, else why would they appear only in this new land where it was said that demons held sway?

Shortly after the sight of the cool fire in the water, Marguerite noticed that Damienne had made herself a sort of rough Rosary, knotting up a cord with small granite chips, and tying a cross at the end which she had carved from a twig.

Although she said nothing about the matter, Marguerite felt great disquiet. She, herself, had been slowly regaining her peace of mind and even a certain buoyancy of spirit, slow to return after the death of her husband, but Damienne must be truly disturbed at heart, she thought, if she must have such a talisman to twist between her hands.

*

As the month drew near its close Damienne was more eager to make the trips to the summit than was Marguerite. This might be for the best, thought the younger woman, since deadfalls now had to be dragged for longer and longer distances, and the work thus took a great deal of time. Besides, it was too heavy for Damienne to do, except as a helper. Soon they would have to chop down trees for wood, Marguerite realized, but it was better to gather all the dried wood first.

And in the cooling days they could no longer bring the babe out-of-doors, except in their arms, and well bundled.

He was a quiet babe, and lay in his swaddlings on the bed peaceably enough, not seeming as active as he had been before. When he awakened he would turn his eyes toward the flickering light of the pan-lamp or a twig crackling in the fire, seldom crying unless he was hungry. His mother stepped inside the *logette* with each wood-hauling trip she made, to attend to his needs and to give him his meed of human companionship if he proved to be awake.

So that without much discussion Damienne started to make the trips to the beacon. She took the sword along as her weapon, and she gathered berries, mushrooms or herbs as she climbed, since, unbroken, the long ascent was too tiring for her. Marguerite hoped that her old nurse enjoyed the trips away from the confinement of the *logette* and the garden; they were lighter work than the wood-chopping, or the carrying of stones for the roof.

Later that month while Marguerite was on the roof, placing additional stones, Damienne had made the trip to the summit. Suddenly the younger woman heard a frightful but distant scream from the hill. Damienne was coming down in haste, hobbling around the rocky outcroppings, calling out at every breath. A beast has attacked her, thought Marguerite—she has even dropped her sword! She leaped down from the roof and rushed into the *logette.*

Hastily she seized two arquebuses and the powder-horn, quickly lighting a slow-match at the hearth. Barring the doors of the *logette* and the courtyard behind her she ran up the hill, the arquebuses clattering together on her shoulder.

When the two women met neither had breath to talk. Marguerite shouldered an arquebus and peered uphill.

She saw nothing but the soaring birds.

Damienne was leaning against a boulder, bent sidewise, holding her gnarled fist against her chest. Her face was splotched and empurpled, and she could not seem to catch her breath. "Ships!" she finally gasped, pointing a shaking arm toward the southwest. "Not far, coming this way!"

Marguerite rushed to the summit, lightfooted. Reaching the top, she turned. One ship was well within sight, coming directly toward the island, not more than a league or two away. Another was behind it, farther in the distance.

"They have come for us!" she cried, rushing down the hill toward Damienne. Feverishly unclamping the slow-match, she snatched up a handful of dried brush and dipped it into a rocky rainwater-pool, dropping the arquebuses where she knelt. She rushed to the beacon. Damienne was standing there, her thin arms waving above her head.

Marguerite knelt by the pyre and swept it together with one hasty, embracing gesture. She thrust a handful of dried moss under it, on the windward side, crouching to shield the little flames from the stiff breeze as the coal from the slow-match started them burning. Urgently but carefully she fed the fire with dried moss, pressing it cautiously down so as to feed, but not to smother, the flames. She did not blow her breath on the embers; on this windy hilltop there was draft and to spare.

Without daring to look again toward the ships, lest her fire flicker out, she quickly placed dry twigs against the moss, still shielding the fire with her body.

At last the flames reached upward through the larger twigs, through the center of the pyre. First laying a heavy bough across the top to keep the fire compacted, Marguerite finally dared turn away to look at the ships.

Now she stood upright and looked southward.

The leading ship was in plain view. Marguerite even thought she recognized the hull and rigging of the *Saincte Anne*. "They must see us!" she cried. Hastily she thrust her dampened handful of brush into the fire to make the smoke blacken. It was not enough. The fire was now too hot to smoulder.

She rushed back downhill and snatched up turf, wetting it and hurrying back to thrust it, dripping, upon the fire. Now the smoke blackened and billowed in a dark column away from the crest of the hill. It could be seen for miles, she thought, carried almost laterally by the stiff wind.

And Damienne was still waving.

Across the blue water outside the harbor the ship was now approaching so near that Marguerite thought she could almost see tiny figures of men on the deck. The *vaisseau* was pointing as near as might be into the wind, heading toward the harbor. A white arrow of foam, cut by the bow, crossed the crests of the wavelets which were brushed up by the shift of wind to the east.

Surely they were heading for the south entrance of the harbor, from which they had departed more than a year ago. Both women stood in a tense and eager silence, a channel of tears cutting down through Damienne's furrowed cheeks, a welter of confused emotions reeling through Marguerite's mind.

The creamy sails, more weathered now, were pulled tightly on the larboard side as the ships strained to keep headway and direction. But once in the lee of the outer island, Marguerite thought, they can easily enter the harbor under topsails, assisted by their *artimons*. She wondered if Roberval was on the leading ship and how she could endure to see his face, killer of her husband as he was, as surely as if he had given him his death-blow. *Mon homme, mon homme,* she thought, if you could only have lived to see this day. But often as her husband had gritted his teeth and clenched his fists at the thought of Roberval's treachery, she wondered what he would have done. Challenged him to a duel on the very deck of his ship? She would never know. And how should she, herself, greet the man, guilty as he was of the death of her husband? Her arm fell to her side, arrested in its waving.

Both of the women now stood silently, an arm's length apart, their skirts blowing out like pennants. Damienne was moving her lips in prayer. And Marguerite thought she heard voices from the ship borne faintly on the wind. Orders were probably being given. She thought she knew what they would be; she could almost have given them herself.

Intently she watched for the movements which would preface a northward turn into the harbor entrance. The vessels now were moving very slowly, as was always the case when the heavy *vaisseaux* were forced to point their clumsy bulks into the wind. They were now in the lee of the outer islands, moving into slightly smoother water.

Jean Alfonce's careful charting is proving its value, thought Marguerite, at a time like this, when the ships are fighting for headway. For a moment she felt strangely removed from the problem, as though it did not concern her own rescue but merely an exercise in ships-handling. She wondered if Jean Alfonce, himself, was standing on the quarterdeck, unrolling the chart of depths in the harbor.

Perhaps he is here in despite of Roberval, she thought, perhaps Roberval is on another ship and I need not face him. The thought gave relief.

And now the bow of the forward ship started to veer toward the north, pointing toward the harbor entrance. Marguerite grasped Damienne's arm, preparing to rush down the hill to the cove where the ships would anchor. As she did so she gave the ship a last glance, only to see, incredibly, that it was swinging still farther to the northwest, then to the west, away from the harbor-entrance!

Both women watched incredulously as it swung completely around, stern to wind, picking up headway, then farther still, to point away from their island. The sails were then hauled into place for another close haul into the wind, toward the southeast, away from the harbor entrance, away from their marooned countrywomen.

Marguerite and Damienne could not believe what they saw.

As they watched, dumbfounded, the second ship performed the same maneuver, farther out, and followed the first, a league or so downwind of it. The expedition had veered ship, a procedure which was avoided whenever possible. They could just as easily have come into the harbor, Marguerite knew, to wait for the changing of the wind. Apparently the shifting wind forced them in this direction, she thought dazedly. They did not plan to come for us. They simply did not care. And as it was they could not quite clear the outer island, pointing against the wind.

She looked at Damienne. Damienne's old face looked like parchment, like death. Tearlessly her eyes stared out from under their crumpled lids and scanty eyebrows, toward the receding ships, with such a look of despair as Marguerite had never seen. She threw her arm around Damienne and pulled her head into her shoulder and bleakly she watched the ships haul slowly away, their wakes dying out in the shifting movement of the waves. They were now receding from view, pressing steadily on their eastward course.

Jean-François has had the last word, thought Marguerite. Her cousin was returning to France without stopping at the *Ysles Saincte Martre* for his kinswoman, although their signal must have been clearly seen.

The sea to the west was empty. There were no more ships to pass by.

Marguerite did not stay to watch further, but herded Damienne blindly down the hill, stumbling as if in sleep. As she bent to pick up the arquebuses, then the sword, she noticed the berries which Damienne had dropped from her apron when she ran down the hill with her news of their rescue.

*

That night Damienne crouched on her stool by the fire in silence. She had eaten nothing. Her eyes held a vacant glare, and her hand fumbled absently at her crudely knotted Rosary, pulling it slowly through her gnarled fingers. Her lips moved in and out but no sounds came. She did not even move when the baby cried.

Marguerite tried to talk of daily things despite her own sense of desolation as she cleared up the leavings of their meal and put the baby to bed. She wondered if he would ever see his native land. But carefully she tried to explain to her old nurse why she had lately thought that only the fisherfolk would be likely to rescue them, and that fishing-boats would eventually come.

But Damienne vouchsafed no reply.

After securing the courtyard gate and the doors and banking the fire for the night, Marguerite prepared for bed. But Damienne still sat on her stool in unblinking silence. The younger woman finally put her to bed, like a dazed and sullen child, loosening her faded clothing and slipping off her worn, heelless sabots.

Then she, herself, lay down on her bed, pulling the covers over herself and her babe, and dropping the bed-draperies around them. Sleepily he nursed. Marguerite lay in the bed like a stone, not daring even to think. The fate of her baby son and her old nurse now lay in her hands, and hers alone. Perhaps they would live out their lives alone, here on this island. She did not know when sleep finally came.

September, 1543

—1—

Damienne did not recover her spirits as autumn began. During the first days after the ships passed she had stumbled about her duties in a daze, often standing with empty hands, gazing out across the empty harbor. She had said little, and Marguerite had talked of other things, half-awed by the despair with which her old nurse was so deeply afflicted. There was little to be said now, in any event, thought Marguerite, regarding the colony upriver and the traffic to and from it on the ships' road. All that was past.

They must now look sharply to their own affairs, and plan for the winter to come. But even the ripening garden did not draw Damienne's attention, nor did the baby's cooing or even his cries. When Marguerite placed him in her old nurse's arms, thinking that his warm, squirming little body would comfort her, Damienne looked at him vaguely, as if through a veil.

But although she, herself, had been shocked and saddened by the passing of the expedition, Marguerite did not feel its loss as a deathblow. As she reminded Damienne, they had little reason to miss the colony upriver. Distant as their countrymen had been, their little touch of civilization, their livestock and armaments, and the town they had perhaps built, had had no real value to the exiles on the island. Hundreds of miles away as it was, she and Damienne should not let themselves feel its loss, Marguerite pointed out with painfully-summoned logic, although her own heart sank at the certainty of their isolation in New France.

We are the only Frenchmen here, she thought incredulously, two women and an infant babe!

But she went impassively on with her reasoned argument to Damienne. They had known that Jean-François was not a forgiving man, she reminded her, nor was he prone to admit his own mistakes and cruelties. "It would not have been like him," Marguerite declared, "To come back to this island even to find out if we were alive or dead."

"Perhaps our signal fire let the others on the ships know that we are still here," she added hopefully. That is, indeed, the most we can hope for, she thought, that, and the eventual coming of the fishing fleets in this direction. So she tried to express some of these notions to Damienne who, at first, received them in stony silence.

At last she replied, "The fishing boats have their places that they go, and their places that they do not go." Her voice rasped harshly, "We have been on this island for more than a year, and they have not come here. It is clear to me, therefore, that they do not come here at any season." Her lips closed grimly.

Marguerite did not gainsay her. There was a kernel of truth in what Damienne said. The fishing boats had certain places to which they returned year after year. These they sometimes tried to keep secret from other fishermen, but had any of them chosen this place, with its well-protected harbor, they would have been here ere now. Damienne spoke once more. "It may be that the place has an evil reputation, that it is, in truth, the Isle of Demons. If that is so, none will ever come."

She got into her bed and dropped the bed-curtains behind her.

*

Marguerite now spurred herself to desperate efforts in the gathering and chopping of wood, and in cutting turf and stacking it for the winter's fuel. While Damienne helped, her movements were languid and slow. Finally Marguerite asked her to gather faggots and stack them in the nook between the entrance and the outer wall, to act as a kindling supply. This Damienne did, in a mechanical way, walking to and fro to pick up the dry branches, carrying bundles of them back to the courtyard tied on her bent back. The mindless task seemed to satisfy her. As she plodded wordlessly in and out while Marguerite sawed the larger logs, the younger woman was saddened to notice how her old nurse's back had bent, and how her movements faltered. It was as if all hope had left her, and with it had departed all her former bustling energy and hardihood.

So that it was fortunate, at least, thought Marguerite, that they had completed the heavy work on the *logette* and the courtyard before Damienne had had this loss of heart. Had we not done so, she thought, we would soon have had to return to the cave, and I do not believe Damienne could have endured that. Marguerite, herself, could get in the winter's wood supply, she now believed.

*

Sometimes in the evenings Marguerite tried to re-awaken Damienne's interest in matters on the island which concerned them both. But it became apparent that plans for the winter only made the older woman more depressed. "My blood is running cold in my veins," she said plaintively, "And the thought of winter's coming makes it run colder still." She dreaded the grim and frigid nights, and the loneliness of being shut in together during the dark months to come.

And in the absence of Damienne's companionship only the increased humanness of her child enlivened his mother's spirit as the days rapidly grew colder and shorter. While Damienne was somber, he was daily more alert, reaching to grasp his young mother's nose or hair, and hanging on with a grip of steel. He pulled his head toward whatever he wanted, and his thumb found its way into his mouth, along with the corner of his blanket and his mother's bodice laces.

Mindful of her child's need to hear voices about him, in the face of Damienne's long silences, Marguerite talked to him whenever he was awake. As she fed him she recited to him the grace for infants:

Nous te remercions nostre Pere celeste
Du repas qu'avons prins aussi de toute le reste

While her son was still too young to understand, he might become accustomed to the sound of the words, Marguerite thought, and the food he ate would each day have its blessing until he could prate the words, baby-fashion, for himself.

She wished that Damienne would join her in either talk or prayer, but the older woman's attention seemed to be wandering far from her nurseling, or her nurseling's child.

As the month went along flocks of geese and ducks started to fly over the island, going south, and Damienne formed a habit of standing and watching them as they disappeared from sight. On some days their honking and the beating of their wings was almost incessant, as they flew south in multitudes. Twice Marguerite lay in wait for flocks flying low and close together, and brought down many ducks and geese with a single firing of the arquebus, having thriftily loaded it with many small pebbles of granite instead of larger balls.

Damienne picked and cleaned the fowl, almost mindlessly, it seemed, and at Marguerite's suggestion she again set up her smoking-place in the cave, where she could smoke the birds even during the frequent rains. There she crouched like an old, old woman in the semi-darkness, occasionally feeding a stick of dampened wood into her fire.

The nights grew more chill later in the month, and the first few snowflakes fell. Fearing frost, the women now brought in the vegetables from their garden, carefully packing them away in a deep bed of moss in the storage-place under the low end of the roof. The garlic and shallots were braided to hang on the wall beside the hearth, and a large sack of sea-salt hung beside them, the product of the summer's salt-boiling. Beside it hung strings of mushrooms, and higher there hung the smoked game and fish, and bags of dried berries. Clusters of drying herbs, too, added to the store, along with the bags of millet and barley which had ripened and had been hulled almost grain by grain. A larger bag contained the wild grain which had again been gathered and winnowed out on the hill.

Marguerite thought it a brave and reassuring display, and even Damienne, she thought, seemed somewhat cheered as she viewed it.

The seed plants, although started indoors, had not quite ripened, and Marguerite now took them up and carefully brought them indoors, in bark containers, lest a night frost kill the unripened seeds. She again carried them outside the *logette* on sunny days, and at last they ripened fully, and their seed was put away in little cloth squares, carefully tied with string. Thus there was no fear now that they would not have a garden next year, Marguerite thought, and if need be, the next year, and the next.

Having lived here this long, she thought wryly, we are a well-established colony; our first mistakes have been made, and the worst is past. We know how to do those things that need to be done.

—2—

The nights were now gradually lengthening and growing still colder, and a few night frosts came, turning the berry-leaves into their multicolored state on the hillside meadows. Marguerite glimpsed a mouse that had already turned white, and the small birds were leaving, flying overhead, going southward in swarms like bees.

The women gathered the last of the berries, cooking them into preserves since they could not be dried in the sun any longer. The times when the sun shone were infrequent now, and it did not shine very warmly in its shortening duration. There was a great deal of rain, sometimes mixed with sleet; puddles lay on the granite, and the turf was soggy. Their feet were always wet.

Damienne's sabots did not even save her, since the water

came up over the soles. Wet hose were always drying before the fire, with their wet-wool smell rising on the air.

So that Marguerite now tried soaking a pair of wool hose in tallow and she found that they were then almost waterproof, although somewhat unpleasant-feeling. With pieces of oiled hide sewed around them for soles, fur-side in, they made a sort of clumsy boot that tied at the knee. These wore out fast, she found, especially in the feet, but they saved her shoes from their final ruin and made walking over the soggy ground more endurable.

But after the baby slept each evening she whittled on a pair of sabots to replace them.

And in the lengthening evenings Marguerite continued to talk to Damienne of France, while she lulled her baby son before putting him to bed. He was growing, but he seemed to be more fretful and restless than he had ever been before. One night while she sat before the fire, dandling and patting the sleepless child first over her shoulder, then on her knee, her thoughts returned to Nontron in the valley of the Bandiat in the Dordogne.

She and Damienne had lived there for a while, and Marguerite remembered it fondly, with a feeling of home. She thought that Damienne had enjoyed that time as well, so she chatted along in a vagrant monologue, hoping that the sound of her voice would lull her restless son, as well as soothing Damienne's troubled spirit.

They had stayed in Nontron long enough to make a few good friends, and it seemed to Marguerite that Nontron was a hospitable little village, where folk were friendly to newcomers, the dark-eyed, dignified women nodding and speaking, in the streets, as they passed.

She mentioned the ramparts of Nontron, rising from its rocky outcroppings on its hilltop, its grey stone buildings and red tiled roofs, and the steep, winding streets on natural rock, almost like the smooth granite slopes of the island. There was an ancient château where it was said that Richard Coeur de Lion had received his death-wound hundreds of years before.

The people of Nontron spoke the langue d'oc, which carried a pleasant sound to Marguerite's ears, although she, herself, had had to learn to speak in the accents of northern France, as well. Her cousin, Jean-François, had made much of this matter of a northern accent, since he liked to be considered a gentleman of Picardy, not of the South, and a kinswoman with a provincial accent was an embarrassment. He had made that point only too clear, although, as Marguerite reminded Damienne wryly, "The King himself came from the South, from Angoulême."

But the de la Roques had lived for generations in the South, also, and there Marguerite had felt at home. She had been far happier in Nontron than ever she had managed to be in the fine château at Roberval, in the North.

So she mused aloud to Damienne, mentioning the streets of Nontron, which climbed so steeply to the city square and the ramparts, and the fountains in the walls, from which they had drawn their water. Some of the houses along those winding streets were truly elegant, she reminded Damienne, with the families' coats of arms carved in stone over the doorways. One house even had a beautiful, broad circular staircase of cut stone, finer than would be expected in a small village.

And the surrounding countryside thereabouts was also rocky, she added, and the rock was granite, almost like that of the island. The resemblance somehow pleased her as she recalled it, since to her Nontron had been a homelike place. She hoped Damienne had enjoyed her talking of it.

But the older woman hunched in a stony silence, implacable and unbroken, and she showed little sign of what she was thinking, or, indeed, whether she now let herself think at all.

Gathering and cutting wood for the winter's burning was now Marguerite's day-long task; there was no knowing how much would be needed, but it would clearly be dangerous to be caught short when the deep snows came. So that calling for Damienne to help her when she found deadfalls too large to pull home alone, Marguerite dragged together a pile of driftwood and fallen logs too large to be brought into the courtyard. Only when the pieces were cut and stacked would they fit inside.

She first cut them into lengths of a size to carry in, thinking that they could then be covered with canvas, and sawed into shorter lengths inside the entry-hall if the deep snows caught her before she was done.

Daily she missed the strong arms of her husband, who last

year had wielded the heavy cutting axe, and had pulled the big, two-handled square saw so rapidly through the logs. Sometimes she asked Damienne to help her use the two-handled saw, since it was hard to use alone, but it was discomforting to see her old nurse working across from her instead of her gay young husband, so that now she simply used the hand-saw although it sawed more slowly.

And now the woodland was beginning to look as neat and closely picked as a copse in France, so that although the two women had to go farther afield for wood, the look of impenetrable wilderness had vanished. It would now be harder for beasts to lurk close by, bold as they had become.

*

In the misty, gloom-ridden evenings Marguerite tried persistently to regain Damienne's companionship. If her old nurse did not want to talk of some matters, she thought, perhaps others would arouse her interest and bring her mind forth from behind the sullen wall of silence she had built up.

So that one evening she remarked brightly that the geese passing overhead had reminded her of the baying of hunting-hounds in the Forest of Compiègne. François Premier loved to hunt there, and her kinsman, Roberval, had often been in the hunting party. How fine the hunters had looked in their high leather boots and their brightly-colored, warm clothing! Thinking covetously of those warm garments, Marguerite glanced meaningfully toward Damienne and remarked that they were often made of the luxuriously-fine wool called Camelot, woven right there in Picardy, and most of the jackets and capes had fur collars or linings, making a rich array. Even the horses had embossed bridles and saddles, and the very collars of the hounds had been decorated. It was a goodly sight, to say nothing of the noise! The clamor of the hounds, the soundings of the hunting-horns and the shouts of the hunters, the thunder of hooves—a hunt in full cry could be heard for miles.

Damienne hunched toward the fire as if she could peer through the flames into the forests of France, and in Marguerite's arms her baby son dozed, his lips hanging slackly against a curled hand.

So that as she enjoyed her recollections of past splendor, Marguerite continued her tale. Entertaining the huntsmen was an affair of great import, she reminded Damienne, since they both had had to assume the duty from time to time, and it was an onerous one especially if the King, himself was among the huntsmen—which he often was. The many great houses in and around the forest made preparations to receive the huntsmen with due ceremony if the game-trail they followed brought them nearby. It was a great honor to have the King stop at one's château, and he might even stay for the night, a still greater honor. When he was known to be nearby the ladies dressed in their gayest garments, so that they might be ready on a moment's notice to welcome the hunters and serve them refreshment.

Damienne rocked back and forth on her stool, her eyes staring, unfocused, as if she looked back into the very courtyards of Picardy. "Oh, aye," she said dreamily, bound, against her will by the spell her nurseling was weaving, "François was ever a one for the ladies." She even smiled a bit and nodded. Marguerite was almost giddily encouraged by this unwonted show of interest.

"Yes," she agreed vivaciously, "He collects them as he does his Italian works of art." It was a known thing that the King had a weakness for the ladies, she rambled on, although he had had only two *Maîtresses en Titre* during his reign. And the second, from what she had heard, she said, was a cold-hearted and calculating vixen, with an eye to her own advantage, Anne de Pisseleu de Heilly, the Duchesse d'Etampes. Marguerite had only seen her at a distance, but she was a radiant beauty.

Damienne again showed a certain interest. "When he asked his first mistress to return his jewels, she sent them back melted into ingots!" she rumbled forth with a certain ironic satisfaction that François had received a comeuppance of sorts. "But Françoise de Foix was ever a high-spirited woman. She is dead now, of course, this few years back, but it is said the King loved her well."

"The King has always attracted women. Even before he took

the throne, he apparently knew how to win them," said Marguerite, smiling at certain risqué rumors she had heard concerning his methods. She and Damienne had seen him, many times, on his incessant travels throughout France, for it was said that the Court did not stay in one place more than fifteen days at a time. Then its twelve thousand horses, its six thousand cavaliers and men-at-arms, its Court ladies, its servants and its baggage of tapestries and gold and silver plate were all packed up and moved again.

Chambord, Fontainbleau, Chenonceaux, Angoulême, and again back to Paris. All France was visited sooner or later, and the courtiers became weary with constant travel. François had once said, "A Court without ladies is a springtime without roses," and, wearied or not, the ladies followed after him.

Well both women remembered. François Premier was a tall man with a faunish face, and a long nose which came down somewhat over a short upper lip, and well did Marguerite remember that striking visage, sensual but kingly. And his sister looked exactly like him. Between them, she now remarked to Damienne, they had made their strange looks fashionable, since both of them had great charm. And after the two wives François had been successively required to marry for reasons of state, Marguerite went on, few could blame him for finding for himself some pretty and spirited mistresses. His first wife, Claude de France, had been a sweet-natured woman, but plain and lame; his second, Eléonore d'Autriche, Charles Quint's sister, had been a sort of dwarf, with stumpy legs. So François had drawn other gaiety around him and had made himself the center of a frivolous and dissolute Court, while still remaining the idol of his devoted sister, Queen Marguerite, and of the French people.

His subjects had irreverently nicknamed him "Big Nose," Marguerite smiled to recall.

But Italianate influences had shaped François Premier's thinking, and it seemed that he must now be a disciple of Machiavelli, who had advised princes to be strong, not over-scrupulous, and to study naught but war. Thus François' alliances shifted rapidly. Before the expedition had left it was rumored that he had intervened with the Pope himself, in behalf of Henry of England, the Eighth of his Name, who had fallen in love with a lady of his Court, and who now wanted to divorce Charles Quint's aunt, Katharine of Aragon. That move would cause a real ferment, Marguerite predicted darkly.

But now that the King was getting old he was suffering from a recurrent abscess, it was whispered, and his health had declined greatly. "Perhaps Roberval may soon lose his protector," Marguerite continued, her gentle voice betraying a certain vengefulness toward her kinsman. "Unless, of course, he re-establishes his claims of family connection with Diane de Poitiers." Thus, of course, he would gain influence with François' successor, since Diane was already the Dauphin's mistress. Probably Roberval had long since taken steps in this direction, both women agreed, since he had long been a courtier, and he was adept at trimming his sails to whichever direction the wind blew.

It was almost *lèse-majesté* to talk so openly of the King's illness and his successor, and for a moment both women had instinctively lowered their voices.

But here on this remote island we can at least speak freely, thought Marguerite with a fleeting sense of liberation, and of this point she reminded Damienne, who was again sinking back into her accustomed silence. For a few moments she continued her efforts at conversation, talking of this matter and that one. But again the older woman did not respond. As Marguerite recalled the evening, it had been largely a one-sided effort. As she lulled her baby son, swinging little objects for him to grasp, she felt as if she were telling tales to two children, one too young to understand, and one too old.

And that night as she laid her sleeping son in the side of her bed, where his father had lain for so short a time, Marguerite gazed down at him somberly in the flickering light of the pan-lamp and wondered what her child's coming lifetime would bring him.

The evening's conversation had brought back thoughts of her homeland, which she ordinarily pushed back into the furthest recesses of her mind, and these memories now came forward with a bitter poignancy as she thought of her son's birth-right as a nobleman of France.

Would he ever go hunting in the Forest of Compiègne, and be presented, richly-garbed, at Court, to whomever might then be King? Or would he grow to manhood on this savage island, learning only what she and Damienne could teach him? His mother feared that this might well come about.

October, 1543

—1—

The coming of winter now seemed a more ominous thing, since the hope of rescue had dimmed with the passing of the ships.

Even Marguerite, in spite of her disclaimers, had unconsciously pinned her hopes on the return of the *vaisseaux,* knowing that the movements of the fisher-folk were mysterious and unpredictable.

And as if to add to their despair, cold rains were now frequently coming down, with occasional sleet; the days were shortening, and the wood supply was still very far short of what would be needed.

Rain or no rain, more fuel must be brought in and cut.

During the spring days in the *logette,* Damienne had remembered the farm custom of making workmen's bonnets out of caps which were first knitted, then soaked in hot and cold water and pounded between heavy stones until the fibres matted solidly together. They then became windproof and nearly waterproof. Partly to keep busy while awaiting the birth of the child, she had made such a helmet, which tied under the chin and covered the hair, like a huntsman's hat. It had proved to be very warm, and to stay in place while one worked.

Now Marguerite oiled it slightly on the outside, to make it shed the rain, and wore it daily. She also felted and oiled a pair of wool hose, wearing them in the wooden sabots which she had finally finished carving out, and in this garb she looked like a veritable peasant and field-worker, she thought wryly, whether male or female she did not know. And in the constant rain she found that she could only use the axe to cut wood; the saw-blade bound when the wood was wet.

But Damienne's sturdy endurance had faltered since the sighting of the ships. All spirit seemed now to have left her. She did her accustomed duties as if in a trance, often pausing and staring vacantly into space, an unreadable expression in her eyes.

Try though she did, Marguerite was now seldom able to divert her old nurse or to lure her mind away from what were apparently dark thoughts. So she tried to spare Damienne from duties which demanded exertion or care, and she herself resumed the trips to the signal pyre, since ships of the fisher-folk might still pass by. Her daily trips should soothe Damienne, she thought, and give her continued reasons for hope.

On the way she took slightly different routes, to search for dried deadfalls, and once she disturbed a black bear which charged out from a little rock shelter on the northern slope, where it would probably hibernate. Marguerite did not kill the creature, since after charging threateningly toward her, it did not pursue her, but she became still more aware that the beasts were returning, more and more, to their old lairs on the island.

Now, as she trudged down the hill with her heavy but indispensable arquebus on one shoulder, hauling a deadfall behind her in her other hand, Marguerite wished heartily for a less cumbersome weapon which could be hung from her belt. Her husband had told her of hand guns and pistolets, describing them with a boyish relish which she now remembered with a pang of love and longing. He had said the rare little guns were small and light, and could be fired with one hand, and that he regretted that they did not have one, instead of so many heavy arquebuses.

However, Marguerite recalled, he had also said that the small guns did not shoot very far, nor did their bullets strike with the crushing impact of arquebus balls. Indeed he had seemed to believe that they might not have much effect on the larger beasts of the island, and these were now to be feared, since they were becoming more bold and menacing than they had been during the autumn before.

—2—

Later in the month the baby grew more and more fretful. He nursed often, but did not seem to be satisfied, and he cried oftener and for longer periods of time in his raucous baby wail, filling the *logette* with unease. Marguerite did not know how to comfort him, and Damienne sat stolidly on her stool by the fireplace, not arousing herself to help her harrassed young mistress.

Marguerite thought that the baby might be hungry, even after his nursing, so she asked Damienne how to make him a barley-broth, since this was the food given to nurselings even before they were weaned. Making the broth, Marguerite knew, was a complicated matter, but Damienne responded only rather vaguely, answering the questions which Marguerite asked her, but hardly raising her eyes.

It seemed that the grain had to be rinsed in cold water, drained, and set to one side, then the broth, alone, was to be brought to a boil, and Marguerite learned that it should be a simple strained meat and vegetable stock. In another pot the liquid was to be poured on the grain, when the stock was done, not the other way about, and it must be stirred just once. Otherwise the grain would become gummy.

A baby this young, of course, could not yet be given any of the barley-grains, only the broth.

With her wailing baby on her arm, and no further help from Damienne, the younger woman cut up the vegetables and meat, made the stock, strained it through the horsehair sieve, and then made the broth. It took her several hours, and in the meantime the baby was not being helped, and the brief daylight was vanishing, with no additional wood being cut to add to the winter's store.

And a certain amount now had to be cut every day until the deep snows came, Marguerite had worriedly decided, or they would not be able to keep the *logette* warm enough for so young a child.

And her son was now in a frenzy of anger and impatience, throwing his head from side to side and dashing the soft little yarn balls which were his toys impatiently aside, as he thrashed his thin little arms about and kicked his swaddlings into disorder.

At last Marguerite reached the end of her patience, her nerves rubbed raw by the baby's rasping voice, and her own helplessness. She screamed at Damienne to get up and help her, and said that she could not do all the work of the household by herself.

Shocked out of her lethargy, Damienne got to her feet and took the frantic child into her shaking old hands. Marguerite had never before lost her temper with her old nurse, since outgrowing the inevitable tantrums of early childhood, and behind Damienne's stolid expression, she was appalled and sick at heart. But she attempted to quiet and feed the baby, and after an embarrassed moment his mother pulled on her outdoor garments and went out to work in the courtyard.

And yet the baby would not be soothed. So that at last Damienne poked up the fire and took him on her lap in its reflected warmth, carefully drawing away the layers of swathing in which he was wrapped. She examined him carefully, pressing and probing his little body with her gentle old hands.

His color had yellowed, and his legs and arms, she now realized, while they had lengthened, were no longer firm. His chest and neck were thin, but his abdomen was distended and tender. In shock and dismay Damienne drew his wrappings back around him and again fed him some of the barley-broth which his mother had prepared. He could not keep it down.

Then for a long time Damienne sat with him in her arms, bleakly staring into the fire, until the baby whimpered himself into sleep from sheer weariness. When Marguerite looked in on them from time to time, the old nurse remained silent.

She had seen babies in France whose bodies took on this certain look. They seldom lived.

—3—

The next morning Marguerite awoke to find that Damienne had already left the *logette.* Only the baby was there with her, lying silently on his side of the bed. She tried to nurse him. Apparently her milk was drying up, for he pawed at her fretfully, and cried. She finally poked up the fire and fed him some warm barley-broth, which he vomited almost at once, down over the front of his linen swaddlings.

They had so little barley, if he needs must be weaned, his mother regretted the loss of even a mouthful. She had hoped to nurse him throughout the winter, since babies were usually nursed until they were over a year old, and he was so thin, as it was.

Marguerite finally laid him on the bed, thinking she would try again later. The angry voices of the day before had probably disturbed him too much to digest his food, she thought, especially if she could no longer nurse him. So she soothed him until he fell asleep.

A spark of anger now flared up in Marguerite's mind as Damienne did not return. Where could she have gone for such a long time? Finally, reluctantly, Marguerite dressed to go outside and seek her, carefully barring the door as she left the *logette,* since she did not like to leave the child unattended if Damienne was not nearby. She dragged the courtyard gate shut and barred it, also, then walked down the path to the shore, calling Damienne.

The water-birds wheeled and screamed, dropping into the water with splashes of white, but Damienne was nowhere to be seen.

Perhaps she had gone for faggots? That was a never-ending task; the wood supply could not be too large, they both knew. Damienne had gleaned most of the branches near the cabin, and thus nowadays she had to gather them from farther away. Marguerite called out, "Damienne, Damienne!" as she climbed upward through the trees to where the woodland diminished near the western side of the island, close to the high cliffs of the shore. But Damienne did not reply.

Retracing her steps past the *logette,* with a quick look at the sleeping baby, Marguerite searched the lower marshy places toward the northeast. Perhaps Damienne had gone there to get a late-season supply of roots or herbs, to hang beside the hearth with the rest of the winter's food supply. But Damienne was not there.

Finding another deadfall, the younger woman dragged it thriftily back to the courtyard, and again looked in at her child. He was still asleep.

At last, half-unwillingly, Marguerite decided to climb to the summit. There was no reason for Damienne to go there, but perhaps she had done so for some unknown reason, perhaps to seek herbs, or thresh more grain. After a hurried and increasingly apprehensive climb, Marguerite reached the summit and stood near the pyre which had been scattered by the wind. Little use to build it up, she thought somberly, the time was nearly past when fishermen would come. But she walked farther northward, down the hill, calling Damienne as she went.

Why Damienne would have gone to the north shore or the clay-bank, her mistress did not know, and now her growing alarm caused her to search feverishly over their limited domain. She clambered anxiously up and down the banks, back and forth on the north side of the island, standing on each of the taller ridges and calling Damienne's name. But again Damienne neither appeared nor responded.

A chill fear creeping into her mind, Marguerite now climbed hastily back toward the summit by a more westerly course. With a deadly apprehension she peered into the bear's den there. To her relief Damienne had not been dragged away by the beast, and she rushed to the nearby topmost summit of the island, calling as loudly as she could, through cupped hands, "Damienne, Damienne!"

From this vantage-point, she thought, I could be heard almost anywhere on the island, except for the extreme southern part. So she raised her hands and called again, facing in each direction, but there was no answer.

Sternly reining in her near-panic, Marguerite told herself firmly that Damienne was probably already back in the cabin. But as she walked down the long, slanting slope of the granite cliff toward the *logette,* she decided to go close to the edge which overhung the valley and see if Damienne was anywhere in sight. Perhaps Damienne's hearing was failing, as were her eyes. Perhaps she had even gone to the cave for some reason, thought Marguerite forlornly, although there was nothing left there now.

The cliff was sheer and tall on the east side of the cave, a steep, straight wall higher than that of most castles. One could not climb directly down to the cave from there, since no footholds were to be found on it, and the way around was long. Marguerite stood at the edge and called down over the side, "Damienne, Damienne!" The echo from the rocks on the other side of the valley was her only answer.

Greater fear now came to Marguerite. Unwillingly she cast her eyes downward.

Almost directly beneath her, at the foot of the sheerest and highest part of the cliff, far below, lay a huddle of cloth, as weathered as the rock itself, but greyer. In deadly horror Marguerite fixed her eyes upon it, flinching with utter dismay. It was Damienne.

Marguerite never knew how she got down the ridge. She dimly remembered, afterward, of plunging downward, to the east, and climbing down the lower portion of the cliff, hand over hand. She tore her way through the meshwork of scrubby growth, feet slipping through the prickly branches whenever she missed a step, tearing her legs, her clothing and her hands. Even her face was deeply scratched.

At last she bent over Damienne. Damienne was dead. Her flesh was already cool.

—4—

Marguerite stood insecurely on the matted underbrush gazing down at her old nurse, flooded both by guilt and by a bleak despair. A sort of darkness seemed to creep in behind her eyes, from cold and hidden corners within her skull and her ears rang as if her head were inside a bell. The reality of this death was unacceptable to her stunned mind, and all her senses rejected it. She felt as if she were floating away from herself, borne on a dark cloud. Moments passed.

How will I get her out of here? she finally wondered dazedly. I do not know how I got in here by myself.

So that closing her thoughts to anything but the problem of carrying Damienne's body out of the thicket, Marguerite at last gathered together her forces of will. Time for grief and remorse later, she told herself, time for remembrance. But now Damienne must be carried out through this entangled brush, with none to help with the task. The beasts would eat her if she lay here even for an hour unattended.

In her complete desperation Marguerite did not attempt to extricate or even to compose Damienne's body, caught, as it was, in a cleft of rock, between branches. But, climbing back over the treacherous meshwork, she returned to the cabin for the hatchet. There, in the merciful oblivion of infancy, her son still slept.

Returning, Marguerite hacked out a desperate path through the branches, toward the bottom of the cliff where Damienne lay. It was not easily done. The branches were not large, but they were tough and springy, and they seemed innumerable, each one barring the way to the solid earth beneath, each one enmeshed, it seemed, with a hundred others. They sprang back as she tried to cut them, and even after they were cut they were so inextricably matted and intermeshed that it was hard to pull them out of the way.

Once, as she straightened her back and wiped her sweating face on her sleeve, Marguerite thought with grisly logic, the beasts will not come for her while I am nearby.

But at last she reached Damienne's body again and took her hand. It felt like a cluster of damp, gnarled twigs. I will not drag her out, Marguerite thought dazedly. She deserves gentle treatment.

In the midst of her horror and pain she remembered how she and Damienne had borne her husband to his grave, with some showing of gentleness and dignity, heavy with child though she had then been. Nobody to help me, this time, she thought numbly, but at least I have my strength back; I am not great with child nor weak from childbirth.

Gently she pulled Damienne upward and turned her over. Damienne's face was peaceful; her eyes and lips were closed. With a surge of determination Marguerite stooped beside the body and worked her hands under the knees and behind the limp arms. Bracing her feet, she heaved her body upward with a sudden motion and found herself standing upright with Damienne's body sagging in her arms.

How thin she is! thought Marguerite aghast, but even so I could not have done this a year ago. She had continued to think of Damienne as the buxom, sturdy woman she had always been, but now she was no heavier than a tall child.

The body drooping between her arms, Marguerite stumbled down the rough pathway to the cabin. Branches tore at Damienne's dangling feet, and at their tattered clothing. At times Marguerite had to turn sidewise to get them both through the narrow way she had chopped out.

Reaching the *logette* at last, Marguerite laid Damienne on the table and straightened her body. The baby still slept, unmoving.

For a moment Marguerite stood before the body of her old nurse in silence, gripped by a spasm of anguish, of unreality.

Then, almost mechanically, she took off Damienne's faded and torn clothing, washed her body, and dressed her in the neatly-folded garments from her garde-robe, even managing to get Damienne's thin arms down through the sleeves of her black silk dress, and fastening it in front. It fit, she found in guilty dismay, as though it had been made for another, and larger, woman. How could she have failed to notice her old nurse's frailty, the falling away of her flesh? Marguerite asked herself dismally.

But she combed back Damienne's hair and pinned it up as best she could, finding that it was whiter than she had realized, and thinner. With faltering hands Marguerite smoothed the scanty wisps into neatness and tied the small bonnet over them. She crossed Damienne's hands over her bony chest, and looked around for her Rosary, which she had taken to carrying in her pocket.

But as she looked through the pockets of Damienne's limp, discarded garments, she found that the Rosary was not there.

Numbly Marguerite again retraced her steps to the cliff. There it lay, a cluster of pitiful tied pebbles, looking like rubble from the cliff above it. Marguerite took it back to the cabin and wrapped it around Damienne's hands. Then, again, she parted the bed-curtains and looked at the baby. He was still asleep. Ah, my poor little one, his mother thought, it is not fitting that you should lie here in the room with a corpse. But Damienne will not harm you. She loved you well. You will be her only watcher.

*

And now there was no time to be lost in the burial. Marguerite remembered how suddenly the deep snows had come down upon them during the winter before, and how difficult her husband's burial had been. Now, at least, she thought again, I am not heavy with child.

So that retrieving the hatchet Marguerite went to her husband's grave. Damienne would lie beside him, and perhaps she would rest easier at the side of her young Lord, thought Marguerite, since Damienne had always felt safer with a man about. After a moment's repining, as she gazed back through the dark, lonely shadows of the trees, Marguerite knelt and started chopping a line around a narrow rectangle to edge the grave. She even lay down on it herself to judge the length, and, for a despairing moment, she wished she could stay there, mindlessly staring upward at the gray sky through the dark branches.

But there was the baby to think of, she told herself with stubborn realism, as well as Damienne.

At intervals she went back to the *logette* to see to the babe; he only ate once, and then but little. She did not offer him her breast, for fear of arousing him again to an angry frenzy as he suckled in vain. Milk should be a gentle thing, she thought, and mine may now be bitter as gall, akin to a witch's brew, damned by heaven as I surely seem to be.

But by evening Marguerite had the grave hacked out, down

to the granite. She laid green boughs across the bottom, as before, and propped them against the steep sides. The evergreen spread in a soft, springy mat, covering the harsh stone at the bottom of the grave, and the sharp points of the chopped-off roots along the sides. Marguerite stood and looked at it for a moment. The second grave I have dug; she thought with bitter irony, I am becoming an able gravedigger in truth.

Returning wearily to the cabin, Marguerite wrapped Damienne's body in a sheet, tying it closely about her, head and all, after a last look at the worn, peaceful face. The calm of the familiar features steadied her, as though she had been again a child. Damienne looked as serene as she might have done, years hence, Marguerite thought, in our own château at home in France, lying between candles, in all honor, waiting for the rites of burial after a long and useful life. But I have even forgotten the candles, she thought sadly.

As she lifted the body this time she found that it had stiffened, and was somehow even easier to lift. She carried it to the grave across her arms with an eerie awareness that the body of her faithful old nurse was even less weighty than a fireplace log, and she laid it down beside the grave-hole. Then she walked around to the other side, knelt, and reached across it, to slide the body down as gently as she could, face upward, on the soft branches. I am sorry, Damienne, she thought. There is no seemly way for one person to do this.

She decided to cover the body first, before reading the burial rites, lest it become too dark for proper precautions against the night-beasts. So she laid the layer of evergreen boughs over the shrouded body, soft as they were and clean-smelling, somehow comfortingly alive and real. Over the branches she laid flat stones, across the whole bottom of the grave, taking them from the stack which was laid up against the courtyard wall. Between the stones she packed the spongy peat, then pressed turf over them. Another layer of boulders, a layer of turf. She felt an odd flash of satisfaction at the thought that she was now able to carry larger stones, this time, than she had for her husband. They would better ward off the beasts.

At last the grave was filled, and a long mound of boulders heaped up over it.

Marguerite straightened her back and again walked wearily to the cabin. It was nearly dark. Her mind seemed to be washed clean of all feeling, all thought, as she trod the pathway which her husband and Damienne had so often walked. In the *logette* she lighted more pan-lamps, and washed herself, dressing in her dark, warm dress. There was blood on the washing-cloth, she saw, from her scratched face and torn hands. Not looking into the mirror, she combed up her hair and knotted it into place by mere habit, not caring to see her own face in the mirror's dim surface, nor to look into what she might see in the eyes that would have gazed back at her.

She then stolidly picked up her baby, who had awakened, and wrapped him in a warm, woolen cloth, taking the Bible from the mantelstone. Her very heartbeats seemed to echo dismally in her own ears as she turned away from the empty *logette.* The fire was nearly out, and the room was chill.

Her little son lay supinely in her arm as she returned to the burial-place, where, standing at the head of the grave, the silent child in her leaden grasp, she suddenly remembered Damienne's horror of being buried in unhallowed ground. Now she must lie here, on this island she had almost thought to be accursed.

Marguerite raised her eyes to the darkening sky and said firmly, aloud, "But for this babe I am the only Christian soul here, and I now bless this ground." She held her arm out woodenly over the grave. The forest was still.

Then in the dimming light, she read the remembered words from her New Testament, adding to them the Lord's prayer:

Nostre Pere estant lassus es cieulx
Sanctifie soit tō nom precieux . . .

The sky darkened as she read from the tiny volume, scarcely larger than her hand, its red and yellow illuminations glowing faintly in the fading light. The rich leather cover, the gold-colored edges and the creamy pages, so familiar to her touch, lay before her eyes in unreality, like a link to a lost civilization. She peered at the elegant print in the near dark, but between the gathering night and her tears she could no longer read the pages.

So that closing her eyes, she recited one of the poems she remembered from Queen Marguerite's devout writings:

O doulce mort, gratieuse douleur
Puissante clef delivrant de malheur
Ceulx qui par mort estoient mortifiéz
Pour l'estre en vous et votre mort fiéz . . .

The appropriateness of the words steadied her, somehow, as though she were surrounded by a company of friends sharing her sorrow. As she finished the prayers she stood silent for a moment, desolate but somehow undestroyed.

Then, remembering Damienne's return, of late months, to the Old Religion, she tried to remember what Latin she could, and murmured it, as well.

*

As the sky grew dark Marguerite stood for a long while before the grave, holding the silent child in her arms, her mind vacant of thought. Night-sounds began.

Then, remembering that for once she had left the arquebus behind, she returned languidly to the cabin. As she paced slowly back the dark path, holding her baby son in one arm and her Bible in the other, she forced herself to preserve a steely calm. Only one thought went though her mind, unbidden, before she could turn it away. Until my babe learns to talk, she thought, I will never hear the sound of another human voice.

She closed her mind completely, then and forever, to the question of whether Damienne had fallen or jumped.

November, 1543

—1—

Alone on the island with her child, Marguerite fought against an increasing sense of unreality. At times it seemed impossible to her stunned mind that she should be here alone, cast away in this isolated place, and that her husband and Damienne should both be gone. In the mornings, during her first waking moments, she seemed clearly to hear them talking together nearby in their well-remembered accents.

They inhabited her dreams, and whether this was comfort or torment she did not know.

The greatest unreality of all was a thing she barred from all conscious thought. Not to be borne was the realization that she and her baby son were the only human beings in all of New France, except for the fierce and warlike savages, and that she now stood alone as the protector of her child.

In the first days after Damienne's death, Marguerite found that she had to hold her thoughts unflinchingly into certain narrow channels, preventing them from straying into places where horror and dread lay in wait. Now I am preparing the barley-broth, she would tell herself firmly, or now I am feeding my son; I will think of that and nothing other. Like a falcon under its hood or a terrorized mare in blinders, she blocked off all wandering thoughts from her mind, lest she drift into madness or sink into a despair from which nothing would arouse her.

Only an animal-like urgency to protect her child sustained her. Like the beasts, she thought, I care now only for the survival of my young, thinking of naught but how I must feed him and keep him warm.

And food she had, in plenty, she thought mournfully, since the stores had been gathered together for two, or even three, but no milk was to be had for the child, and it was milk he needed, Marguerite knew.

Soon a desperate fear for her child submerged even her deep shock and sorrow at the loss of Damienne.

The baby was restless, seldom sleeping for long at a time, and little she fed him seemed aright. The sucking movements of his mouth told her that it was the milk from her breast he needed, not broth from a spoon or a cup. And in Marguerite's inexperience she did not know how much an infant of seven months should eat. Barley-broth was all she dared give him, but it was the customary weaning-food; on that she pinned her waning faith, even as his stomach rejected it, and as he grew weaker.

Idle to wish for milk for him, from oxen, or goats, or even for asses' milk, Marguerite told herself. All of these were sometimes given to weanlings when a wet-nurse could not be found, Damienne had told her, and all could have been tried, Marguerite thought in blank despair, if only we could have carried him back to France. Milk for her baby, she thought desperately, was as unattainable here as a full-rigged ship in which to take him home.

So that now even Marguerite's dreams centered around the feeding of her little son. Once as she dozed at his bedside she dreamed of a unicorn, stately and white, its neck arched and its single horn twined with flowers. It sat, gently submissive, in a tiny, encircling fence of withes, surrounded by a thousand flowers, like a picture in a tapestry. In her dream it spoke to her in bell-like cadences, and willingly gave its milk, as if by magic, for her little son.

Even in her sleep, thankfulness had welled up in her, dissolving into near-tears as she woke into the reality of her son's fretful whimpering.

She could only pray, she told herself in her increasing torment, that he would somehow be weaned on the foods at hand, and pray she did, with increasing urgency. She even called on Damienne to help her, from wherever she had gone, but the comfort Damienne could give had vanished even before her own departure.

When her now-frail son was awake, Marguerite talked to him, trying to reach him with the sound of her voice, willing him to live. When he slept, lying in his swaddlings, more motionless as he grew weaker, Marguerite stole out into the courtyard and worked on the winter's supply of wood. If her son was not sturdy, he must at least be kept warm. So she feverishly dragged in one deadfall after another, sawing off lengths as the end lay over the chopping block in the dooryard, and peering into the *logette* as often as she dared.

Sleet and snow now fell at intervals, but the rows of cut firewood around the inside of the courtyard wall continued to grow. The wood was piled as high as Marguerite's head, and it extended once around the whole courtyard. Now the second row was well along. She worked desperately, telling herself that even more would be needed, with only her breath and her child's to warm the air inside the draperies of the bed.

*

But grief for Damienne, Marguerite found, was as deep as sorrow for her husband. After his death she had sometimes taken his hunting-jacket and held it across her face, to breathe in the remembered scent of his body. Now her old nurse's belongings, when they caught her eye unexpectedly, cut her like a sudden wound. At last she put all of them away in Damienne's garde-robe.

But Damienne's bed, with its well-remembered hangings, also proved to be too sharp a reminder. The older woman had embroidered the draperies years before, as she sat watching her nurseling in the early years of Marguerite's childhood. She could almost remember when each flower had been outlined, when each entwined stem had been stitched into being. Later, when Marguerite had been given a full-sized bed of her own, they had both embroidered its curtains, and some of her own faltering stitches were still to be seen on it now.

The memories were too hard to endure, too rending, of Damienne sitting under this tree or that, placidly wielding her needle, and looking up now and then to see what her nurseling was about, or to soothe away the sudden tears of childhood.

Finally, with a spurt of energy almost rebellious in its intensity, Marguerite dismantled Damienne's bed. She folded the draperies and canopy into the garde-robe, and moved the straw mattress and the feather-bed, pillows and *pallaisse,* onto her own bed. They would add warmth, she told herself, and warmth might well be needed.

She then stacked wood all across Damienne's bed and along her side of the room. Several rows of it would fill up space which would then not have to be heated, and the wood would be dried and ready to hand.

While making these changes, Marguerite took down her husband's *citre* and her flute and packed them carefully away in his sea-chest. Reminding her, as they did, of the early gaiety on the island, when they had sung and danced in the evenings, she could no longer bear the pain which the sight of them caused.

*

Before Damienne had died, the two women had packed pond-ice into the storage compartment in the rear of the *logette,* and had put away several catches of fish in the ice, to break the monotony of the winter's salted food. Now, in her concern for her son, Marguerite took two arquebuses and went out to hunt for game, since winter was near and the flesh would stay frozen. Her trips were hurried, so that she would not be long absent from the child. She would feed him a broth of newly-killed rabbit, or fowl, she thought; perhaps one or the other would sit better in his stomach than did the barley-broth.

The hares, rabbits and grouse had already assumed their winter coloring and were hard to see against the snow, but Marguerite shot a fair number of each, carrying them into the courtyard for cleaning. The last of the geese and ducks had left, she noticed even during the haste of her foray, and only the winter sea-birds now soared or roosted in their accustomed haunts.

And the harbor had frozen over with a leathery coating of gray ice. No matter, thought Marguerite bitterly; we have already salted away enough fish, and more, than I will need alone.

Returning to the courtyard, Marguerite carefully skinned the hares and rabbits, saving their soft, white-furred pelts to make a robe and a cap for her son. She had been told, she thought, that the small, thin hides could be softened and cured by merely rubbing them between one's hands, and the work would calm her mind during the anxious hours she now spent sitting beside her fretful baby son.

And since the harbor was now frozen the trips to the lookout could now be abandoned, Marguerite realized thankfully, and in any event she now could not leave the weakening child long enough to make the trips. As the snow fell and the waters froze, it was more discomforting than ever to gaze out across them, knowing that no human eyes except her own were viewing that bleak and barren immensity.

Also, the beasts had become still bolder, especially the wolves and the bears. On one of her earlier trips to the summit she had returned to the *logette* to find a bear trying to dig his way in through the lower part of the roof, attracted, perhaps, by the child's weak cries. With shaking hands she had shot the beast and repaired the roof.

My son would be a tender mouthful for the beasts here, thought Marguerite; best if I stay nearby, or even go no farther than the courtyard from now on. So that with a strange sense of enclosure, of succour, she retreated within the *logette.*

—2—

Her child was now sleeping most of the time, and whimpering rather than crying aloud when he was awake. Marguerite devoted herself completely to finding some broth or posset he would relish, trying brews of game, of fish or of vegetables, but even when he swallowed a few mouthfuls, his tiny stomach rejected the food more often than not.

Ah, my small one, thought his mother despairingly, would that your body could take what I can obtain for you! Naught else is to be found here! But in increasing agony of spirit she still tried to find a food that would fit his need.

From deep in her memory came the thought of porridge made of steamed millet, and puddings made from the coarsely-ground grain. She tried them both, in increasing desperation, but neither seemed to be relished; as she spooned them into her little son's mouth, his tongue pushed out more than he would swallow, and the attempts at feeding him often ended with both of them in tears.

When he slept, his mother doggedly cut wood, partly to occupy herself with the hard work, and partly because she hoped that the intermittent sound of the axe might deter the beasts from becoming too bold.

Large stones now lay inside the fireplace to hold heat, and smaller warming-stones lay on the hearth. Already Marguerite was wrapping them in cloths and placing them around her small son as he lay under the heavy coverings, in a furred hood she had made for him. He sucked his thumb as he slept, but his tiny face now seemed old, not babyish.

When her few tasks were finished, Marguerite spent her time beside him in the bed, trying with the warmth of her body to sustain her child, and to give him comfort.

Once, half-dreaming there, her mind wandered far afield, into the past, as if to seek relief there from grief she could no longer ward off, and she remembered with a strange clarity her very first sight of the archipelago of islands which now surrounded her. The memory passed through her mind as vividly as if she were living it again.

She was standing on the starboard side of the *gaillard d'avant,* looking out toward the west as the ship moved west and south. She was wearing one of her lighter dresses, which Damienne had somehow freshened for her, creased though it had been in her sea-chest. The weather had warmed, and she had been wearied with her heavy, dark shipboard clothing. And she had tied a hood over her head to keep her long hair back from her face, but a few strands had escaped and they blew across her eyes.

The shoreline was a maze of islands and inlets, along which the ship moved steadily toward the southwest. Seemingly the mainland along this north shore was far distant from the ships' road, guarded by ranks of innumerable islands and shoals which were scattered between the mainland and the open sea.

Although the ship was a safe distance offshore, Marguerite's keen young eyes could see the shoreline of the islands. It was not an inviting sight. This must be the part of the New World, she thought, which Jacques Cartier had been describing when he said it was the land that God gave to Cain! There was no sign of the fertile meadows and tall trees which she had been told appeared farther to the South. Here the shores were of red granite, sometimes sloping, sometimes rising in steep cliffs against which the surf broke high and foaming. The trees were dark spruce and fir, rearing their near-black pointed tops only in the valleys. The crests of the hills and cliffs were bare, or nearly so, with ragged carpets of low growth reaching downward to slightly higher scrubby plants and bushes that intervened before the edges of the woodlands. The taller trees grew only in the bottoms of the little valleys, tapering to shorter, more straggling trees farther up the valley-sides.

Sea-birds wheeled and cried and perched on the cliffs in sweeping masses. Some of the rocks were white with their droppings. It was a landscape of bold colors, blue of sky and water, red of cliffs, somber greens of trees and moss, dashed with the white of birds, bold and stark colors, without softness.

The same scene, with slight changes, had passed before her eyes ever since Blanc Sablon, an unchanging parade of islets, islands and cliffs, the surf breaking against them endlessly, as far as eye could see.

The wind grew chill, even in July, and Marguerite suppressed a shudder, reminding herself that they were going much farther south.

Suddenly she noticed a seaman run up the ratlines and pull

a signal flag up to the tip of the mainmast. What is this, she wondered, for which there is a need to signal, as we go upriver, offshore, straight up the ships' road? She turned to watch the decks behind her with greater attention. Inquisitively she listened. Voices from the quarterdeck gave orders. Other voices passed them along.

Jean Alfonce, she saw, had bent to call an order to the helmsman below him. Members of the crew came forward to their assigned places along the rails and at the masts, checking the running rigging. Several of them climbed the ratlines to each mast. They were going to change direction; that was apparent.

Marguerite watched them with a certain critical expertise. She knew enough, now, about the setting of the sails to wonder why so many seamen were ordered to their posts unless the captain planned a complete change of direction. It would be understandable, she thought, if they were to veer farther to the larboard, to take the *nef* out to a safer distance from shore. There were uncharted shoals and random rock outcroppings just under the water's surface near these shores, she knew. She had wondered why they were staying so near within sight of the shore, when the sea had become wider here, after leaving the *Étroit de Belle Ysle.* It had perhaps been done, she thought, so that Jean Alfonce could map the shoreline as they went southward through the Grand Baye.

The ship now fell off course slightly and picked up speed. The seamen cleared the sheets. Even the cook had come up from his smoky den under the forward hatch to help with the *écoute de misaine.*

The cry to the helmsman rang out and the ship lumbered hard over to the starboard. *Écoutes* on the starboard side were released, and those on the larboard side were hauled in and secured. The *voile à livarde* below Marguerite filled first; it was smaller and more quickly hauled around. The huge triangular *artimon* in the stern was next to fill, and the boat now swung more rapidly around to its new direction.

But now the *grand'voile* and the *misaine* were being furled! The seamen in the *nids de pie* were securing them to their *vergues.* This was a strange procedure, indeed, for the time and place, unless they were going into harbor for the night. And knowing the need for haste if the expedition was to have time to plant its crops and build its shelters before winter, Marguerite was baffled. It was possible, she knew, to sail all night safely in the long, bright northern nights at this time of year.

A strange sense of unease came into her mind. Picking up her billowing skirts, she descended the steep, ladder-like stair from the *gaillard d'avant* to the *pont,* to seek out someone who knew the reason for this change of course.

And after that, before she had even seen Jean-François, her sharpened senses had told her of grave matters afoot, matters, apparently, that affected her.

The whole affair made a bitter remembrance, Marguerite thought, shocked into wakefulness from her trance-like reverie. Those were the last moments when there was any pretense that I was yet a sheltered and cossetted young *Damoiselle,* worthy of respect, entitled to be gay and carefree and protected.

She remembered, still, the glances of the sea-men as she had passed them that last time—looks she was accustomed to receive, as a young and attractive noblewoman. They had looked at her as men look at a pretty woman who is beyond their station, but not of a forbidding mien. All women liked to receive such glances, whether or not their properly lowered eyes showed their pleasure.

And now Marguerite's hands lifted unconsciously to her gaunt and weathered cheeks. No man, she thought dully, would look at her in quite that way again.

—3—

For the rest of the month her son weakened, day by day.

Urgent efforts to arouse him and to get him to eat became less and less successful, and finally they seemed to his despairing mother to be merely cruel. Once she cried out aloud in her agony and hopelessness, and as she clapped her hand across her mouth in dismay at her loss of self-control, she saw that in his somnolence he had hardly been disturbed.

Finally, after days of increasing lethargy, he opened his eyes and looked squarely up at Marguerite with an almost adult look of weary patience in his drawn face. It was as though her husband's eyes again looked into her own, ill as he too had been, at the last.

She fought her despair. Finally she held her little son in her arms, day and night, spooning a few drops of liquid into his mouth whenever he awakened. But at last he no longer even whimpered, and one morning she awoke to find that his breathing had ceased.

*

Marguerite never knew afterward what she had done then.

Days later she had come to herself, huddled like an animal inside the *pallaisse,* the bed-hangings closed. The fire was dead, and the room was in complete darkness. Groping her way to the hearth like one arisen reluctantly from the dead, she found the fusil and started the fire, lighting a pan-lamp from the first flames.

She found herself as dirty and disheveled as a mad-woman. Her very sabots were gone, and the room was in wild disorder; even the hides on the floor had been scuffled this way and that.

And her son's body was nowhere to be seen.

In growing horror, Marguerite searched outside in the courtyard and then she went to the place of the graves. There was a third mound of stones, untidily piled. The son lay beside the father who had never seen him.

Somehow, Marguerite thought, even in my madness I must have buried him. The beasts have not gotten him.

Numbly she returned to the *logette,* chilled in both mind and body, to sit for a long time before the fire, distraught, mindlessly staring into the flames. At last she cleaned herself, put her hair to rights, and changed her shredded clothing for her last decent, warm dress. Putting on her furred cape, she resignedly took the New Testament from the mantel and returned to the burial place.

Standing over her son's grave in a desolation so stark that it fringed the edges of madness, Marguerite read once more the words of Christian burial. She even added prayers from some strange recesses in her memory:

Atant fais sin soeur Marguerite
Priant Dieu que par le merite
De son tresaymé fils Iesus lassus
Nous puissons parvenir
En nostre maison paternelle
Ou est paix et vie eternelle

Into her mind, unbidden and unwelcome, came the thought: when I die here there will be none to do this for me, but she raised her voice still more loudly in fervent prayer, pressing away from her consciousness the still more unwelcome thought that she, herself, would lie unburied and a prey for the beasts, when her strength at last failed.

Finally her voice faltered and trailed into silence. The cries of the sea-birds reached her, sounding mournful over the shores. The woodland itself was silent; all the little singing birds had gone away.

Clinging to her Bible as though it were the hand of a friend, Marguerite bent over her child's grave. *Répose-toi doucement,* she said, my son, my little son.

Numbly, blinded by tears, she slowly returned to the *logette,* barring the gate and securing the doors behind her without conscious thought. It was as if she sealed herself into the solitude of her own tomb.

*

Alone, more alone than any living thing, Marguerite now waged a stubborn defense against utter madness and despair. Mechanically she finally went about the work she had planned so much earlier in the year; as the winter storms came on at the end of the month she put more stones on the canvas which covered the stacked wood in the courtyard and shut herself inside the *logette* with a sense of finality.

There, stubbornly fighting against her utter loneliness, she feverishly occupied herself with one small task after another, whittling another pair of sabots or patching her tattered work-dress.

Desolately she tried to bar from her thoughts all the memories which she now found unbearable, sitting before the fire doggedly plying her needle in the flickering light of the pan-lamps, her mind a roaring void of incredulity and despair.

No desire to live sustained her; only her body's persistent life went on and on, heartbeat by heartbeat, dragging along her reluctant spirit with it.

On one such night, as she had the worn dress nearly patched together once again, Marguerite noticed that the wind was howling more loudly than ever across the chimney-top, and she got to her feet stolidly to build up the fire and to move the warming-stones into place. She would go to bed when they were warmed, she told herself, after the mending was done.

The room seemed even more empty than it ever had, like a dungeon or a tomb, and her mood became still more somber, try though she did to pin her mind to her homely task.

At last she laid her mending aside and prepared for bed, wrapping the warming-stones to lay between the covers, and banking the fire for the night. A chunk of peat smouldered for a long time and held the heat, as a green backlog held the fire until morning.

Within the bed draperies, in the total darkness, Marguerite had hoped that sleep would come soon and mercifully. Her tired body had always won through to a sleeping state quickly, even in the midst of fear and care. Now she could not sleep. The space beside her where her baby son and her husband had lain seemed like a chill void, deathly and ominous.

Awake, she could govern her thoughts; half-asleep, terrible sorrows and longings raged through her mind, back and forth, like rival armies battling for her sanity.

The wind, howling across the roof, clattered the overlapping stones she had laid there, and vibrated the very logs of the heavy little building. It would be almost merciful, Marguerite thought uneasily, when the deep snow and ice engulfed the *logette,* as she had seen it do during the winter before, enclosing it from the bitter cold and the wailing of the wind. As she and her husband had looked down at the drift-covered cabin from the height of the cave, they had thought it looked helplessly submerged in its casing of ice and snow.

Now she thought of the snow almost as a friend who would seal her away, as if in a cold and peaceful tomb, away from all earthly suffering, away from the insensate fury of the wind and the savage beasts who must be ravenously hungry by now.

Even as she drifted into a disturbed slumber the gusts of wind kept her half-conscious of wilderness, savagery, and things unknown, in the vast country over which the wind had come.

December, 1543

—1—

Dungeons in France sometimes had solitary cells, wherein some poor wretch or another was chained, alone, for forgotten periods of time. Lying in solitude and darkness, unknowing what was next to befall, and of what events might be going forward outside his stone-lined tomb, such prisoners often went mad, Marguerite remembered with an unsparing realism. Sometimes, when mercy of a sort was finally shown, they were brought out, blinking and cringing into the light of day, white-haired and frail although perhaps still young, often never fully to regain their senses. Marguerite had heard of such cases, and she had been told that some prisoners survived long confinement by exerting a stern discipline over both mind and body.

This, she now somehow resolved in the midst of her sorrow and despair, she, herself, must do, as she felt herself trembling on the edge of utter desolation or even of madness. And in her isolation she fought against a sense of unreality that seemed to be borne on the very air as the darkness lengthened to envelop the shortened days into dismal, wind-haunted, endless nights. Going outside into the courtyard was of no avail, hardly relieving her sense of being imprisoned in the *logette,* since outside it she was imprisoned in the courtyard, and outside that, on the island.

The *logette* was warm enough, as yet, with its thickened walls and roof, but Marguerite now found unease and restlessness within its walls, with little to do and only the memory of her dead to keep her company. The outdoor tasks, as she worked alone, had been bearable; indoors the duties she set for herself, however much she attempted to make of them, did not distract her mind from the utter solitude about her.

Sometimes in her desperation she determinedly governed her mind by reading from her *New Testament* or her *Book of True and Perfect Prayer,* hour by hour; sometimes she turned her thoughts to France, and tried to bring into her mind remembered scenes, meticulously complete in each detail, to divert herself by tracing travels she had taken and places she had visited in the years before.

On one such lonely, wind-beleaguered night she deliberately pictured in her mind the procession from Roberval to Paris, of which she and Damienne had been a part, going to attend the celebration of the reconciling between François Premier and his kingly rival, Charles Quint.

Propped in her bed, hangings draped aside so that she could watch the fire, Marguerite readily brought to mind those momentous days.

The two rulers had never liked each other, and their hostility had kept their principalities at intermittent war, for two more different men, Marguerite believed, could hardly have existed, Charles, a coolheaded planner, six years younger than François, but seeming older because of his self-contained nature and disdain for sports. François was hot-blooded and impetuous, fond of women and physical activity, changeable as the seasons, and more likely to give in to the wishes of his friends and intimates than to negotiate politically in a sustained and logical way.

The two had been reconciled, it was said, by the urgings of Queen Eléonore, who was François' wife, but also Charles' older sister, and in bringing together these two rulers who had so long been at odds, the Pope himself had also played a part.

Scarcely three years ago, Marguerite thought wistfully, and what festivities there were! Charles and François had made a ceremonious entry into Paris for a full week of celebration.

Marguerite now thought wryly that it had probably been because it was an almost inescapable obligation of her station that she had been permitted to go down to Paris from Roberval, riding splendidly away through the little village of Rhuis, near the château, where the peasants and freeholders and their wives and children had come out of their doorways to wave and smile at the cavalcade. As the procession had gone along they had joined other members of the seigneuralty from neighboring holdings, to travel south with them through Picardy, bundled in their furs, with the breaths of the horses rising like smoke on the crisp air. Closing her eyes, Marguerite could almost hear the clinking of harness, armor and spurs, the sonorous voices of the men, and the light, quick twitterings of the women, as they renewed acquaintances and commented on each others' clothing and their marriageable children.

The party had clattered through the cobbled streets of the prosperous little villages, where booths with canvas roofs or porchlike awnings narrowed the way, which was still more crowded by peddlers crying their wares with the traditional tuneful rhymes, and apprentices running to and fro from one *artisinat* to the other. Dogs ran between the horses' legs and barked as they passed; the tradesmen held out their offerings. Well did Marguerite remember that din, here where the only sound was the crackling of the fire and the sounds of the wind and the sea.

But that had been a gay time. Draperies and pennants hung from the windows, some painted with the likenesses of the two monarchs, François' nose and Charles' lower lip and jaw lending themselves well to such rude and unflattering portraiture.

And the *echoppes* or stalls in the towns were still wide open as the procession rode past them, sometimes with a blazing hearth to be glimpsed inside, along with the tailor, barber or other tradesman, working away at his calling, while his gaudy sign swung over the shop to attract the passers-by. Savory smells of food came from the doors of the inns or the trays and baskets of the food vendors, and a whiff of the smell of crusty white bread, from a bakeshop, now crossed Marguerite's consciousness with a pang of hunger and craving. She had almost forgotten the taste of good, white, French bread, let alone its fresh-baked aroma.

With a pang of real physical longing she hastily turned her reverie to less tantalizing thoughts.

The villages and towns had looked very well-furbished, she recalled, in honor of the celebration, partly because much new building had already been done, and the houses were now designed for comfort and appearance, not as in earlier years only for security. Now the roofs were tiled instead of thatched, and there were diamond-paned windows and covered chimneys giving promise of coziness within. The fashionable stucco and timber construction had endless variations, sometimes with portions built in carved stone, sometimes in brick. Balconies, porches and even turrets and dormer-windows were to be seen.

The merchants were building houses for themselves that only kings and queens could have afforded but a few short years before, and it had greatly astonished some of the more impoverished provincial noblemen, who seldom ventured far from home, to see for themselves how affluent the artisans and tradesmen had become.

As their cavalcade neared Paris, she remembered nostalgically, they had progressed through the small town of Saincte Ladre, also bedecked for the festivities, and had gone on past the northern moats and walls of the City of Paris itself, through the Porte St. Denis, draped with banners and pennants for the great occasion. There was dancing and celebration in the streets, with roving bands of street musicians attracting crowds, as their party pushed its way on down the Rue Saincte Denis and across the Pont au Muniers, which one would not have known to be a bridge, since the waters of the river were not to be seen over its sides. It was lined solidly with houses and shops.

Marguerite again closed her eyes, and pictured their passage through the bridge. It was almost like a tunnel, since the upper stories of the buildings were extended over the passage-way. And as they left the bridge, the towers of Nostre Dame were within sight on their left, while they passed the castle and church of Sainct Michel, with its formal gardens which extended to the tip of the island. Then they progressed on, at a stately and interrupted pace, through the Pont Sainct Michel, also enclosed with buildings, to seek out their various lodgings.

Paris had been crowded to the rooftops, and their Parisian host had jested that the only unoccupied space was out on the bare little islands in the middle of the Seine, to which there were no bridges. The Ysle aux Vaches, for example, he said jovially, could have housed some of the multitudes, had they cared to pitch tents there.

Huge efforts had been made to show off Paris to good advantage to Charles Quint, and even the reconstruction of the Louvre had been hurried along to completion in honor of his visit.

The many ceremonies of that week Marguerite now remembered, with the two monarchs making a great show of their new-found camaraderie. Her cousin, Jean-François, had been much in evidence, standing as near to the King's elbow as he dared to place himself, and she had thus seen little of him during the entire time.

But Charles Quint had stayed in France for a full three months, even visiting the Connetable of France at his splendid residence in Chantilly, and, all in all, Marguerite reflected wryly, the cost of the reconciliation may well have equalled the cost of a war.

And she smiled a little, now, ironically, to remember that the two kingly rivals had already fallen out again, the very next year, in a squabble over an alliance between Soliman of Constantinople and François, to which Charles Quint had taken exception.

So for all the rejoicing by the people at the grand celebration, little lasting peace had been achieved.

And now Marguerite leaned back in her wild goose-down pillows, half-reclining, staring at the fire. She wondered what had happened in France since then. Less than two years since the expedition departed, she thought incredulously, and much must have gone forward since then. War, with its shifting political, military and religious alliances had again seemed probable, even as they had left for New France.

—2—

The weather grew colder and the winds seldom abated. Drifts formed and reshaped themselves at the winds' whims. Even with a blazing fire, the edges of the room were chill. And there was a sense of depression in huddling constantly by the hearth, or in the bed, alone, perhaps forever. Loneliness engulfed her.

As during the winter before, strange sounds came from the sea and the wind. The ice froze, cracked with the tides, grated together, and refroze, giving forth agonized creaks and groans which seemed to travel not only through the air, but through the very rock of the island on which the *logette* sat.

When Marguerite went outdoors the blown snow stung her face like shot, freezing over her nostrils. There was a sense of mighty forces battling to have their way; the gales pushed in one direction, the tides and ice in another, in massive conflict. Man amounted to nothing here. Even legions of men, she thought, a whole civilization, could have done nothing to control the forces here displayed.

It would take great determination and endurance to colonize this land, thought Marguerite grimly, and unless there was a prospect of immediate gain in it, she realized that such a costly effort might not be made, at least not by François Premier.

*

As the month went by the dismal weather and the isolation began to take their full toll on Marguerite's spirit, try though she did to combat their effect. The wild and weird sounds of the sea and the wind, and the occasional howling of the wolf-pack, were sometimes broken by short intervals of piercing, still calm, which were strangely still more nerve-wracking. The utter silence was then so complete, when the wind died and the harbor ice froze together, that she felt as if she had been struck deaf.

Once she awoke at such an interval of calm, surrounded by the total darkness inside the logette, to wonder how she could tell whether she had gone blind, as well.

And at intervals now her limbs became numb and would not respond to her will, weakened as it seemed to have become, and she would lie in the curtained bedstead with eyes straining from her head, urging her body to move, to get up and lay a log on the dying fire, or to prepare food. Sometimes her legs and arms would finally obey her, sometimes not, and she would lie like a corpse on the bed, slowly drifting off into a half-sleeping, half-waking daze.

—3—

Once Marguerite awakened, her body still warm but her face chilled, to lie lethargically listening to the wind. Its perpetual howling seemed to have taken on a more sinister note, a tone of insensate malice, almost as though it were directed against her, personally, or as the lone representative of mankind hereabout.

The room was chill, and the fire should be tended immediately; that fact Marguerite's mind dimly acknowledged, but, again, her reluctant body refused to stir itself. Her inert arms lay beside her like dough, and her legs felt like the appendages of a cripple, totally without feeling or the possibility of movement. But somehow this did not distress her. She floated in an oblivious, dreamlike state, lying in the darkness, feeling, for once, no responsibility for her own survival.

The gale increased in force. It drew the last remaining warmth up the chimney and blew the traces of it away across the frozen sea. And the wind seemed to suck the very air out of the room.

Strange sounds now came to Marguerite's ears from overhead. The stones on the roof, heavy though they were, seemed to be disturbed. They made clattering noises, which became progressively louder, almost, Marguerite thought vaguely, as if someone were scuffling upward on the roof over her. Several times she heard a heavy, grating scratch, as if a wet, cloven hoof were pawing at the roof.

The howling of the wind increased and took on an even more eerie note. It no longer sounded to its lone listener to be alike to the simple winds of nature, but rather like sensate beings, who did not wish her well. She pulled the covers closer. And against her will she remembered the horrid tales of the Isle of Demons, and the monsters which were said to inhabit New France, some with only one foot, larger than their bodies, on which they hopped about to do their evil, some with leathery wings, who flew from tree to tree, and one which even the savages feared, *Atce'n,* since they said that it ate the flesh of men.

In her horror, Marguerite's mind became slightly more aroused. The raveling wisps of Damienne's St. John's wort came into her thoughts, and half against her will she was glad that it was still hanging over the doorway.

The wind now blew in still more violent gusts, and with it came the sound of heavy rain or sleet. The roof was buffeted and swept, and the air outside the *logette* seemed to have been strained and pulled out of the chimney, leaving nothingness within.

Then a still more sinister sound came to her ears—a heavy slapping, as though of wet, leathery wings. Marguerite's scalp tightened. She remembered the pictures she had seen of demons. There were different kinds, but most of them had batlike wings which trailed from their arms, ending in claw-like fingers. Some did not even have legs, but rather had bodies which ended in thickly-tapering, coiled serpentine tails, sometimes terminating in forked ends, like prongs. Some had feet with claws, some with hooves. And their tails and lower bodies were leathery or covered with scales.

And Marguerite hardly dared remember their heads—the glaring fiery eyes, darting forth flames and evil, the wolflike fanged teeth, the horrid little horns. She cowered. A scream rose in her throat, but at last she was able to move, her body arousing itself from its torpor.

With an incredible force of will she restored her self-control, her reason. If these creatures had waited to come for her until she was alone, she told herself with painfully-summoned logic, they must be cowardly things indeed. And Monsieur Cauvin had taught that Evil had power only over those who did not have faith in God and the desire to cast off evil. So she laid back the coverlets with a determined movement and stepped down into the frigid room. Renewing the fire from its last skimpy coals, she built up the blaze and lighted all the lamps. They guttered and flickered in the draft, casting strange shadows on the walls.

The cover of her thick little New Testament felt chill in her hands as she gathered her fur-lined robe about her shoulders. For a moment she stood erect before the fireplace, her face set in stern planes, appearing little like the soft-faced bride of last year, but more akin to her stern ancestors whose countenances were carved on their Crusaders' tombs.

She opened the Book. With a steady voice, as the wind howled above her and the roof-stones clattered, she read aloud:

> *O Dieu, écoute ma requete et prête l'oreille aux paroles de ma bouche . . .*

*

The month dragged along. Marguerite could not tell day from night, and ceased trying to distinguish them. Thoughts of her little son, lying outside in the wet and cold, haunted her, as did the manner of his burial. All his toys and garments were gone. She must have snatched them up, she realized, in her despair and frenzy, and buried them with him, like a barbarian.

Sometimes her fire again died out completely, and she had to fumble with the fusil, shivering in the cold and darkness, to start it again. This was dangerous, she told herself, but for the first time her body did not arouse itself with sharpened senses to the challenge of danger. Harangue herself though she might, long hours of deadly lethargy still came upon her, and her will to govern her own behavior faltered. So she lay in the bed, enclosed in its draperies, for longer and longer intervals, numb, unable to arouse herself.

At last she lost all accounting of the days. But toward what she judged to be the latter part of the month, during an interval of greater self-command, she thought of the Christmas season. And still half be-dazed, she took her New Testament from the mantel-shelf and read the ancient words:

> *Quant Iesus fut né en Bethleem cite de Juda au tēps du roy herode: voicy les saiges . . .*

Her voice arose thinly in the chill air, scarcely breaching the silence and the solitude around her, sounding forth impotently, without much sense of comfort or even conviction. At last her voice trailed away, and she stood silently gazing into her fire.

It was hard to rejoice in the birth of another infant, so long ago, she thought sadly, when her own little son lay in his grave, beside his father and Damienne.

January, 1544

—1—

Arousing herself from the deadening trances which now afflicted her became Marguerite's most difficult task.

Some traitorous spirit within her seemed to have convinced her daunted body that all was lost, that it need never arise again. Even her mind, muddled and dazed as it had become, often acquiesced in this capitulation, so that sometimes she would lie willingly motionless for hours, in the darkness. But at still other times she would lie immobile in utter anguish, her spirit making demands on her body to rise up, but it would not obey her commands.

During these times of half-sleep, half-trance, strange and unpleasant visions traveled through Marguerite's mind, and she was unable to avert her thoughts from them. It was as though every ugly gargoyle she had ever seen, from childhood on, moved through her consciousness as a living entity, intent on carrying away the last shreds of her sanity. All the paintings and carvings of cadavers and demons, to whose horrors she had been able to steel herself even as a child, now paraded, unbidden, before her, as though painted against the darkness.

As one will sometimes have, even during a nightmare, the comforting awareness that it is not real, Marguerite occasionally had a flash of realization that these visions were only false entities called into being by her own sick imaginings. She even comprehended, albeit dimly, that their danger lay in the fact that they might lull her into a stupor from which she would never awaken.

Had only another person been present, she thought longingly, so that they might have awakened each other by turns, or even diverted each other's minds, she believed that the peril could have been averted. Another human face to look into her own, another voice to break the silence—between her and the shores of France there was not one human soul whose words she could have understood.

So that as it was, she told herself starkly, she must somehow save herself.

It seemed an impossible task. Sometimes the effort of raising just one arm seemed insuperable and required enormous efforts of will, bringing cold sweat to her brow. Finally, after what Marguerite realized must have been a long period of semi-consciousness, she dragged herself out of bed, forcing first a leg, then an arm, to move and do her bidding.

The warmth of her body, under the thick, heavy coverings of the bed, had been preserved, and this had apparently saved her from freezing, she now realized. The inside of the *logette* had become so frigid that the air seemed to sear her skin like hot coals.

Marguerite fumbled her way across the icy floor to the hearth in the total darkness, found the fusil and the basket of moss, lighted lamps, and rekindled the fire. It had died out so completely that there was not a sign of warmth in the stones of the fireplace or hearth. Shuddering uncontrollably, her cold hands held close to the small flames, Marguerite belatedly deliberated on the danger into which she had allowed herself to sink, and as she trembled in the chill room her mind sluggishly aroused itself from the deadly langour into which she had declined.

At last some pale vestiges of her dauntless courage revived. For shame! she told herself sternly. Your husband, who for love of you came here and built this *logette*, and gave his life, alas, so to do; he is ill served by the way you use it! You waste this good lodging, and food and fuel Damienne helped to gather, old and ill as she was!

Berating herself harshly for ingratitude to those who were dead, and who had loved her, she thought bitterly that they would never go back to France, but neither would they be pleased to see her snivel and lie in bed, failing to use the comforts they had worked to provide.

Walking to her pedestal mirror where it stood on its shelf beside the hearth, Marguerite looked herself squarely in the eyes. A wild, emaciated stranger stared back. She ran her fingers upward through her disordered hair, still looking into the mirror. "Marguerite de la Roque," she said aloud, "If you let yourself die, it will be small loss!" Her words echoed through the icy room like the condemnation of a judge. But the sound of a human voice, even if only her own, steadied her. And while reminding herself that only madmen talked to themselves, Marguerite decided to grasp at the meager comfort of her own spoken words. So she directed herself to put her dress to rights, and to prepare food. Stepping outside, she gathered a pot of snow for water, putting a handful into her mouth as she did so. Her thirst told her that she must have had no liquid for a long time.

The strange time of unknowingness and half-sleep must have endured for many days.

*

It took a long time to thaw out the *logette* and to let the warmth of the newly-built fire penetrate the hearthstones and walls. But forcing her weakened body to exert itself, Marguerite lighted all the pan-amps and brought a frozen grouse out of the ice-storage in the crawl-space, as well as a *morue* to thaw for the next day's meal. She took a few carrots and turnips from deep in their moss packing on the other side of the storage-space, as well, and while the fowl was turning on its spit, and the vegetables were boiling, she sat drinking a hot potion made of Damienne's herbs. Crouched on a stool which she had pulled close to the hearth, bundled in her furred cape, she extracted firm promises from herself to behave as became her circumstances.

Deadly peril lurked in these waking trances, Marguerite warned herself, aghast at her own derelictions. Perhaps it was during such times that evil spirits gained power over men, when their wills were weakened and dazed. It was evident from her visions, she thought, that such creatures skulked about, although perhaps their existence was only in men's minds, at times of weakness and despair. But whether these evil beings came from within or from without, their presence and attacks must be fought off, since from them rose the deadly uncaringness that might well end in death.

Astonished at her own body's weakness, Marguerite arose. Even after her son was born, she had not been so lean, nor so infirm in her step. She forced herself into the customary duties of setting the table and tending the food. And while she waited for the grouse to finish roasting, she combed up her hair, washed herself, and even pounded some grain for a pasty.

The odors of the food aroused her long-dormant appetite, and when it was ready she found herself eating ravenously. At last she checked herself, lest she sicken from overeating after so long a fast.

Then, as the bedclothing aired, Marguerite sat before the fire for a long time, first reading her *New Testament,* then knitting a sock from the last of Damienne's wool. She kept the hearth-fire and the pan-lamps well-fueled, and they flickered with a comforting light, casting warm reflections on the plates and silverware, the hanging pots and pans and the stacked arquebuses. And in the increasing warmth the tablecloth and the bed-hangings again took on a familiar and homelike look, so that once more the *logette* looked like a home and a refuge, instead of a void of horror and dread.

But Marguerite almost feared to surrender herself again to sleep at last, lest she slip away into the strange, half-waking daze which could become so deadly. Firmly she vowed to herself that she would devise work for her hands to do, whatever it might be, and spend less of her time in the bed, however tempting its warmth should become. If her body was always weary when she went to her rest, she reasoned, a deep and dreamless slumber might come to her without delay, shielding her from the unwholesome langour and its attendant visions.

—2—

A few days later wolves came to the cabin, after howling and barking nearby for several nights. At first Marguerite decided to stay inside the thick walls of the *logette,* relying on its safety. But the beasts became bolder. At last she could hear them digging at the roof, near the ground, having apparently scented out the frozen game and fish which were stored there. Telling herself that they clearly could not be allowed to destroy the roof, nor to get at the food, Marguerite reflected that if the whole pack were close together, perhaps she could rid the island of all of them at once, while the wary creatures were within firing range.

So she carefully cleaned and loaded four arquebuses, while planning how to kill the beasts without losing her own life in the process. From the sounds there were many of them on the roof, doing their best to dig their way in. But going outside, around the outer wall of the courtyard, would be dangerous, and probably impossible, she decided, in the deeply-drifted snow. The wolves were at the rear of the *logette,* outside the stockaded courtyard, but the slant of the roof would permit them to clamber up to the very top, and possibly make their way down into the courtyard itself by way of the roof of the entryway and wood-piles, down onto the drifted snow.

She decided that she could climb up to shoot them by the same route.

So that holding one arquebus ready to fire and carrying the others, Marguerite stole out through the entryway as quietly as she could, and silently climbed up to where she could peer over the edge of the roof, thankful for the snow which silenced her movements. Five wolves were digging at the roof, snarling and snapping at each other as they fairly danced on their forepaws.

The slight wind, coming as it usually did from the northwest, had not carried Marguerite's scent to them, she was glad to realize. Quietly she shouldered the arquebus and aimed, but the small, unavoidable grating of the serpentine caught one beast's attention, and he looked up just before she fired.

Shaking her head after the explosion and flame, to which she was now unaccustomed, Marguerite quickly regained her balance from the heavy recoil, grasped the second arquebus, and readied it to fire. The wolves, she saw, had been frightened, and some were hurt, but none had evidently been killed. They snapped at each other and at their wounds, and one of them now looked squarely up at her. He would lead the pack to the source of its injuries, and that quickly thought Marguerite.

Fear clutched at her throat with a strangler's grasp. Foolhardy to have made this venture single-handed! A pang of longing for her husband's steady-hearted presence assailed her, forever lost as he was in the grave. But in the midst of her repining, feverishly, as if by their own volition, her chilled and stiffened fingers worked with the stubborn slow-match and triggered the serpentine. Again the powder spluttered, but only a fizzling and smouldering resulted. The gun misfired.

Incredulously, stunned, already knowing how the wolfish fangs would feel as they tore her throat, Marguerite seized the third arquebus and cleared it of snow. The beasts were starting to look up toward her, and one, apparently the leader, climbed warily toward her, up the roof. It was now too late for retreat to the *logette,* she realized desperately; if she clambered back toward the door the swift creatures could spring down upon her.

So with faltering fingers, heartsick with fear, Marguerite hastened to hold the slow-match in place, and to ready the third arquebus for firing. In her fear and impatience the process seemed endless, and in her extremity she thought of Damienne, who could have loaded the guns, who would at least have lent her support, fear-struck though she might have been.

Alone! she thought. To die here alone, eaten by wolves! She smelled the very odor of the approaching beasts before she had the weapon readied. When she looked up to aim the beasts were advancing cautiously but steadily toward her, coming upward across the ice-covered roof.

Marguerite hastily aimed the heavy weapon in such a way as to catch as many of them as she could in the field of fire. And as she pressed the serpentine into firing position, waiting the necessary instant for the powder to ignite, she prayed that the gun would not misfire. If it did, the affray was lost.

But mercifully the weapon fired. Its heavy recoil almost threw her down from her perch. Blinking her eyes and reaching for the fourth gun, Marguerite found that two wolves lay dead, their heads nearly torn off. Caught at point-blank range, they lay almost within arm's reach of her, near the top edge of the roof.

The others had retreated, one badly wounded. Trembling, Marguerite thought longingly of a return into the *logette,* leaving the remaining animals to fill their stomachs on their fallen pack-mates. But this was a chance, she told herself sturdily, to rid the island of the beasts. So that readying the last remaining arquebus, she crouched in wait until the living animals approached their dead. The scent of the blood had acted as bait, and thus she waited coolly until the beasts were close together and near her. This time, also, the arquebus fired forcefully, throwing her back off the roof of the entryway.

Marguerite hastily gathered herself up from the snowdrift beside the doorway, climbed upward, and looked over the top of the roof. All the wolves were dead or dying.

She breathed a few words of relief, of thanksgiving.

But their bodies, left on the roof, would tempt other beasts to come there. So that climbing back down into the *logette,* Marguerite pondered as she cleaned and reloaded an arquebus. The other wolves had been skinned, she remembered wryly, partly to make that first affair less frightening to Damienne. Well she remembered her husband's agile huntsmanship that day, long ago as it now seemed. Ah, *mon homme,* she thought, *mon homme.*

Then a strange thought came to her. Slowly, with reverent hands, she opened her dead young Lord's sea-chest and gently removed from it his work-garments. Musingly, standing before the fire, she put on his clothing, with its well-remembered feel and odor. Love and longing engulfed her. He had not been much taller nor larger than his bride, and even his hunting-boots, which had been so carefully oiled and stored away, were well-fitted to his tall young wife. And in his garments Marguerite felt a resurgence of strength, as though her husband's courage and steadfastness enfolded her. He would have wanted her to use his clothing, she told herself wistfully, since a woman's hampering skirts would make the climb to the roof nearly impossible. Picking up the freshly-loaded arquebus with a new feeling of lightness and agility, she left the *logette,* climbed nimbly onto the roof and stood for a moment there, looking out across the harbor, the woodland, and the cliffs of her small domain. The wind had died down to a faint breath, or the cold would have been too biting to be endured.

She now saw that the tracks of the wolves encircled the *logette* and the stockaded courtyard; they had sniffed their way around it many times and would probably have gotten over the drifts and into the courtyard before long, she realized.

The snow was too deep to drag the carcasses very far away, she found, but she beat a path away from the *logette* and dragged them as far as she could, their bodies already stiffening in the frigid air.

The beasts had not managed to do much damage to the roof, she found, since the corner where the meat was stored was near the ground, and the ice and snow had protected the bark under the overlapping stones. So that after a last careful survey of her surroundings, Marguerite climbed lithely back down into the courtyard and returned into the *logette,* to build up the fire again and clean the guns.

After the kettle boiled over her fire, she brewed a hot potion of dried berries.

It was strange, she thought, but she now felt better than she had in a long time, more confident, more alive. Even the misfiring of the arquebus, and the resulting danger, did not recall itself to her mind in a way which alloyed her sense of well-being and satisfaction.

Remaining dressed as she was, Marguerite prepared her meal, ate it with relish, and then sat, legs asprawl, before the fire, like a tall, lean boy.

How much more comfortable men's garments are than women's, she reflected somnolently, and how much easier it is to move about in them.

*

But it was still no easy thing, in solitude, and during the dark time of the year, to ward off the attacks of depression and lethargy. At last the weather became so cold that stoking the fire was almost a full-time duty, and in a strange way this made Marguerite's life easier; it acted as a demand on her time.

Again she read and reread her books, mended clothing, and spent time preparing her food with unwonted care, meticulously blending, chopping and basting, as if for honored and critical guests. And sometimes, again, she sat propped in her bed, purposefully keeping herself awake by spurring her mind to exact recollections of France.

Nontron often returned to her mind, and once she set herself the task of remembering the customary trip from Nontron to Périgueux, a much larger city, where she and Damienne sometimes went to see tourneys, do official business, or visit the provincial Court. It was south of Nontron, and the well-remembered way to it wound south along the river Dronne to Brantôme, which was about the halfway point; they usually stayed overnight at Brantôme, going on to the châteaux of either Bourdelles or Merlande for the next night on the way.

The entrance into Périgueux was always exciting. Sitting in her chill bed, vigilantly watching her fuel-devouring fire, Marguerite remembered how her young heart leaped up when the towering cupolas of St. Front could first be seen from afar, and when at last they rode down toward the river to where the parapets of the town rose steeply from its basin between the high hills around it.

The bridge and walls of Périgueux were among her earliest memories, and they were very old and massive, above a wide stone *quai* which extended along the south shore of the river, where fishermen lounged.

Then from the *pont*, the streets climbed upward into the town, mostly winding or weaving back and forth, since the hill was steep as one went up to the center of town. And just across the bridge rose the House of the Consul, overlooking the river, with a parapet which formed a long gallery, and beautiful dormer windows. The winters were so mild there, Marguerite remembered nostalgically, that *pensees* could bloom in their flower beds all season, surviving the occasional short spells of chilly weather. And she suddenly remembered a little bell-shaped purple flower, too, with scalloped leaves, which she had also loved.

The town of Périgueux had grown so greatly that there were houses outside the city wall along the river at the lower part of the battlements, beside the slow-moving river Isle. And from there it was a steep, winding climb to the *Allees de Tourney,* crowded, if it was a tournament day, with noisy celebrants who filled the wide streets with their gaiety.

And many members of the high nobility were often present.

The d'Albrets, into which great family Queen Marguerite, herself, had married, had holdings thereabout, and they often attended the tourneys, as did Guillaume de Montfaucon, the capitaine and Sénéchal of Périgord, along with Éléonore de Vendôme and her splendid array as Comtesse de Périgord. Guillaume de Bretagne, the Comte de Périgord, was often absent, but he presided over the tourneys when he was in the city, riding splendidly through the narrow streets to the tourney field, followed by his retinue of men-at-arms.

But always there were the splendid but familiar houses and *échoppes* of Périgueux, many of them narrow and tall, facing on narrow streets. For a moment a pang of longing stabbed through Marguerite's mind at the thought of the familiar faces, the human companionship, the sense of enclosure in those streets. In her mind's eye she could see them, crowded with passers-by, sturdy, dark-haired and dark-eyed Périgordiennes, stepping along with their firm, energetic tread, bustling in and out of the shops. For an instant she closed her eyes as they suddenly prickled with unshed tears of loneliness and longing for home.

It hardly seemed possible that her countrymen still thronged the streets of Périgueux while she, herself, sat on this remote island, alone. Waves of unreality engulfed her.

A sharp sense of desolation swept through her mind. Surrounded as she was by vast, uncharted wastelands, the memory of Périgueux was almost too poignant to be borne. Her diligently-summoned memories had brought little solace.

But at last a saving sense of indignation, even of wrath, flooded through Marguerite's consciousness, and she vowed hotly to herself that she would somehow live to return to Périgueux. Pulling her body erect, she stared back toward France with a new and steel-hard determination, a clearly-forming resolve.

"Some day," she said aloud, "I will return there, and I will ride back into town through the old Roman gate as those of my family so long have done." But before her lips the cold air formed a blinding vapor.

February, 1544

—1—

The voyage from France was one of her most comforting memories, Marguerite found, since in spite of the conditions on shipboard, she had loved the sea. It had been an enviable thing not to have a tendency to seasickness, as so many did, and to *avoir le pied marin,* so that one could keep one's balance on a pitching deck. As she lay propped in the canopied bed, thinking only of those things from which her mind might take assuagement, Marguerite found that thoughts of the voyage often merged into endurable dreams.

So that in her chill, log-walled chamber, behind her closed eyelids she carefully envisioned the *Marye,* where Jean Alfonce was standing beside her on the *gaillard d'arriere,* performing his interminable calculations. He had seemed to enjoy having her at hand, she remembered, since she had shown an interest in his duties, which was more than Jean-François had done. Jean Alfonce was a kindly man, she reflected, a man of great integrity, and he had expressed at some length his stern views about the responsibilities of pilots. "It is a great charge on the conscience," he had once written, "To undertake things in which, if we are not skilful, we may cause death and peril to so many by our ignorance and stupidity."

And it was told of him that he had never lost a ship. In his stiff but kindly way he had taught Marguerite something about ship-handling and navigation as the voyage went on. As chief pilot under the order of the King, and a respected authority on rigging, sail and navigation as well, it was Jean Alfonce's duty to make an accurate record of all latitudes and longitudes traveled, plotting the exact locations of shorelines and harbors.

And who else, Marguerite thought, would have taken his wife's last name on marriage! His own name had been Jean Fonteneau. The very thought of him was warming. If anyone would try to help me, Marguerite thought, it would be Jean Alfonce.

But her kinsman, she recalled, had seemed to be jealous of his master-pilot because of the high esteem in which the King held him, and the great responsibilities which François had laid on his shoulders. Jean Alfonce had been put in charge of the *nef généralle*, the flagship of the expedition, to record the distances covered, the course directions, the depths of the soundings, the fitness of the sea-bottom for anchorage, and such other information as would be helpful in identifying landmarks and mapping the new lands which were to be colonized.

This alone was important work and a heavy responsibility. But Jean Alfonce had confided to her that he was also conducting an experiment in improving the accuracy of navigational methods. This was an exciting and important disclosure indeed, since navigational mistakes were dangerous as well as embarrassing. Any improvement would be of diplomatic and military value to France.

Such an assignment had been undertaken before, in 1529, by one Pierre Mauclerc, an astronomer, Jean Alfonce had told her, who had performed such double duties when he sailed on *Le Sacre.* Now Jean-Alfonce had been appointed to continue the work. He tried to explain his process to Marguerite.

It had to do with the use of an azimuth and a tide table, sighting the sun with a cross-staff. Then north and south declinations had to be taken, together with the finding of the pole's height by taking the sun's altitude above the horizon. Thus the precise time of the observations could be known. And the sun was sighted backwards, surprisingly, over the shoulder, by the use of a new device called a forty-five degree backstaff, and a quadrant was also used.

Marguerite had hated to admit that she did not understand his explanation very well, or to ask him to explain again. To her it had seemed akin to astrology, or even witchcraft, and he did her great honor, she thought, even to discuss it with her at all.

Jean Alfonce de Xanctoigne, she thought dreamily, that serious, dutiful man. She could almost see his closed, intent face, and hear his voice. Xanctoigne was not far from Angoulême, in Aquitaine, and he spoke with the accents of home.

And I probably owe my very life to him, she thought gratefully, since he stood up to Roberval, at some risk to himself, and forced him to bring us in to this sheltered island for the marooning. Then the thought seemed absurd, and in her solitary room Marguerite snorted with wry laughter that she should feel grateful for such a back-handed favor.

But her days with Jean-Alfonce had been enjoyable, since he had treated her as a thinking person, capable of learning some of the things he knew, and not merely as a decorative toy. So she tried to bring back to her mind a certain afternoon aboard ship, when she had asked him to teach her more about the way the ship was sailed. She had found, she told him, that she felt more secure when she understood what the seamen were doing, and what the commands meant. It was somehow discomforting to see feverish activity in the rigging and on the deck when one did not know its meaning, she had explained, and Jean Alfonce had found this to be quite a reasonable point of view. He had not treated it as a pretty fancy of one whom he must humor since she was Roberval's kinswoman.

So that he had explained with seeming enjoyment that the matter was really very simple; the ship moved because the wind pressed against the sails, and it was necessary to be able to control the direction and speed. That was why sails were moved about, and why they were placed and shaped as they were. The sails and other parts of the ship all had to have exact names, too, he had explained, so that commands could be quickly and precisely given, and so that the seamen could follow them briskly, without hesitation or blunder. Everything had its place and its name, he said, since fumbling or hesitation could result in shipwreck.

Lovingly, almost like a litany, Marguerite now searched her mind for all she had learned. The tallest mast, in the middle of the ship, was called the *grand'mat.* It carried the huge square sail called the *grand'voile,* the largest and most powerful sail on the ship. This hung from a long wooden yard called a *vergue.* And above it was a smaller square sail, called the *grand'hunier,* which caught the higher winds, and added power. Between them these sails put such a strain on a vessel, Jean Alfonce had told her awesomely, that the mast holding them had to be set right into the heavy keel at the very bottom of the ship. And Marguerite herself had noticed that the *grand'mat* was more than two feet thick where it met the deck, and was heavily reinforced by the banding which encircled it.

Almost as a memory-game, she now taxed herself to remember the remainder of the sails. The mast ahead of the main-sail, toward the prow, was the *mat de misaine,* and the square sail it carried was called the *misaine.* Jean Alfonce had told her somewhat scornfully that English seamen, however, in their ignorance and confusion, often called the sail at the stern of the ship the "mizzen" and they had to be corrected when they found themselves serving aboard proper French vessels.

And at last she recalled the name of the sail which was hung above the *misaine,* also a square sail, the *petite hunier.*

At the bow of the ship a long spar extended outward and upward, called the *beaupre,* and under it hung a crosswise spar holding a small square sail called the *voile á livarde.* This was used more to aid maneuverability, Jean Alfonce had remarked, than to add power. Since the influence of the rudder in steering was restricted and slow, it had been found that this small sail, so far out in front of the ship, was an aid in turning.

The *mat de misaine* stood on the *gaillard d'avant,* the deck above the fore castle of the ship, where the leadsmen often stood, and at all times it was a favorite gathering-place for the compagnons of the expedition, and certain of the ladies. For a poignant moment

Marguerite could almost see their faces and remember the gaiety of their voices, their very gestures. How light-hearted we were, she thought, how unknowing. Sadness assailed her for those lost days.

Brusquely she returned her mind from its fruitless repining, taxing herself with completing her self-imposed inventory of ships' rigging. The mast in the stern of the ship was called the *mat d'artimon,* named for its huge triangular sail, the *artimon.* The name of this sail dated back to Roman times, the master-pilot had told her, and it was helpful, too, in changing course, because of its fore-and-aft rigging.

Under their feet as they stood on the after-deck they could glimpse the helmsman as he straddled firmly on his half-deck, receiving his orders through a small square hatch above his head. Marguerite could recall how she had learned the orders which were given him, as well as the orders which had to be given to manipulate the running rigging of the ship. Jean Alfonce had been so proud of the *nef* that he had taught Marguerite to love it, as well. And as she had grown to understand the working of the sails and the rigging, the constant sounds of the ship, the squeak of tightly-strained hemp pulling against metal or wood, the tapping of lines against a mast, became to Marguerite well-understood sounds, sounds of safety.

Alone now in her chilly bed she could almost feel the movement of the ship, and somehow comforted she slipped into a calm sleep.

*

Whether by reason of her own determination or because of the less oppressive weather, Marguerite's depression disappeared as the days lengthened. While still bitterly cold, the days were now clear and dry, somehow stimulating, and suddenly she found many tasks that needed to be done, both inside the *logette* and outside in the courtyard.

All the chests and trunks had to be unpacked and their contents sorted, aired and tended. Marguerite even used the smoothing-stones to press out folds that might otherwise have become too firmly creased into the rich fabrics. The fine garments, so useless here on the island, brought back memories of more carefree times, and the task was somehow pleasant. It was even comforting, somehow, to recall when she had worn this garment and that one, as though the feel of the silks and satins proved her own existence in those far away places and times, the faint traces of perfume bringing back warm memories of youth, of France.

But the problem of constructing outdoor clothing was a puzzling one. It must not hamper her movements, she knew, since one miss-step could be deadly now that she was alone, but none of their clothing was really protective enough against the arctic cold. The long fur capes got dangerously into the way while handling an arquebus, to say nothing of their interference with climbing or running, as did the sweeping, full skirts which entangled her legs, while not affording much warmth as the high winds blew them about.

And now Marguerite was in a virtual fever of impatience to get outside the *logette* as the weather grew more brisk, albeit still frigidly cold.

The skills of a needlewoman were all that I was taught, except for music and my letters, she thought, so that surely I can contrive a sort of hunting costume that will serve me, here where none can view me in it, or condemn its immodesty.

So that after much measurement and comparison, Marguerite decided to use her husband's clothing as a basis, knitting several pairs of long socks to make his boots fit more securely, and quilting heavy, feather-stuffed undergarments for warmth. She even quilted mittens and a hood with a draw-string to cover her head and most of her face.

But an outdoor trial of the new garments proved disappointing. The icy cold still cut through them. Furs would be best, Marguerite realized, but she knew no way of softening the hides, which were as hard as boards.

At last she found that tufts of fur could be cut off and pulled through fabric with a knitting-hook, making a sort of fur lining. Laboriously she lined the quilted garments and climbed into them at last with an odd sense of achievement, for she needed no mirror to tell her that in them she looked like a very corpulent man, or even like one of the white bears, she thought in amusement.

The days of sun had glazed a heavy crust on the snow, so that walking across it became possible and confinement in the *logette* was no longer necessary. After numbing her face with frostbite and spending several days, as had Damienne, with burned and watering eyes, Marguerite also made herself a sort of mask which she wore on days when the sun was bright.

Thus garbed, an awesome sight she was sure, she went forth hunting and exploring. And the outings, as well as the fresh meat, restored her strength as well as her spirits.

*

While Marguerite had failed to mark her calendar during the days of depression and near-madness, she knew that the month of February must be drawing to its close, since that was the time of year when the snow's crust glazed over. So she resumed marking her calendar accordingly, estimating the days as best she could, with a view to the spring planting, and to starting roots indoors as Damienne had done.

Since the summers were so short, a close calculation in these matters would be necessary.

As she marked the calendar Marguerite suddenly remembered that now a full year had passed since the death of her young husband. A renewal of grief and longing swept over her, sharper than ever before. It struck like a lash, like a bludgeon, without warning, all the more cruel since she had believed that she had come to terms with her loss. But the harsh, racking grief for her husband was of a different sort from her sorrow for Damienne and the hideous pain of losing her child.

Thinking again of her dead, Marguerite wept in stormy rebellion, pacing the floor of the *logette* and choking out sobs from the depths of her being. But thus she released for the first time her full sense of despair. And like blood gushing from a wound, which cleans it so that it will no longer fester beneath the skin, the outburst brought healing.

March, 1544

—1—

The worst of the winter had finally passed, and the wood supply, although depleted, apparently would last out. The sun, while still more bright than warm, now appeared at more frequent intervals, again glazing the snow into an ice-like hardness. The urge to get outside the *logette* and to rove about the island became irresistible, since the confinement of winter, and its darkness, had been overlong. So that without a real need for emerging into the cold and possible danger, Marguerite devised outdoor errands which took her from one end of the island to the other. The sun seemed to have a bracing effect, she found, like strong tonic or wine.

Wearing her new-made garments, Marguerite felt nimbler and safer than before. The trousers did not catch the wind and blow about her limbs, as had her heavy skirts, which had required constant attention as they caught on obstructions, tripping and encumbering their wearer. It was no longer a matter for wonderment to Marguerite that peasant women kilted up their scanty skirts as they went about their work in the fields.

With an early-spring craving for greenery, she dug moss, lichens and green herbs from the shallower snow against the cliff-sides which faced the sun, and took them back to the *logette.* Some of the leaves, which had remained surprisingly green under the snow, made a savory flavor in her ragout, and one of the mosses, when boiled, proved to make a thick jelly. She boiled this up with dried berries, thus flavoring and coloring it, and the crude confection seemed to satisfy her eternal craving for sweets.

Marguerite devoured it like a greedy child, first with a spoon, and later as a filling over coarse pastries which she made of pounded wild grain, baking them under the bell-oven in the fireplace.

And to satisfy her hunger for bread, she ground part of her hoarded store of millet, using the coarse flour for puddings and flat cakes.

Among her errands, Marguerite brought in fresh pine boughs to sweeten and scent the *logette* as they burned, and gathered branches from the dead trees in the northern end of the woodland, distant from her cabin, but now easily reached over the crusted snow that covered the thickets and crevasses. Apparently some animal had girdled these standing trees, stripping off their bark nearly to the tops. And since the deadfalls were covered, these trees were a good source of fuel, now that they could be cut and easily slid or dragged to the *logette.* Since the days had lengthened and but few additional indoor tasks could be devised, Marguerite decided to replenish the wood supply. It kept her warm, she found, to chop down and haul the trees, and it was pleasanter to do this heavy work in the cold, clear air than in the rains and fogs of spring and summer.

But the work was not without risks. Hungry animals were on the prowl, and were to be sighted slinking about at ever-narrowing distances. The sound of Marguerite's axe did not deter them. They seemed to have sensed that she was now alone.

*

In the brighter sun of the lengthening days, Marguerite found that she had to wear her face-mask whenever she went outdoors, since even on an overcast day the weather on the island was quick to change, and without her mask she had to retreat ignominiously to the *logette,* squinting against the glare.

As she returned one afternoon, weary from woodchopping, she caught a glimpse of herself in her mirror as she removed the mask. The incongruity of heavy work-garments and a masked face brought a gasp of startled laughter to her throat, for ladies wore masks in France to protect their complexions from the sun, and sometimes, also, for purposes of coquetry as they rode about traveling or watching the hunt. But now I have scant fairness of skin to preserve, though Marguerite ruefully. And she recalled her first *touret de nez,* as the masks were called, which signalled her departure from childhood; she had worn it on a trip from Nontron to Angoulême. How proud she had been that her unformed features might contain charms worth concealing!

But the honor of wearing the mask, like the more confining garments which accompanied it at that time, had been dearly bought. The mask was hot, and it sometimes slipped up across her eyes as the palfrey plodded along, Marguerite remembered, amused at the proud pretensions of her childhood self.

And there was no really comfortable way for women to travel, she recalled as she went about the preparation of her solitary meal. Only peasant women rode astride, and even they did not do so in the villages, or within sight of strangers. And there were only three carriages in all of France. Queens, princesses, and very old or very pregnant noblewomen rode in litters with leather and silk curtains to shield them from mud or dust, and Queen Marguerite was said to do much of her writing to while away her time in her litter, although how she did so was a marvel, with the swaying, tipping and jolting, to say nothing of the presence of her little pet dog which she kept at her side.

And other ladies, if they did not ride pillion behind a husband or a groom, simply rode their palfreys sideways, on a sort of perch; it could hardly be called a saddle, since it had only a narrow edge which did little to give security or support. Both feet were placed side by side on a flat little single stirrup which hung down from the saddle, and the precarious seat was tiring, since one had to twist forward at the waist to control the horse.

But everyone rode, nevertheless, from childhood on, thought Marguerite as she filled her water-kettle and swung it on its crane, for there was no other way of getting about, although the length of a day's journey had to be limited if women were among the party, since they had to ride slowly because of the way they were mounted; and the strained position of their bodies, swaying eternally from side to side as the horse moved along, was wearying. Stops thus were frequent, and progress slow. Unpleasant although conditions were aboard ship, they were preferable to those on overland journeys, Marguerite thought ruefully, at least for women.

As she cooked her meal, elaborating in its preparation to pass the time, Marguerite thought of that trip on which she had first been fully burdened with the garments and deportment of a lady. Winding down from Nontron's high cliff the cavalcade had moved east, toward Javerlhac, where farmsteads stood with their buildings on both sides of the road, in the valley which led to Angoulême.

They passed through Variagnes with its stone buildings and red roofs, on through Feuillade, with its low round tower and into Bandiat where they had stayed, she recalled, at the château. After winding through Rochepine, Bouex and Soyaux they had finally sighted Angoulême on its hilltop, and had stopped to night over so that they could clean themselves and change their dusty, horse-sweated garments. Angoulême had an elegant Court, and provincial noblemen did not like to ride into the city, Marguerite smiled to remember, reeking of their beasts, like peasants going to a village fair.

Some of the men of the party had donned their caps with flowing plumes, their doublets, hose and surtouts, multicolored and embroidered, and the women wore their low-cut, wide-sleeved velvet or satin dresses, impractical for riding, but of requisite elegance to be presentable at Court.

For a moment as she knelt before her lonely fire in her oddly-assembled work-garments, Marguerite paused to remember her anticipation, her excitement, on that far-off day. How the horses had pranced, sensing that the end of their journey was near! How the silks and satins had swirled and glistened, like molten jewels!

And there had been much gaiety and clowning as the long

journey ended. By the time they filed through the city gates they were laughing and singing, and one young chevalier with a nimble-footed mount had ridden it right up the steps into the castle hall to announce their arrival.

And greatly had her childish eyes been impressed with her first viewing of Angoulême. It was an elegant city, not a town, and the people had seemed to her to be more formal, even arrogant, in their city ways. And although their party had received a gracious welcome at the Court, dissipating her youthful apprehensions of awkwardness, or even, horrible to contemplate, some monstous *faux pas,* she still thought of Nontron as a friendlier place, a refuge, a home.

*

The first rain of the year fell late in the month, with water running down over the glazed crust of the snow without seeming to melt it. Water dripped inside the *logette,* coming from nowhere, since Marguerite did not think the roof had leaked. Clothing and bedding had to be dried before the fire, by turns, and the canvas was brought in from the woodpile to cover the bed.

When the rains stopped, fog still hung in the air. Being always wet was one of the great discomforts of the island, so that after some hesitation and a great deal of planning, Marguerite took apart one of her silk dresses at the waist, removing from the voluminous folds of the skirt enough of the precious material to make herself a sort of long, hooded jacket, which she dipped repeatedly in warm oil until it held water.

It had seemed wasteful, almost a sacrilege, to cut apart the costly garment, and Marguerite artfully redesigned it so that it could be again worn.

While it was probably already out of style, she told herself sadly, it was too valuable to be spoiled. And although it was now too elegant and gaily-colored for her to wear again, widowed and raw-boned as she was, and probably impoverished, into the bargain, the material was valuable, and the money it would bring was not to be disregarded, Marguerite thought with an unfamiliar frugality, if she were able somehow to return to France.

*

Although the arquebus did not seem to fire with its usual explosive force, Marguerite loaded it with small pebbles and brought down several land-fowl late in the month. Picking them up by their furry legs as they thrashed about, staining the snow, she carried them home to her chopping-block, beheading them and drawing out their entrails with even less squeamishness than Damienne would have shown. I have changed, thought Marguerite ruefully, since I came to this island. Once I could not have put my hands into this mess; now I am working away like the veriest market-wife.

Smiling at her own earthiness, her peasant-like failure to indulge in sentimentality, she made a savory stuffing from wild grain and herbs and set the fowl to roast. Afterwards, changing from her hunting garments into a warm, dark dress, she ate at her table, saying grace before she served herself with food, and sitting erect and alone on the cushioned bench, once again a Damoiselle of France.

Sometimes Marguerite told herself that the formalities of suppertime were unnecessary, perhaps even grotesque or pitiful, but having had her taste of the rapid descent to near-bestial living which had occurred when she had ceased caring for herself, she resolved to live at all times as if she were on public view, in such a manner as did not bring her shame.

*

And now she never permitted her hands to be idle. She chopped wood during the days, and when the weather forced her to stay indoors, she sewed, scraped leather, or carved wooden implements. Boiling caribou-hide, she made boot-soles with knit hose to fasten to them, and one pair of soles she shaped to her feet in a pair of crude strap-sandles such as peasant women wore, heelless and toeless, the straps tied at the ankle.

Using her husband's whet-stone, she sharpened the knives, the sword, the axes and even the sickle and saw-blades, afterward coating them with oil. Keeping her hands busy in homely tasks helped to push to the edges of her mind the thoughts of her loneliness, her dead.

Old women in France who walked the streets knitting or even spinning, came into her mind as her hands worked away, now functioning as theirs did, almost unconsciously, with practiced skill. She thought she understood them now. As a certain age was reached, loved ones had been lost; husbands, parents, friends, even children, were in their graves. Thoughts, left to wander, were like to be somber. Some of the bustling industry of the old wives, she now thought, must have been like her own, a defense.

And with a sense of compassion she thought of the old noblewomen, as well, whose activities had sometimes seemed trivial to her, their needlework, their music, their poetry, their games of *tric-trac* and cards. Many of them had small dogs, as did Queen Marguerite, which they carried around on their arms, and even fed from their plates.

All a defense, I suppose, thought Marguerite. The men, even when they are old, are still able to go about busying themselves with large affairs. And they are at least consulted when decisions of heavy import are to be made. But the women are most often on the edges, or behind the scenes, using their influence, if any, at a remove.

No wonder they make small things important, Marguerite thought with new-found understanding—a change of hairdress, the hang of a sleeve. Even the men at Court occupy themselves in such frivolous matters, since they, also, are forced to be idle.

Her work-scarred hands hung for a moment, motionless, in her lap. At least, she told herself sturdily, I have important things to occupy my time, here on this island.

April, 1544

—1—

The pale color of the oiled-silk jacket may have saved her life, Marguerite thought, on the day the polar bear came.

A fresh snow had fallen, and she had taken her arquebus to shoot a few more of the white chicken-like fowl, before they assumed their speckled, brown, summer plumage, and their shy summer habits. The fowl often hunted berries along the south hill and Marguerite started out in that direction.

In the untrodden snow which had fallen the night before, the bear's tracks were clearly to be seen, and enormous. Marguerite's own foot, in her husband's boot, was just over half as long, and the bear's track was trailed by claw-marks that looked as though they had been made by the tines of a haying-fork. There were smaller tracks, too, those of cubs.

Instinctively Marguerite crouched, looking slowly about her, for even to her unschooled eyes, the tracks looked fresh. She had seen the huge white bears far out on the ice-floes or swimming slowly along in the open water offshore, where they apparently caught fish or seals, but none had appeared thus far on the island itself.

She saw the bear immediately. It was downwind, plodding along, hips higher than forequarters, head down, followed by the cubs. The white of their fur was hard to see against the glare of the snow; it was easier to see the moving blots of their shadows, blue-green on the ice. As Marguerite watched, motionless, the bear raised its head on a long, tapering neck, and snaked it smoothly around into the wind, remaining motionless for a moment. Apparently it had scented Marguerite. And the beast was directly downwind of her, Marguerite realized in horror.

The bear was huge. As it reared up on its hind legs it stood taller than a man could reach. And Marguerite doubted that she could defend herself against the huge creature with arquebus fire, especially since the gun was only loaded lightly, and with pebbles.

From the space between the tracks, the beast could move swiftly; there would be no chance to reload if a killing shot were not fired at the first attempt. And the weapons had now misfired at more and more frequent intervals.

It would be better, Marguerite hastily decided, if she could escape.

Staying crouched down, she moved as rapidly as she could, not directly away, which would have been upwind, but laterally to the beast's approach, crosswind. From the movements of the animal's head, she judged that it had not seen her, but was following her scent. It came swiftly along the shore to where she had first stood, its breath puffing out ahead of it like smoke, claws scratching the ice, saliva stringing from the corners of its mouth. The cubs tumbled along behind.

The bear moved swiftly. There was no hope of outdistancing it, although Marguerite moved away as fast as she could progress from one point of concealment to the next. At last it was so close she could see the black spot of its nose, and hear its huffing breath, the scratch of its long claws on the granite and ice.

Suddenly the beast stopped, and seemed to be picking up some object in its clumsy paws. It dropped the thing, and reached for it again. Finally it even sat down. Marguerite took swift advantage of the delay to make off toward the woodland and to return hastily to the *logette* by an indirect path. As she barred the gate and the heavy door behind her, shuddering, she found that one of her gloves had been left behind. That, she realized gratefully, must have been the puzzling object the beast had scented out, had picked up, giving her the chance to escape.

The animal's curiosity and its apparently poor vision had interfered with its pursuit of her. Like the white winter feathers of the birds, Marguerite thought, my light garments did not show plainly against the snow. That is what saved me.

Hands shaking, she brewed herself a hot potion of herbs and huddled thankfully over her fire. And later that day, when the beast and its cubs had traveled far northward, Marguerite went out to hunt and fired the already-loaded arquebus at a flock of the white fowl near the *logette.*

The gun misfired.

A few days later the herd of grey deer again crossed the island. Marguerite heard them coming; their cup-like hooves on the hard crust of the snow sounded like a troop of horsemen crossing cobble-stones. And although there was no need to hunt the creatures with a store of smoked venison at hand, Marguerite climbed the woodpile to where she could watch them pass. They moved along directly under her eyes, between the stockade and the withed fence of the garden, past the graves, horns tapping, heels clicking, without knocking down either fence, like a herd of cattle. Their odor on the air smelled like a cattle-yard in France.

Smiling strangely to herself after they passed, the Damoiselle de la Roque, Dame de Sermet, de Sauveterre, d'Allas and de la Mothe, and Co-Seigneuresse de Saint-Popoing took a large basket and went out to pick up manure.

*

The next day Marguerite saw a *gerfaut,* a gyrfalcon, soaring above the harbor, its long wings and short body unmistakable, as the quick sharp strokes of its narrow wings carried it upward in a long, spiralling climb, from which it dropped like an arrow onto its prey. The bird was pure white; in France it might well have graced the wrist of a King, since the lordly *gerfaut* was the king of falcons. Even great seigneurs contented themselves with well-trained *pèlerins.*

Her husband had had a *faucon pelèrin,* he had told Marguerite, a black one, which he had hated to leave behind. The bird was well-trained and gentle, he had said fondly, but it could not have been carried along on a long sea-voyage, and he clearly regretted its loss. Perhaps his falcon is still alive, in France, Marguerite thought sadly, riding out to the hunt on another man's wrist.

*

That night Marguerite's half-waking dreams combined the falcon and the deer, and she remembered the last hunt she had seen, in the forest of Compiègne. It was in the late autumn of the year before the expedition departed, and François Premier, himself, had dropped in for a surprise visit to their château at Roberval. Jean-François, her cousin, had been taken aback, she remembered, for Roberval was a bit modest for the King's entertainment and Jean-François had been at a loss. But then the skies had cleared and the hunting-party had ridden gaily off again, after having hardly entered the château.

The King was heavier in the saddle than he had been, Marguerite remembered, but still an avid hunter, and he had wanted to start for the hunting-forest again almost before the cold rain had ceased. In earlier years, a be-ribboned courtier had muttered thankfully, he would never have stopped at all because of a mere wintry rain.

A little later that day she and Damienne had ridden sedately off past the *coulombier* and down the road, past the stone buildings of Rhuis and southward toward the hunting-forest, past the walled courtyards and châteaux, where other ladies joined them, dressed in the gayest garments they dared wear on horseback. And as they passed through Verberie they listened for the hunt. Then they heard the hounds from time to time, and changed direction to follow.

The forest was beautiful. Still carrying their leaves in shades of gold and ruddy bronze, the huge trees cast a mottled shade on the rolling woodland turf. The Forest of Compiègne looked like a park. Not a fallen branch littered the ground. In some places tall, golden-tan fern-like plants grew, in masses of pale color. And where the trees were farther apart, the grass was still green.

At last the party of ladies had wound its way to the Etangs de St. Perrine, with its walled court, towers, and mirror-lake, on the shores of which the hunters had stopped for refreshment. The ladies had been glad to rest there, too, and to admire the stag which the hunters had brought down. As the ducks and geese had paddled in the lake, sending their small ripples to the shore, the lords and ladies had taken their ease in the pale sunlight, and the talk had turned to falcons.

All of them had known a great deal about the great hunting-hawks, since falconry was a stamp of nobility, and there was great argument that day, Marguerite remembered, as to whether the best hunting falcons were to be gotten by catching a wild hawk and taming it, or by finding an *eyas*, a freshly-hatched hawk, and raising it in captivity. Opinions were heated, and the King's falconer was consulted, since his views were held in great respect.

Arguments abounded among the King's retinue as to the best methods of accustoming falcons to the *jesses* which held them to the hunter's wrist, and the kinds of *varvels*, or identification rings, which were best to be used. And the kinds of hoods were also a source of weighty debate. The ladies, while not entering into the arguments of the huntsmen, murmured occasionally to each other of favorite hawks, since they, too, understood and treasured them. Many a little lady's first attempt at sewing was in the making of a tiny jeweled and plumed velvet hood for her father's falcon.

Female falcons were usually trained, since they were larger and stronger than the males, and, some said, more intelligent and trainable. The birds were then fierce and ruthless hunters, but a well-trained falcon was very gentle to the humans with which it was familiar, and could be fondled like a pet.

In her loneliness Marguerite thought longingly of the white *gerfaut* she had seen that day. She hoped that it had a mate, and that the pair would nest on one of the high cliffs over the harbor, where game would be plentiful. It would be comfort of a sort, she thought nostalgically, from the depths of her solitude, to watch the swift birds as they soared in courtship or dived with thrilling speed to strike their prey.

*

As the month drew on to its close the geese and ducks began to return to the island, and rain was almost unceasing. When she went outside the *logette* Marguerite wore her sabots. But little needed to be done outdoors, in truth, except to carry in the wood to be dried for the day's burning.

When the wind was off the land, it was now somewhat warmer, but when it blew from the sea it was almost as wintry as ever.

As Damienne had done during the year before, Marguerite now made bark containers for a carrot and a turnip, which she soaked in water overnight before planting, and thereafter kept covered and damp on the warm hearth until they showed signs of life. As she did so she thought of Damienne and of her husband. How much they had taught her! Without their training, ignorant as she had been, and helpless into the bargain, she could never have lived on here in their absence. A sense of deep gratitude to them for their staunchness, their love, grew in her, warming her heart even as she felt the chill void of their absence.

Their graves were still hidden under the snowdrifts, but she had carved out round-topped markers for Damienne and for her son which she would set into the ground when it thawed.

A row of three graves, thought Marguerite, and I am the only one alive to tend them. And that night she again heard the insane laughter ringing over the water of the harbor and echoing through the dark woodland beyond.

May, 1544

— 1 —

The ice in the river at last broke up, crashing and crushing its way out to sea, followed by the harbor-ice, which had earlier melted along the shores of the islands, so that it moved up and down with the tides. Thus the island was no longer locked in by ice. Every declivity and swale ran with water from the melting snow, and the days were long.

The waterfowl had returned, passing overhead in such numbers as to cloud the sun and gabbling in the waters of the harbor which still floated with chunks of ice. They strutted on the shore, courting or fighting, and Marguerite again became accustomed to their cries as the ordinary sounds surrounding her on the island. The birds now found her a familiar thing, and they stayed barely outside of arm's reach as she walked among them.

So that it was the birds who warned Marguerite, one day as she was casting her fish-net in the water near the shore, of approaching danger. Their cries took on a strident note, and all of them flew or swam northward. Marguerite hastily retreated from the water's edge, mindful of her experience with the white bear, and crouched down behind a rock outcropping, peering out toward the source of the birds' alarm. She had snatched up the two arquebuses which she carried nowadays, and they lay beside her, along with her fishing-net.

The birds continued to move away in even greater haste, uttering panic-struck cries of warning and alarm. Marguerite now heard a faint, rhythmic splashing in the water, hardly detectable over the sounds made by the waterfowl and the slight rippling of the tiny shoreline wavelets.

It was too late to run for the *logette,* she decided; better to hide here than to expose herself to view. So she moved still farther into her shelter and crouched down, eyes fixed on the direction of the sounds.

Across the water now came the thump of a drum! Barking, guttural voices rang out, not of any civilized tongue. Savages! Her scalp tightened and her mouth grew dry.

The urge to flee was almost irresistible. Marguerite wondered how it must feel to have one's scalp cut off, whether it was done while one still lived. Hardly moving, she reached out for a few branches of scrubby pine, broke them off, and propped them around her, giving herself a better concealment and yet one through which she could safely peer out.

In the midst of her shock and fear Marguerite thankfully noticed that her work-garments had faded into dull colors like those of the dried seaweed, and that they thus blended with the shades of the moss and the rock's shadow. Thankfully she breathed to herself that the pale color of her rain-jacket and hood would have been easily seen, now that the snow was melted. God's providence be thanked that she had not worn them!

Panting between parted lips, Marguerite waited. Before more than a few moments passed, she saw the first of the war-canoes coming past her in the harbor. They must have entered through the south channel, the one by which the ships had departed.

One after another they came into her view, seven men to a canoe, paddles flashing in short, sharp strokes, the narrow, rounded craft moving sleekly through the water. Marguerite's heart pounded with utter terror.

And the war party stayed agonizingly close to shore. The breeze was from the northwest, and the water was quietest in the lee of the island, helping their progress. Frozen into immobility, afraid that faintness would overtake her, Marguerite stared through her pine branches into piercing black eyes which seemed to gaze directly into hers. If the thought of never seeing another human face had once distressed her, that longing was put aside as she gazed into the fiercely painted faces of the warriors.

These may well be the last faces I will see, she thought blankly.

The war-party was a large one, painted and bedecked for combat, carrying hide shields and bone-tipped spears and lances, bristling with bows and arrows and an occasional *casse-tête,* waving pennants of dyed hide, and tapping occasionally on painted war-drums.

Marguerite thought they looked as if they came from Hell itself.

The warriors' hair was gathered into topknots through which bones and feathers had been stabbed, and their thick bodies were bare from the waist up, with writhing muscles glistening under a coating of oil or sweat. The set of their faces was alert, cruel and fierce, fixed for war-making. In truth they looked more animal than human to Marguerite, more savage, by far, than had the northern indigenes who had worn clothing over their bodies and had not painted their faces.

The sound of Marguerite's own heartbeats pounded heavily in her ears, as if to echo the sound of their war-drums. And one decorated canoe after another came into her range of vision. They dotted the sea.

Fighting to hold herself immobile, Marguerite's mind thrashed about in a frenzied desire to escape. Savages were said to have keener senses than other men. Perhaps they would scent her out, as had the white bear!

And they must be on their way to make war, so they would have no use for a woman such as herself, except to pillage her belongings, taking her life, to the bargain, as the most casual of gestures. Her husband's warnings of their barbarous cruelty flew through her mind.

Alas! she thought, if only she had resumed the trips to the summit! She should have done so when the ice broke away. Vain to regret it. But her mind raced on. Even if she had hidden herself in the cave, they would still have sought her out, once they saw the paths criss-crossing the island.

Then her mind rushed to other tell-tale signs.

The fire in the fireplace! But fortunately it had smouldered out; during the last few warm days she had built it up only for cooking. That was a merciful thing, since they would have smelled the smoke, or even have seen it from a distance. But she could not believe, keen-sighted as they were said to be, that they would not notice the *logette* or the garden fence. If they came ashore anywhere on the eastern shore, they would scent her out like hounds! She had heard of their demoniacal skill as trackers.

Numb with fear, she watched the white canoes pass, checkered with their lines of blackened pitch caulking, against which the short, dark paddles flashed like the legs of scuttling insects. Bronze skin glistened, harsh voices barked out strange syllables, pennons fluttered, with an occasional waving circlet of long, black hair like horses' tails. These Marguerite finally recognized, in horror, as the skins from the heads of their dead enemies, kept and displayed.

Thunderstruck, her lips moved in prayer.

Legs and arms growing numb, since the slightest movement would have shaken her screen of branches and betrayed her presence, Marguerite waited, ears alert to hear the grating of watercraft being hauled ashore farther north. But no such sounds were to be heard.

The last of the war-canoes had passed from her view. Watching with straining eyes and ears, and moving only very slightly to ease her arms and legs, Marguerite waited for a long, long time in her shelter. Stragglers might still appear, she thought, following the main party.

But the geese and ducks gradually came back and resumed their fishing and courting along the water's edge, and their behavior reassured her. They are as good as watch-dogs, she thought, to warn of danger before it is upon us, scant time though they allow, with their wings to save them!

Finally, much later, she crept cautiously from her shelter and stole away behind bushes, then between trees, up the western side of the island to its summit. Peering around a high outcropping, her breath rasping in her dry throat, Marguerite could see the war-party disappearing into the distance, to the northeast, across the bay.

For some time she sat in thought, her senses gradually restoring themselves to a vestige of composure. Savages, as well as wild beasts were now clearly to be reckoned with.

She went to the signal pyre and laid it down still more flatly to the ground. Never would she pile it up again, to be seen silhouetted against the sky. Fortunately for her, this time, the winds of winter had scattered it so that its outline had not betrayed her, but, she reflected dismally, it is well for me to take thought that in this land the savages are now more like to pass by this place than are my own countrymen.

*

Why the warriors had not seen the *logette* or the garden, Marguerite could not afterward understand, close to the shore as these had been built, having no concealment around them. So that later that evening she went down to the water's edge and crouched to the level of the paddlers in the canoes, peering up at her clearing. From no point along the shore could the top of the *logette,* or even its chimney, be seen. The withes of the garden fence were also beyond view, concealed by the rise of rock along the shore. And the savages had passed, she remembered, at the time of low tide.

It was almost a miracle, Marguerite reflected thankfully, that her foolish efforts toward setting up a French farmstead had escaped notice. What folly to plant flowers along one's walls in this savage place! And the natives would almost certainly pass by again, if only to return from their war. This time they might stop, and then there would be no possibility of concealment.

At least she must be careful that nothing here should attract their notice, thus they might again pass by. Carefully she paced up the shoreline, deciding where she would walk, only on stone, so that no pathways would be beaten down in the greening spring vegetation. And no fish must be cleaned nor game skinned within view of the shore.

In a way the wildfowl would protect her, she thought hopefully, not only by their warning cries, but because they did not take alarm when she moved among them, which would have betrayed her presence. And every morning, at first light, she vowed to herself, the inspections from the summit would be made, with due caution. Perhaps, Marguerite thought apprehensively, remembering how rapidly the canoes had moved along through the sea-mist, she had better watch several times a day for their return.

—2—

That night, as Marguerite again gave thanks for her deliverance, she wondered if the evil reputation of the island was known to the savages, and if that had caused them to pass it by, or if, as it seemed, they were simply moving on in haste to attack their enemies.

Remembering their gaudy array and the pennons which fluttered above them, outlined against the towering granite islands across the harbor, Marguerite now recalled a war-party which she had seen, as a child, leaving Carcassonne.

They, too, had been gaudily decked out and bristling with weapons, barking directions and commands, with bronzed faces sternly set. Dark eyes, dark hair, there too, she thought, and even feathers on their heads, albeit in velvet caps. They, too, had had shields on their arms and lances and pennons held upright and menacing.

How alike men are, she thought, the world over, sallying forth to wage their wars, and leaving the women at home to bear their babies and attend to the dull work at home!

And she thought of the savages' women-folk, far upriver, readying their gardens for the planting, even as she herself would shortly be doing, making clothing, grinding grain, doing the same work. If she could slip in among them, somehow unnoticed by the warriors, she thought dreamily, or if one of those women could somehow be stranded here, we could become friends. Perhaps we could learn each other's language, she mused in her loneliness, and I could again hold a baby in my arms, one of their babies, not my own.

Foolish daydreaming, she reminded herself, and almost dangerous, in truth, if one took into account how savage were the faces of the warriors. And if Jacques Cartier and his armed men had felt cause to fear the indigenes, toward the last, she reminded herself desolately that a lone woman would be a fool, indeed, to throw herself on their mercy.

*

But as the savages did not return, her apprehensions slowly relaxed and she resumed her accustomed ways.

The geese and ducks were now laying their eggs, and Marguerite devised omelettes and souffles from stealthily-removed fresh eggs, beating them with newly-gathered herbs or mushrooms, or the shoots of the shallots which now pierced their way through the soil. Each day the bark containers were set out into the sun and the plants in them were sending up their first leaves.

And although she had watched several times daily for the returning war-party, the soil of the garden had also been turned, with eggshells, ashes and dead fish from the shore spaded under in the furrows, along with the manure from the herd of grey deer. The soil seemed more friendly now, and less savage. It crumbled in Marguerite's hands, somewhat, and trickled through her fingers to the ground in a more friable way, like honest earth.

But sand from the north end of the island still would have to be hauled on the carrying-yoke, in readiness to cover the seeds. It would be a burdensome task, a long climb and descent, carrying the necessary two arquebuses, the yoke and the spade, but Marguerite no longer dared to trust to one firearm for protection. The powder was losing its force; there was no further doubt of that, and the beasts, seeming to sense this, were becoming bolder.

*

On an early morning trip to the summit later in the month, Marguerite scented smoke, coming from the west. Instantly she dropped into hiding, scanning the water for the canoes of the savages, since this must be the smoke of their campfires. Like a hunted beast she hugged the ground, immobile.

But the smoke was not coming from fires on her own island, she found. It came from the mainland, leagues to the westward. So that cautiously arising, Marguerite inspected the distant shoreline. The smoke was too wide-spread for cooking-fires, she decided, and she could see flames, now, in the tops of the trees. The forest was on fire!

A flock of the grey deer now left the mainland, swimming toward the scattered islands offshore. Marguerite hoped that the smaller animals were also escaping, but that the large and savage beasts would not be driven to her own island in their retreat from the fire.

How had the fire started? Marguerite wondered. Perhaps the natives had left a cooking-fire smouldering; perhaps lightning had kindled a dead tree. Such things were not unheard-of. Watching the spreading devastation on the mainland, Marguerite was glad for the wide bay between her island and the shore. While ashes and charred flakes were now reaching her on the wind, live sparks and brands could not be carried so far.

A fire here on her island would be a disaster, indeed. Without doubt it would destroy the *logette* and all her supplies and goods, even the garden. And Marguerite did not believe that she could endure going back to the cave, alone, there to face the memories of her husband in his illness, and Damienne, and the last hopeful months of waiting for the birth of her child. How many times must one begin all over again, she asked herself, after the heavy blows an unkind providence deals us?

So she stood for a long time watching the progress of the fire on the mainland. If the wind increases, she thought, sparks will reach here.

But the wind died down, and the fire abated, stopping at the shoreline. Below her on her own shores the humpbacked deer were now scrambling ashore. They looked defenseless, many having dropped their horns, and as they made their way, dripping and shaking their heads, across the northern part of the island, the slinking shadows of a few wolves followed them.

*

During the last days of the month the night-frosts ceased, and Marguerite planted her garden.

The bark containers were set into the ground, with their seed-plants already half-grown, and again Marguerite saved away a small store of seed in case her crop should somehow be lost. The rest of the seed she planted in tidy rows, covering them with sand and pressing them down firmly as Damienne had done in the years before. Inside their neat fence of withes, the rows of turned earth looked like a corner of a well-tended farmstead, somehow comforting.

And after the seedlings were watered each day, Marguerite now cleaned and aired the *logette,* leaving the door open to let in the warm air, and even sweeping out the courtyard in a veritable passion of neatness. The hides were taken out into the courtyard and sunned, then scraped, again, of their still-odorous remnants of flesh. Marguerite wished, again, that she could tan hides, but it was an art unknown to her, as it had been to her husband and Damienne.

With less fear that her cabin-smoke might betray her presence, since it now mingled on the wind with the scorched odor of the fire still smouldering on the mainland, Marguerite built up her cooking-fire each evening as it was needed. The savages did not move at night, she had heard, and if she watched for them in the mornings, the warning-time would have to suffice.

*

To cheer up the look of her home Marguerite had moved a few wildflowers into the corners of the courtyard and along the garden fence, where they nodded their gay colors against the weathered wood.

How cruel it is, Marguerite now thought poignantly, that only my eyes are here to see the coming of summer-time! Death's capriciousness, its insensate lack of justice, angered and confounded her. Sometimes she paced the pathway under the dark trees hardly daring to realize that her dead could never return to her, never return her love.

But a jug of flowers now sat on her table, and each day she picked small nosegays to lay on the three graves, where the mounded stones were already growing a covering of grey-green moss.

June, 1544

—1—

As if to give solace for tragedy and despair, the summer came on earlier and more clemently than it had in the years before. The nights were not as chill, and violets bloomed. Small singing birds which had never before appeared, now came to the island, trilling their unfamiliar songs as they nested in the woodland. Some of them resembled the little birds of France, to which Marguerite had paid scant heed while she had lived there.

With less work to be done than in the years before, since the *logette* was finished and the garden tillable, Marguerite found herself taking more time to sit and dream, and to look at the things which were to be seen on the island.

After planting the little field of barley and millet, she walked around the island, carrying her arquebuses, and sometimes she sat on the high rocks of the summit to watch the distant views of water and land.

The remains of the snowdrifts had all melted, but large floating pinnacles of ice still floated down occasionally from the Strait of Belle Isle, and one, shaped like a ship under full sail, was pushed into her very harbor by some vagary of the tide.

There, gradually melting, it floated back and forth, sometimes stranding itself here or there until the high tide again floated it adrift. Once as it passed before Marguerite's gaze, it reminded her of the many ships that passed Honfleur and Villefrançoise de Grâce on their way upriver to Rouen, making it so busy a port that it had become the second city of France. Villefrançoise de Grâce was getting to be known by its nickname of Le Havre, she recalled, and it had been a special project of the King's. Even before she, herself, had been born, he had already chartered work to be done on it, for defense of the realm or to make war on England, always a possibility.

Roberval had often had to go there, and since he had always taken Marguerite along on his travels, she had gone along. Now I think I understand, she thought wryly, why he kept me ever so closely under his hand.

But thus she had seen much of France, and Le Havre was in truth an impressive fortification, surrounded by high walls and a wide, moat-like waterway, fed by many streams. There were only two roads into it, protected by drawbridges, and the harbor, itself, was inside the walls, with a huge, round, crenellated tower guarding it, so massive in girth as to seem rather low and squatty. Inside the fortifications, also, were the streets and buildings of a sizeable town. It was an impressive defense, thought Marguerite, and a tribute to the acumen of François Premier, feckless though he was in many ways.

But Le Havre was primarily a military port, and the merchant shippers and explorers still preferred to use the ports of Dieppe, St. Malo and Honfleur.

So that it was toward Honfleur that they had later sailed, Marguerite recalled dreamily, watching the melting iceberg in her little harbor, up the broad Seine past the older port of Harfleur, already silted-in, and on through the wide, flat valley which extended north of the river to the chalky-white steep *falaise* at its edge. Forests, abbeys and châteaux were to be seen along the way, and the river-traffic was heavy; the pointed sails of caravels bulging out in the wind as they hurried along. Honfleur was only a few leagues upriver from Le Havre, and had been quickly reached.

It, too, one of the sea-captains had later told her, was beginning to silt in, and to become shallow, as were many of the rivers of France. Something would have to be done, he said, if they were not to have to go about their affairs in rowboats!

And later, during her various long waits in seaports, Marguerite had heard that the great Leonardo himself, sketching away at the Manoir de Cloux in Amboise, had worked out plans for movable wooden dams to deepen the water in rivers and harbors, while still allowing ships to pass without reloading.

Remembering the problem of silting, in France, Marguerite looked out across her own harbor with a knowing eye. No problem with silting here, she thought, hardly a loose grain of sand to be had, as she well knew. This harbor would remain deep enough for any ship. And what a site for fortifications! The high cliffs on the outer islands, looming above their narrow inlets, were a natural defense.

Four or five cannon could protect this goodly harbor from an armada, she thought sanguinely, if a settlement were ever to be built here, augmenting what we have already done. The harbor, itself, was as good a shelter for ships, she thought pridefully, as the much-praised harbor of St. John.

Some day, she dreamed with unvanquished hopefulness, ships are sure to return here.

*

Among the things which now plagued Marguerite's solitude were the demoniacal bursts of laughter during the nights. More disturbing than the savage sounds of the beasts, it even occurred during the day, pealing around her as she went about the island.

At last, one day along the shore, she noticed two duck-like birds with long, pointed bills, floating rather low in the water and diving for fish more nimbly than did the other ducks and geese. One bird was grey; the other had a black head. And as the lighter-colored one flew heavily away, beating to rise above the water, the other raised its head and opened its stork-like beak. Out poured a peal of the evil laughter, answered a little later from the shore by a higher, more insane, cadence.

Birds! In her relief Marguerite laughed aloud, with a sound, she feared, as wild as theirs.

The beasts, however, were not an idle fear. They were now

her greatest danger. Seeming to sense that Marguerite was alone, and that her weapons were losing their strength, they became more and more bold.

While her husband and Damienne had been with her, Marguerite remembered, the beasts had stayed their distance, whether because of the unfamiliar human scent, the sound of their voices, or the frequent arquebus fire, there was no knowing. Now they pressed in upon her, she felt, as if in some dim way they knew their advantage.

The wolves, the bears and the *carcajou* which had stolen the arquebus, she decided, were the most to be feared. And from time to time all of them stalked her. At first Marguerite had planned to rid the island of them, but now she knew that more would only come from the mainland, attracted by the seafowl or the caribou migrations.

Only in the *logette,* at night, could she relax her vigilance; during the day she needs must be as wary of danger as any other morsel of prey. But the others had their own defenses, she thought, swiftness of foot, or the ability to fly or swim away, or to climb a tree, or to hide. One creature even had needles on its back which stuck into the mouth of whatever attacked it.

As a member of mankind, with its tender flesh, lacking in fangs, claws or wings, Marguerite thought, I have only my wits and my weapons. If the one fails me, I must truly rely on the other.

And the arquebuses were no longer dependable. They now misfired almost as often as they fired.

*

The worst attack came on a warm and pleasant day. Wearing her skirt instead of her husband's clothing, Marguerite had walked to the crest of the south hill to hunt berries which had just begun to ripen on the meadows. Picking them was a pleasant task in the clear air and the warm sun, with flowers blooming on the hillside and bees buzzing among them. The landscape seemed peaceful, even dreamlike.

But suddenly a brown bear shambled out from the treeline, coming directly toward her, and Marguerite reached for her arquebus to put it in readiness. Why the animal seemed to be attacking, she did not know; it may have had cubs nearby, or this may have been its favorite berrying-patch. When there was no further doubt of the beast's intent, Marguerite shot it, at closer range than she would have formerly chosen. It was a fortunate chance that she did so; the arquebus fired, but judging from the slight recoil, she feared that it had not fired very strongly. The ball would not have carried far.

Shot through the mouth, the animal died quickly, but Marguerite had lost her taste for berrying.

By habit she immediately reloaded the arquebus which had been fired. The berries which she had gathered lay on a cloth which she then gathered up and tied together at the corners, carrying it in one hand, the arquebuses in the other, as she headed downhill through the waving meadow-grasses toward the shoreline.

Almost immediately a crashing through the branches told of the advance of another beast; when it came into view it seemed to be the first bear's mate. Setting down the berries, Marguerite hastily readied one of the arquebuses. There was no doubt that this animal, also, meant to attack.

Having in mind the problem of misfire, Marguerite had earlier loaded both guns, firing one as soon as it could be ignited. The bear had reared up and was weaving its head back and forth from side to side, so she shot for the heart.

This time the arquebus fired strongly, but the animal lowered its forepaws and continued to charge toward her as she fumbled to fire the second weapon. The bear then stumbled and fell, only a few paces from her, its jaws snapping and slavering with blood, before she could fire the second gun.

Again reloading, somewhat tremulously this time, Marguerite continued her retreat toward the *logette.* Then, as in a nightmare which repeats itself endlessly, still a third animal charged out of the woodland toward her. This time, in her increased anxiety, she fired immediately, while the beast was still some distance away.

The arquebus misfired.

But somewhat deterred by the smoke, the beast paused and wove back and forth, taking a few paces this way and that. Hastily Marguerite prepared the unfired weapon and shouldered it, as the animal rebegan its charge.

She did not manage a killing shot, but stopped the beast's advance, hastily ramming home a charge to reload the weapon. The first gun, having misfired, would have to be cleaned before it could be fired again. Now, in spite of her resolve to carry a reserve weapon, she had only one which possibly would fire.

Continuing her retreat more rapidly, nerves at a breaking-point, since the beasts seemed to be on a real rampage, Marguerite hurried up the shore toward the *logette.* In her blind haste and heedlessness she disturbed still a fourth bear, this one yellowish-white. The white bears, unlike the brown, had often threatened to attack, and this beast, she realized, was the most dangerous of all.

Much larger than the others, she knew that it was also swifter, as well, and more deadly. The beast had not yet charged, but it was preparing to attack, and it barred her way.

With only one weapon fit to fire, there was no scope for mistake.

Arquebus readied to fire, she held her slow-match ready until the last second, fearing a weak shot that would not carry the distance. As the huge animal rushed down upon her, its charge carrying it past the place where she had stood, she fired and leaped quickly to one side. Then, hastily reloading, she shot the huge beast again, through its thrashing head, at close range.

*

After she gained the courtyard she hastily barred the heavy gate, then both doors, kindled the fire, and lighted the lamps. Her mouth was still dry, and her hands shook.

But as the light flared up in the homelike surroundings, her fright slowly diminished. She even laughed a bit when she noticed that, incredibly, the berries had not been left behind as she made her much-interrupted retreat to the *logette.*

As she sat before her hearth drinking a potion of hot berry-juice, a rebellious anger grew in her. If the beasts wanted war, so be it.

Getting to her feet, Marguerite stripped off her dress and put on her husband's hunting-garments, strapping his sword-belt around her waist, with the powder horn and skinning-knife. She then loaded not two, but three arquebuses, and thus heavily burdened returned to the dead bears.

Their coats were ragged and dull from their winter's sleep, but one by one she skinned them, taking her time and watching the woodlands belligerently. She even carved fillets from each side of the youngest bear's backbone, and dragged them home on the white bear's hide.

July, 1544

— 1 —

The beasts now kept a respectful distance, whether because they had filled their bellies with flesh from the bears' carcasses, or because they accounted her as an enemy to be reckoned with, Marguerite did not know. Whatever its reason, she enjoyed the peaceful days. Lavendar, bell-like flowers were again in bloom and the garden was thriving.

Although the wild beasts were now staying at a remove, Marguerite decided to sing and talk to herself as she worked. The animals should have no lack of human voices, she told herself, to deter them from becoming over-bold again. Birds and animals seemed to mark out their domains and to warn off others by their songs or cries, she had noticed; she would do the same.

So singing and talking in what she hoped to be diverse voices, she worked energetically in the garden or chopped wood to the bouncing rhythms of peasant dances, and culled flowers and berries to the delicate *airs de Cour* of Claudin de Sermizy. And the sound of her own voice dispelled her sense of utter solitude, she found.

Even her prayers at the graves, formerly silent, Marguerite now sang or recited aloud, using sometimes Bible verses, sometimes the psalms of Clement Marot, and sometimes the prayers in poetic form of kindly Queen Marguerite, who had also lost an infant son, only slightly younger than her own. For an agonizing moment, Marguerite's arms ached for the warm, clinging body of her baby son. Now he would have been more than a year old, almost a toddler. For a moment she could nearly see him as he would now have been, and her voice faltered as she continued her recital of a psalm.

Slowly she left the place of her graves, and climbed the cliff overlooking the harbor.

And now Marguerite's eyes, which had learned the sea's ways, turned to it in hope; the sailing weather was so perfect that it almost seemed to command the presence of ships. The pyre on the summit had been visited every day since the appearance of the savages, but neither their canoes nor sailing vessels had come into view.

As she made her trip to the summit, she now gave thought to the habits of the fishermen who might come here as other fishing-grounds and harbors gradually became more crowded. It might be wise, she decided, to place another signal-pyre on the southern summit of the island, which she could reach more quickly, at need.

The fishing-boats were small, with correspondingly short masts, and it might be that they would be hidden behind the high cliffs of the surrounding islands, visible only when they passed an inlet. This would allow but little time for the long trip to the north summit. And in truth, while the beasts were peaceable now, they had made the trip to the northern signal-pyre perilous, and if the powder continued to lose its strength, the shorter the trip, the better.

*

Roberval had surely gone back to France, Marguerite was certain, since he would not willingly stay away from Court so long, fearing to be forgotten and supplanted. And, if he had stayed thus overlong in New France, François Premier would probably have sent for him by now, since the King was not a patient man and had always had frequent errands for Roberval. Indeed her cousin had often received messages from Court, and had bustled about on mysterious duties afterwards. For many things which a King could not be seen to do for himself, he could entrust to a henchman who was in no position to disappoint him.

And by thus doing the King's constant bidding, Roberval had gained a certain influence with him, so that if she did gain passage back to France, through God's mercy, her greatest problem would be that of dealing with Jean-François, her cousin Roberval.

Except for her mother's jewelry and the clothing she had brought along on the voyage, Marguerite reflected somberly, Roberval had sole custody of all she owned, her whole inheritance. Without some settlement from him, she would be impoverished, and such a settlement could probably never be obtained. Foolhardy, she told herself, even to try.

Her own young Lord, Marguerite knew, had depended on the support of his own family when they returned to France, and he had often told her of the loving welcome they would receive, of the comforts of his home château, sitting among its fertile acres and its woodlands handed down in his family as their native seigneuralty.

And when he had known that Marguerite was to bear his child, he had talked still more frequently of the welcome in store for them when they returned home with a family heir. Even as he neared his last days, he had seemed to want to leave that thought in her mind.

But now her arms were empty.

It would have been a different matter, Marguerite reflected sorrowfully, to ride up to the château of parents-in-law who were strangers, when one bore their grandchild in one's arms. Her eyes clouded with tears. It was a scene she had pictured many times after her husband died, seeing herself riding up to his family's home, through the mist-green trees of a French spring, or the bronze of a French autumn, carrying his son to his father's home. It would have been like giving her husband life again, thus to take his son home, not to take his father's place, but to continue his line, and to offer his lady-mother solace.

But now she, Marguerite, the cause of her husband's death,

could not so assuage his family's grief.

Already they must have been told some story about his death in this savage land; her cousin would have seen to that. Long years as a courtier had made him expert at covering his tracks and tying up loose ends. No-one would challenge him, nor succeed if they dared to try.

And for a widowed bride to turn up on her in-laws' doorstep, bearing only trouble, and having no proof of their duty to her but entries in a Bible, in her own hand, and marriage lines for which the only witness was dead, and her signature a mark—No! It would not do. Old wounds would be opened to no avail.

But more to the point, Marguerite admitted to herself, she did not think that she could bear to find her husband's kin less generous-hearted than he.

And the King, himself, was known to be inclement to those whose interests ran counter to those of his family or friends. His mother or his chosen associates could do no wrong, in his eyes. The Semblançay affair, which Marguerite remembered clearly, was an instructive example of what could happen when an able and honest man, of high station and great service to the crown, had interests which ran counter to those of someone close to the King, in that instance his mother, Louise de Savoie. The Queen-Mother had been clearly in the wrong, but that had not helped Semblançay, who had died for his poor judgment in pressing for his rights. Even Clement Marot, under François' thumb as he was, had written a poem crying out against that execution:

Haut élevés en fortune et pouvoir
Haut élevé en gibet m'ont pu voir!

The ironic words ran through her mind. And the Charles de Bourbon matter was another such instance; he was said to have spurned the advances of Louise and he had been ruined for it, the story ran.

But perhaps, in their absolute power, Kings always behaved in this way, Marguerite reflected, for a hundred years ago, Jeanne d'Arc, protected by Heaven as she was said to be, and having been of great service to her King in saving the realm of France, had been cynically written off by that same monarch when her usefulness was past. Such a one as she, innocent, saintly, famous and well-beloved by the people of France, had been sent to an agonizing death by the verdict of both the French clergy and the professors of its university, and her King, deeply in debt to her as he was, had not lifted a hand to save her.

Thus how frail a chance would she herself have, a minor noblewoman, the forgotten relative of a King's close crony, accused of adultery, having no witness, no defender, and being of no service to her King except to cause another embarrassment? None, Marguerite told herself, none.

Better to return quietly to the South of France, to Périgueux or Nontron, she decided, where I have kin, albeit distant cousins, and to hope that there I may have been remembered.

And outside her own kin there would be certain records. After her pledge of Faith and Homage to the King, Marguerite remembered, in the same year, her name had appeared in the *Denombrement de la noblesse du Perigord*, and she had been assessed one archer for the King's forces by the Seigneur de Daultefort, Gouverneur de la Maison de Navarre. He would have little cause to remember one obscure *damoiselle* among many, but he would have his records, since these were made at the command of the King. They would prove her identity, but they would probably not go far to regain her inheritance.

There was little hope of justice under law, Marguerite reflected, unless one had real power to enforce one's right to that justice. Only the naive and credulous, she thought bitterly, believed that it was freely given to all.

She and Damienne had received word that Marguerite must be ready for a journey far to the north, to Amboise, to sign her oath of Faith and Homage to King François, the first of his name. So that money was hastily spent on rich materials for the dress to be worn at the ceremony of the signing, and for her traveling costume. She had grown tall, and in the new formal clothing, with her hair smoothed back under the hood she later found to be out-of-fashion, she had looked like a grown young lady.

And Damienne, too, had had new garments, as was proper, both to stand at the back of the chamber for the signing, and to wear on the journey to Amboise. New horses were bought and caparisoned in a fitting manner, and the retainers who were to act as outriders were also newly outfitted. It was an exciting time.

Finally Jean-François had come with his own retinue, and they had set out for Amboise, staying in various châteaux and castles along the way. Chenonceaux, mirrored in its ornamental moat, spanning its river, came into her mind when she thought of that journey. The trip to sign one's Faith and Homage was an accustomed requirement on the nobility, and her arrival had been greeted with interest. She, Marguerite, as a substantial heiress, had been a marital plum at the age of thirteen, she now realized. It was no marvel that mothers from nearby holdings had shown a ladylike interest in behalf of their sons! But even at the pledging ceremony, Roberval had kept her closely hemmed-in. She was hustled from her horse to the signing-chamber in the hall at Amboise, to appear before Raoul de Lestrade, seigneur de Floriac, who accepted her procuration as Dame de Sermet, de Sauveterre, d'Allas, de la Mothe and co-seigneuresse de Saint Popoing, and as heiress of the house of Jean de Sermet, her grandfather.

She had placed her signature and its flourish without awkwardness nor spluttering of the quill, she remembered, signing as being of the Seneschaux de Périgort, her home country. She remembered her feeling of pride that her signature was clear, since some of the noblemen who signed before her, grown men though they had been, had signed their pledges with illegible scrawls. Even Roberval, she remembered, had a rather clumsy signature which he started off with a gallows-like scrawl, having the letter "J" rudely intertwined over the "F." Marguerite had earlier decided to practice a fluid and regal signature, with a sort of scroll, such as she had seen used as a distinguishing flourish. Fortunate for her young self, Marguerite smiled to recollect, that it had come off so well!

Ruefully Marguerite remembered that she had often thereafter affixed her splendid signature to papers whenever she was asked to do so, documents which were not read to her, nor allowed to be read. And she had not asked for explanations. Ah, well! she thought, had I done so, it would merely have hastened the hour of my downfall.

Her mind wandered back to the splendid presence-chamber at the Signing at Amboise. What a splendid company it had been! Some of the other families from the South were present, and would have liked to show a little flurry of recognition for her, as a new signer, and now a land-holder in her own right. Many of them seemed to have known her parents, and her grandparents. And now Marguerite remembered how she had longed to talk with them, with the craving, so common among orphan children, to learn more about her dead parents from those who had known them. But Roberval had hustled her away. She remembered glancing back over her shoulder as they left the assemblage, for a last look at the rich setting in which she had for the first time played a part.

Those properties for which I swore my loyalty are gone by now, thought Marguerite cynically; if Jean-François has a free hand, no records will ever be found.

She could see him, in her mind's eye, hunched over the coffer of documents at Roberval, hastily sorting out those that bore her name.

—2—

The summer was rapidly passing, and not a single ship had been sighted in the Great Bay beyond the harbor.

The *fleur de lys* were now in bloom for the third summer on the island, and Marguerite laid daily offerings of them on the grave-mounds, where they displayed their stiff and elegant outlines like paintings on a blason. It now seemed as if she had lived here forever, and a solitary existence was her only reality. Husband, child and nurse came into her mind only as loved memories, without the earlier pangs of unbearable grief and longing.

Daily, in order to ward off the beasts, and to give herself the comfort of hearing a human voice, Marguerite sang as she worked. Now, without conscious decision, she often found herself singing hymns.

"Mark, Lord, how they increase, that trouble now my peace, and would my heart have shaken," she sang. "O Lord lift up mine head, let them be scatter'ed, that press around to slay me." The words were cruelly appropriate, she suddenly realized; they must have come to her lips from the very depths of her consciousness, for the beasts were again rampaging. They now showed little fear of her, even when she shouldered an arquebus, but stalked her constantly, as they would any other succulent prey.

The cause, Marguerite decided, was the powder. There was now no way to deny that it was losing its strength. No matter how she rearranged the loading, varying the amounts and kinds of ball, bullet, pellet or charge, none of the arquebuses now fired strongly or dependably.

Gunpowder, Marguerite had heard, was a mixture of saltpeter, charcoal and sulphur, ground to a powder, which resulted in the dusty black substance she had so carefully hoarded, knowing that here on the island it could not be replaced. The necessary ingredients of saltpeter and sulphur were not to be had.

While Marguerite had kept the powder as dry as she could, she now spread it out on a large cloth, in the sun, hoping that some faint dampness might be causing its loss of explosive power. But no clear improvement resulted.

In the early months on the island the explosion and flame from the guns had resounded and flashed in a frightening way, but now, at best, the powder ignited with a spluttering report, no louder than a brand of wet wood popping in the fireplace.

The beasts were no longer in fear of it.

One evening a *carcajou* climbed up over the roof and jumped down into her courtyard, having scented the game she had hung there to cool. She had had to shoot the beast three times, from close range, rushing in and out of the sturdily barred door of the *logette* to reload, and finally managing to kill it as it dragged itself toward her on her very doorstep. Thus she now had to be wary even in her barricaded courtyard.

September, 1544

—1—

Remembering Damienne as she worked, Marguerite sickled the grain and took it up the hill on a breezy day to thresh it with a heavy stick, and to winnow it of chaff. The crop was good. For herself alone, she realized with a pang of remembrance, she now had more grain than the three of them had been able to raise during the seasons before. This summer had been warmer, with less fog, and the earth had benefited from three years of tillage.

Again thinking of Damienne's teachings, Marguerite gathered and dried berries and mushrooms, and picked the herbs her old nurse had planted or sought out. The salt kettle had been kept boiling intermittently all summer long, and sea-salt was at hand to salt and smoke fish and game in the cave.

So that sitting at the entrance, arquebuses at hand, Marguerite tended the fire and looked down over the *logette* and across the harbor.

Although the island was now a place of plenty, almost of comfort, Marguerite longed for human companionship. Again she thought of her husband, of Damienne, and of her little son. The Lord's ways were harsh and incalculable, indeed, that she herself should have survived childbirth, but that the others should die, one by one. If only they could have lived through the evil times, Marguerite thought sadly, to enjoy the good. But her first wild sorrowing had diminished, and she now thought of her dead with more of love than of longing.

A quick climb to the northern summit had again revealed no vessels within sight, and in the clear air the visibility extended for many leagues. My only real need, thought Marguerite, is for powder, to keep the beasts at bay. If I had that, I could endure here forever.

But the coiled supply of slow-match for the arquebuses was also nearly gone. It was only a rope of loosely-twisted hemp, dipped in a mixture of saltpeter and wine, so that it would hold a coal and burn slowly and steadily, but it, too, could not be replaced on the island unless a substitute of twisted moss might be devised.

Marguerite's husband, she now recalled, had once mentioned his regret that he had not owned a crossbow to bring ashore, but he had not explained this wish, which had seemed rather odd to Marguerite at the time, since she knew that the weapons were heavy and awkward, with cranky little wheels that had to be laboriously wound up. Now she understood the remark; bolts from the crossbow could be retrieved and used again and again; powder would not last forever.

Had her husband also known that the powder would eventually lose its strength? Burdened with despair as he had been, bowed down with his labors and his longing for home, Marguerite hoped that he had been spared that bitter and frightening knowledge.

*

If fisher-folk come, thought Marguerite, I will have to return with them to France. They will have no powder with them, nor would they stay and settle here without their women-folk. They harvest the sea, and must sell their catch in France. Husbandry does not appeal to them. If they come, I must make ready to go back to France.

Tears came to her eyes. It would not be easy to leave this

place, wherein were buried all three of the beings whom she had loved.

But having made her harsh decision, Marguerite tried to think further of matters concerning her return. For soon or late the fisher-folk would come; she knew their independent habits. A shore teeming with fish, a sheltered harbor, fresh water, and a strand slanting into the water, would not forever be overlooked. As the pressure of numbers and rivalry for good fishing-grounds and drying-places increased, this island would inevitably be sought out.

The problem of evading the beasts until then would have to depend on day-to-day vigilance. But before the cold weather came, Marguerite decided, she would cut and quarter a strong sapling to whittle out a longbow. Also, she had noticed, the beasts feared fire above all things. When the powder completely lost its strength, she promised herself that she would devise torches of moss tied to branches and dipped in oil. Several could be carried, and one lighted from the other. Even if the powder lost all its strength, Marguerite vowed to herself, she would not fall prey to the beasts.

*

But the question of how to proceed when she arrived in France was not so simple. So that for a final time Marguerite reviewed the situation that would face her there. It was a bitter thing to relinquish hope of claiming her rightful inheritance, hers by right of blood, and handed down to her, she knew, through generations hard-put to retain it. It was not in their nature, or hers, to surrender tamely.

Again she reviewed the thorny dilemma. The land records would show what was Jean-François' and what was mine, she reflected, and doubtless I could seek them out for myself. Fortunately I learned to read and write, while most girls are taught only sewing, prayer, and how to trace their lineage on their blasons. Indeed, I could well do that too, telling the history of all my holdings, and through what lines of blood they came to me.

I could separate them from those of Jean-François as well as could the *conseillers du roy.*

And much good would it do me, she realized, defeated. If an *eçu* of mine is left by now, it is because Jean-François overlooked it! Better to go back to Périgort, in Aquitaine, and hide myself away, in Périgueux, or even more remotely, in Nontron. There I can buy a small house and garden, and mayhap teach the little girls their manners and their letters in exchange for the tax-moneys.

The *livres* from my husband's money-pouch will have to be used, she thought regretfully, and my mother's jewels can be sold; they would ill become me now, yellowed and spare as I have become. Damienne's sober garments will suit my state better than my delicate satins and brocades. And each of those costly dresses, bought for me by Jean-François so that we could make a brave display will now mean a year's frugal living.

The marriage ring given me by my husband, Marguerite vowed to herself, will be the only jewel I will keep.

*

But even out of sight, in Nontron, unless she used great care, Marguerite feared that Roberval would somehow scent her out. She wondered if Pierre Colombel was still Prévôt de Nontron, and what the local situation might now be. It was hard to guess how safe a haven would be found even in Nontron.

And before starting for Périgort, deliberation would be necessary. Inquiries would have to be made. Best, therefore, to steal into France with caution, when the time came, and, like an animal, to sniff out the air for danger. Jean-François would clearly be the greatest peril. Having squandered her estate over the years, as she suspected he had done, she feared that he would not blink at making certain she would not survive to accuse him. He probably thought her bones had long been stripped clean and scattered on this island. What an embarrassment, she thought wryly, to have her emerge alive!

And still less would he care to receive the news of her return if some of her properties remained unencumbered, Marguerite thought resentfully. He would have full possession of them now, with none to say him nay, and from the sound of his creditors as the expedition left France, he would sorely need them to settle his own tangled affairs.

Briefly she considered the possibility that François Premier, her cousin's kingly crony and protector, might have died during the time of her exile. Whispers had already circulated, even before the expedition departed, that the King's recurring abscess had greatly weakened him and that the doctors had not been able to cure it. His days might be numbered.

But little real hope lay in that direction, Marguerite realized, in defeat. Jean-François would leap nimbly into favor with Henry, the Dauphin, who would ascend the throne as the second of his name, for already Roberval had cannily paved his own way to retain kingly patronage.

By design or by fortunate accident, Henry had already been enslaved by a relative of Roberval's, Diane de Poitiers, his mistress. She was a full eighteen years older than Henry, but a long-legged graceful beauty, and she had been Henry's mistress for some six years now, Marguerite recalled. Known as the *Grande Sénéchale,* Diane made much of her respectable widowhood, at least in public, Marguerite mused sardonically, appearing only in garments of the proper black and white.

She had easily captivated Henry, since the wife allotted him by interests of state had been ill-favored, low-born and sterile, but a niece of the Pope's, for which much had been gracefully overlooked. So that Catherine de Medici had been able to give Diane little competition for Henry's favors.

And she is so much younger than Diane, Marguerite reflected in awe at Diane's complete conquest, only about my own age. And by now Diane had grown bold in her success. She had already conspired against the King's own mistress, Anne de Pisseleu, whom she had hated ever since both of them had served as ladies-in-waiting to Louise of Savoie.

And a rare pair they are, indeed, thought Marguerite, one as cold and self-centered as the other!

But each of them, she also reminded herself ruefully, had

a King or a King-to-be, safely under her thumb. And of course Roberval had providently cultivated Diane, making much of their family relationship. So that even if Henry had already ascended the throne during her exile, he would probably be no more likely to spurn Roberval than his father had been, even though Henry did not favor those of the New Religion. Thus he would consider Marguerite herself a heretic, guilty of an illegitimate marriage, and, worst of all, not likely to bring benefit to the crown. So even if François Premier was dead, she would be in still worse stead with his successor.

*

All this brought to Marguerite's mind another, and even more dangerous factor, which would bear much thought, the matter of the religious climate in France. Even before the expedition had left, Marguerite remembered, trouble had been brewing and persecutions had taken place. Even the New Testaments were being secretly printed, and bound into very small volumes, so that women of the New Faith could hide them in their hair. "Chignon Bibles" they were breezily called by those of the New Religion, accustomed to living on the sword's edge, and indeed they had had to be more cool and wary than foxes to survive when the winds of kingly policy veered against them.

Jean-François rode neatly above the fray, because of his usefulness to the King; others were not so fortunate.

Worse than the Black Death, which had killed off whole villages, and which had also long recurred at intervals, were the religious persecutions that had taken place in France. The Albigensians, or Cathari, as they were sometimes called, were of the South, and they had practiced their strange faith, with its abhorrence of sexual love, for more than two hundred years before Marguerite's birth. Some of the de la Roques, including Jean-François' own father, had been Albigensians.

The crusade against them, led by their own countrymen from the North, had been simply a bloody pillage, Marguerite had early been told, and the South, below the Loire, had been at odds with the North ever since. Feelings ran deep, and the matter had not been forgotten in the passage of time.

While his own father was an Albigensian, Jean-François has cast his lot with the North, and therefore, thought Marguerite, when I at last return to France, I will go to the South. It is my home country. Perhaps even the King will no longer come there, since he now centers the Court near Paris, and I must avoid both Roberval and the King, since his good will toward those of the New Faith can no longer be depended upon.

Perhaps good Queen Marguerite would help me, thought her namesake, but even she has been jeopardized by her defense of the Sacramentarians, and if Henry is now on the throne, he will not be lenient to those he considers heretics. Henry is influenced by his mother, and Catherine de Medici is firm in the Catholic faith.

The clouds are indeed gathering over France, thought Marguerite gloomily, and those of my faith may have few that dare befriend them at the last.

October, 1544

—1—

The fall rains had begun, often coming on without warning, and Marguerite wore her oiled silk jacket and Damienne's sabots as she trudged through the streaming pathways on the daily trips to the summit. A thick skim of ice lay over the fresh-water basins in the rock, and had to be broken as she dipped out the day's supply of water. Night-frosts had now been frequent, and the last one had apparently been a real freeze.

The garden vegetables had been brought in and stored when the frosts first threatened, and again long strings of braided shallots and garlic hung beside the hearth. The turnips and carrots were snugly packed in moss under the end of the roof, and smoked meat and fish hung from pegs in the loft.

Before long the harbor would freeze, Marguerite told herself, and then there would be no need to make the daily trips to the pyre. The fisherfolk would have gone home to France, to sell their last catch there and to spend the worst of the winter in the warmer climate of home.

On a glowering day which she judged to be early in October, Marguerite again sighted no ships from the summit, and as she walked back down the hill the waterfowl flew southward over her head in their arrow-like array as they had been doing for weeks, their resonant, haunting calls echoing over the granite hilltops. As she walked down past the cliff-edge where Damienne's body had been found, Marguerite again remembered that it was now a year since her old nurse had died. Somberly plucking a few flowers from crannies which had protected them from the night-frosts, she carried them along with her, clenching them in the hand which carried the water-kettle, holding the arquebuses over the other shoulder.

At Damienne's grave she laid the sparse bouquet in place and bowed her head, thinking of the long years in which her old nurse had been her only enduring companion. How Damienne had longed to be buried in her home-soil of Normandy!

Making such amends as she could, if comfort could reach the dead through prayer, Marguerite pressed her palms together and softly repeated the familiar words which she had learned at Damienne's teaching so many years ago:

Ie te saluë Iesus Christ
Roy de misericorde
Ie te saluë nostre vie
Nostre doulceur et nostre esperance . . .

*

The ice now froze still more deeply in the fresh-water pools, and Marguerite went up the hill to gather it and pack it in the storage-place under the eaves. Then she went forth to shoot a supply of wildfowl to store without salting. And although the flocks were as plentiful as ever, it was no easy task. The powder had so weakened that her shots did not reach their marks, and even when the birds passed overhead in what should have been easy range, she could not bring them down. It took her all day to shoot a winter's supply, a task which had taken less than an hour in the autumn before.

As she carried the birds to the chopping-block in the courtyard, Marguerite was thoughtful. Her former hunting practices would now no longer suffice; that was clear. During the winter she would have to give thought to the setting of baits and snares, and the making of traps, in ways of which she had heard long ago in France. And for the large beasts, such as the grey deer, travelling as they did in customary pathways, perhaps deadfalls could be built.

Without arquebuses, she told herself grimly, she would have to seek her food stealthily, as did the game-poachers in France.

*

All through the long summer days and the shorter days of autumn, Marguerite had worked to replenish the supply of fire-wood and turf. Last year's supply had easily lasted out the winter, but, she reminded herself, during the weeks of her depression and despair the fire had gone out, apparently for days at a time. That would not happen again, Marguerite vowed to herself. In the loneliness and confinement of the days to come, she would set herself tasks to occupy her hours fully, even to memorizing the New Testament, embroidery, or carving wooden implements and tools. A bow and arrows must necessarily be whittled out and the arrows fletched.

I will even sit and carve the bedposts and table-legs, Marguerite promised herself, before I will again let my mind be a prey to demons and strange imaginings.

*

The fogs on the island had always reminded Marguerite of the fogs of Périgueux, which were also sometimes heavy until mid-morning. And the pathways of her tiny domain were now so familiar that Marguerite went about her planned outdoor duties whether the days were foggy or clear. She even told herself that she enjoyed the fogs, that they were homelike.

Only the trips to the summit were deferred until the fogs cleared, since vessels usually anchored on such days, and had they moved, they still could not have been seen even when the summit stood clear, above the fog.

And on such days, she supposed, even the savages could not be expected to pass by.

Looking out her doorway into a fog so thick that the pointed posts of the courtyard were hidden, Marguerite recalled how often she had stepped slowly through such a thick, damp veil in Périgueux, to see an elegantly carved gateway or arch peeping through it, familiar and reassuring. One such arch was carved with lion cubs at both sides, one of them holding his paw in his mouth. She remembered that from her childhood.

The gutters of the narrow streets in Périgueux had run with moisture during the heavy fogs, even as did the granite swales in the smooth rock of the island, and as one wound downhill, the rough rock felt almost like the cobbled, narrow, sharply-descending streets of that city, as if, just out of sight on either side, ranged the courtyards and entranceways of home, behind which were warmth, and light, and companionship.

A pang of homesickness pierced Marguerite with the sharpness of a spear-thrust. Those well-remembered streets and lodgings were on the other shore of the ocean-sea.

But after a moment of blank desolation and despair Marguerite told herself firmly that Périgueux had stood amid its hills, little changed, for time beyond reckoning. She herself would return, and would find it still the same.

But it would be best to think carefully, Marguerite decided that evening, while she had long hours in which to do so, of what best would serve her need when she stepped ashore in France.

It might not be wise to remain overlong in a seaport town, she decided. Such places were hotbeds of gossip and rumor, and spies collected what news they could in every inn and sailors' tavern. The presence of such a one as herself, alone, would be bound to cause comment. Note would be taken and reports would be made to the King's agents. Three *coffres de voyage* and the other belongings in their bundles would make a notable supply of baggage for a woman of humble station. Perhaps she should pretend to be a servant from one great house or another.

However she was able to return, Marguerite decided, she would pay to have all her goods taken along, and would make arrangements during the voyage for the obtaining of transport as soon as harbor was reached. In the bustle and confusion of landing, she knew, less note would be taken of herself and her baggage, when it was carted away, than if she waited about and made arrangements later, when loungers about the docks would have more time to take note and ask questions.

She should be quickly off and gone. Her tanned face and spare body would attract little attention in themselves, if only her speech and manner were not allowed to betray her.

And, she hoped, the fisher-folk would protect her. They were clannish and independent, and no friends to the King's agents. Secrets were safe with them. And indeed there must already have been talk among the sailors and fisher-folk of Jean-François' leaving his own kinswoman to her fate on an island in new France. Such a deed on the part of a great Lord would not go untalked-of by the seafaring folk, who would know more clearly than their betters what hardship such an act would bring about, and what a vicious nature it betrayed. They, at least, were loyal to those of their blood.

Also, she reflected, many of the fisher-folk were of the New Religion and would hence be likely to shelter one of their own faith, highborn or low, even if agents of the Old Religion now had an upper hand.

But whether the port of return was St. Malo, La Rochelle, or some other fishing-port, an overland journey to Nontron would be necessary, and there lay real danger. Travel by a woman, alone, would require the hiring of horses and outriders, even if a party going in the right direction could be found. Perhaps she could go down to Bordeaux by another boat. That would be safer, and would shorten the land journey. But there was no knowing whether it would be wise or foolish to go through Angoulême. Help might be given there, but danger there might also be.

And land travel would be slow. Nine leagues a day was a fair speed on horseback; roads were bad and bridges were few. Detours had to be made, sometimes because of the condition of the roads or when the streams ran too deep to be forded, or when bandits were known to be about in certain forests along the roads.

Parties of travelers passed each other warily, riding to the left, so that the armed outriders might have their arms toward each other in case of treacherous and sudden attack. And sometimes if a retinue looked too rich and too poorly attended, it never reached its destination.

That should not sorely trouble me, thought Marguerite ironically. My person and my belongings will, in truth, look shabby enough to escape greedy eyes.

—2—

As winter's winds began to blow, bringing their sleet to freeze on the ground, there seemed to be little further hope that sails would be sighted. But out of habit and stubbornness, Marguerite still made the trips to the summit during the shortened days.

Soon enough, she thought, I will have to be penned up in the *logette,* like a mare in her stall, for weeks at a time, and out-of-doors there will be only frozen wastes and darkness.

That day she shot a few of the white, chicken-like fowl, which could be killed from very close range because of their foolish habits. They, at least, could be had, probably even caught by hand, when the powder finally lost all its remaining force. Along with a hare or two she put them away in the ice under the roof, and covered the wood supply in the courtyard with the pieces of canvas.

Again the wood nearly filled the courtyard, and was thickly piled in the entryway and along one side of the *logette.* Preparations for the long winter had all been made.

But although the beasts now stalked her constantly when she was out-of-doors, sometimes attacking and having to be killed, Marguerite felt a great reluctance to close herself into the safety of the *logette* before that needs must be done. The last outdoor days seemed somehow precious, raw as the winds and rain had become. She remembered, too well, the sense of isolation and confinement that had beset her during the winter before.

Even a pet, something to fondle and feed, would make the solitude more endurable, Marguerite thought wistfully, a little dog, or even a cat. Queen Marguerite's little dog came into her mind, and she thought of the affectionate creature enviously. There were those who jested, behind the good Queen's back, because she often talked to the tiny animal as one would to a child. But what harm! Why should not an old woman have a warm little body to cuddle beside her and cosset?

Perhaps next spring a fox cub might be tamed, doglike as the animals seemed to be. Wolf cubs looked like puppies, also, but a fullgrown wolf, Marguerite thought, might be too dangerous a companion. But another creature sharing the *logette* would give her something to think on, something to which she could talk, a playful and loyal pet which might even give warning of the approach of danger.

November, 1544

—1—

Longbows, from what Marguerite had heard, were carved from sections of oak, yew or elm, but only spruce and fir-trees grew on the island. Their wood, therefore, would have to suffice. But from what her husband had told her as they worked on the *logette,* branches made knots in logs and weakened them; thus it would be better, she decided, to find a straight, branchless section of tree-trunk, long enough for a bow. And the search for such a tree was not easy; the straight trees close to the *logette* had been cut, and most of the trees on the island had closely-placed branches.

Carefully examining trees as she went, Marguerite walked upward through the valley, finally arriving near the southern summit. Once there she turned and glanced out across the harbor in a cursory way. It had frozen over the night before with a thin skim of ice, and she had decided only that morning to make no further trips to the signal pyre.

Now, as she straightened her back and looked across the harbor, Marguerite noticed that the sea-birds were flying about, outside the outer islands, in a way that betokened alarm.

Marguerite hastily crouched behind a rocky outcropping and peered out, cautiously holding a shrubby branch before her as a screen. Could the savages be returning so late in the year from their war? But surely the fresh water, upriver, must be frozen across by now, barring the way to their canoes, so that they could no longer return to their homes by water. Could they be coming to winter-over on this island?

The birds continued their clamor. Marguerite stared out at the eastern inlets to the harbor, apprehensive and fearful. Soon, she thought, a procession of canoes will come into one of the inlets, under the screaming sea-birds. If the savages are coming here to winter, she thought in panic, little use to flee. They will seek me out.

At last something moved on the water. High and squarish, it blended its grey with the sea-mist. A sail! A two-masted fishing-boat was crossing the inlet east of her!

Jumping to her feet, Marguerite peered at the vessel, fearing that her desperate hopes were tricking her eyesight. But she could now see the hull, the shape of the sails. It was a fishing-boat! She had seen them by the hundreds in France.

A scream of rejoicing rose in her throat. She jumped onto a rock and waved her arms above her head. But quickly she realized that the vessel was too far away to see her.

So she ran to the nearby pyre and snatched the kindling moss from its dry crevice in the rock, pressing it into place with a pinch of powder, blowing against her slow-match to light it. A thread of smoke curled upward. Against her will, as she nursed the fire along, Marguerite remembered the fruitless signal-fire she and Damienne had built.

At last she dared to rise again and look for the boat.

It was passing the inlet, going out of view behind the island to the south of it. But another was coming along behind it, very slowly. Apparently they were fishing as they went.

Why had she not built herself a little boat? She could have gone to them! As it was, if they stayed behind the outer islands, only a tall column of smoke would attract their attention. Feverishly Marguerite now fed her fire, finally laying sheets of ice on it, which she snatched up from the nearest rock reservoir. These melted, and the blackened smoke arose almost straight upward on the light west wind.

Hastily casting still more fuel and ice on the fire, Marguerite raced downhill toward the rocky shore. There was no knowing whether she could be seen on the summit; its distance from the outer islands was great. And the shore was closer to the inlets. Even from there she would only be seen if the ships entered the harbor.

Reaching the shore, she raced back and forth, north and south along the slanting rocky strand. But no ship entered the harbor. And the outer islands were high. Over them she could not even see the tops of the masts. The ships might have left.

Tensely Marguerite shielded her eyes and watched the inlets. As the boats moved by them at intervals, she waved her arms frantically above her head. There were three vessels, she saw, and they did not seem disposed to come into the harbor. Perhaps the fire was a mistake! Perhaps they thought it had been built by warlike savages!

Panting for breath, Marguerite paused for thought. Her efforts would have to be governed into wise action. If the sailors were fearful, they would search out exits from the harbor before entering it. And they would come in swiftly, if at all. This would mean sailing crosswind, through a southern channel. Thus they would be able to run with the wind out of the harbor, for a quick retreat.

Marguerite rushed to the southern tip of her island to build another fire. Beside it she could stand and signal.

Rushing back to the *logette,* she gathered a kettle of coals, kindling, and dried wood to hasten the building of her beacon. And when it was aflame, scattered with splintered harbor-ice, she stood beside it watching the southern inlets. At least, she thought tremulously, the harbor-ice has broken. They should not fear to enter.

But the fishing-boats went back and forth, slowly, several times, in close order, even seeming to draw close together, as if to confer. Then they disappeared from view.

Marguerite sank down in dejection. Would they be too wary to enter the harbor? This place must indeed have an evil reputation, she thought despairingly.

But after what seemed a very long time the prow of one vessel peeked through the southeast inlet. It moved slowly forward, sailing closely-hauled. Marguerite stood motionless and nearly stopped breathing. But the ship continued to move forward, followed by the second boat, and the third.

When they got into the harbor they sailed slowly north and south, near the outer islands, coming no closer to her than a safe leeway allowed. Their slow movements and the set of their sails told Marguerite that they were deliberately hesitating; ships such as theirs could move very swiftly cross-wind.

Desperately she raised her arms out at her sides, then she knelt and held her arms out imploringly. At this the fishermen brought their boats closer together and seemed to confer, but they came no nearer. It was evident that they were fearful. Matters were at a stalemate.

Soon they will turn away and leave, Marguerite told herself urgently. Desperately gambling that they would be gone when she returned, she rushed back to the *logette.* Without even closing the door she tore off her shabby work-garments and snatched her way into her colorful shipboard dress. With fumbling fingers she swept her hair to the crown of her head, pinning it into a hasty knot. Then she seized a white napkin and rushed back to the shore.

The ships were still there, but seemed to show signs of leaving.

Urgently she beckoned to them, waving the napkin. She thought of firing an arquebus to show them that she was not a savage, but she feared that this might seem threatening. Undecided what to do next, she stood motionless beside her fire, torn between hope and despair.

Her bright skirt blew to one side in the offshore breeze. And at last, cautiously, the leading boat pointed up into the wind again, and moved slowly toward her. Renewing her gestures, Marguerite tried to convey pleading but not frenzy. The fisher-folk might be wary of a madwoman.

At last the ship was within earshot. Marguerite cupped her mouth with her hands and hailed them, first wordlessly, then screaming, "I am a Frenchwoman! Come and aid me!"

Cautiously, still fearing some sort of treachery, the vessels inched forward. At last she could see weathered faces turned toward her, and a rough Breton voice shouted, "Who are you?"

Tremulous with relief and delight at the first human voice she had heard in more than a year, Marguerite called out her name. "My kinsman left me here," she added, "With my nurse and my husband."

A chatter of voices came from the vessel. The speaker finally replied in a loud tone as his ship slowly advanced, "There was talk of that. We did not believe such a thing could have been done."

She gestured the vessels into the cove just north of her, and they anchored in its curving shelter. In their tiny *chaloupes* the seamen came promptly ashore, standing before Marguerite in their rough garments, she thought, like ministers from the Lord himself.

Half abashed, half curious, they looked at her, and she at them. She hardly knew how to act. They seemed somehow to fear her. It would be unseemly, and probably alarming, if she ran forward and threw her arms about the man who had first landed.

A certain formality would probably reassure them. So with calm politeness she welcomed them to her island and invited them to come to her home, where she would give them refreshment.

With amazed looks they fell into line behind her. Whenever she glanced at them she was met with a look of baffled awe, superstitious and wary. And as she turned back toward them to indicate the garden and the place of graves, one of the younger seamen blurted, "We thought you were a she-demon!"

Marguerite laughed aloud in relief. "Not so!" she replied, "And I even have my New Testament to prove it!" The blunt retort, and her laughter, seemed to put the men at ease. Their superstitious fears of the island had indeed been their reason for avoiding it.

With rough camaraderie they surrounded her as they approached the courtyard. What ecstasy to be bombarded by human voices, French voices! And Marguerite felt a certain pride as she opened the gate of the courtyard and ushered them into the *logette*. She lighted all the pan-lamps and the plates gleamed, the silver sparkled; the place looked almost magical surrounded by its rough wilderness. Again a few of the men seemed frightened; this might be some strange spell, something fearful and unholy.

So that first of all, as she showed them her belongings, Marguerite took down her New Testament, rather pointedly showing it to all the men who stood nearby. While they could not read, they seemed to recognize the Book, with its inter-twined cross on the cover. One of them took it reverently into his hands.

*

Although the captain said that they must leave promptly, for fear of being iced-in, they decided to wait for a hot meal. Vegetables would be a treat, they said, since they were weary of fish and salt meat. The venison would be best to serve, Marguerite hastily decided, and while the savory meal was cooking, she made her arrangements, as she had planned, for her transportation back to France. The captain would have carried her home, he said, out of Christian duty and a desire for justice. But Marguerite promised him payment for her passage, in order to take her belongings home; they would take cargo-space, she reminded him, reducing the amount of his catch. She must do so, she carefully explained, not out of greed, but because she would have to sell all she had to secure her living.

His rough face showed dismay. To these fishermen it was inconceivable that a Damoiselle, with her elegant accents and manners, could be hard-put for a living. But he believed her, and he agreed.

As the meal cooked, Marguerite first took the men out to the graveplace. It was comforting to her that they bowed their heads as they stood before the graves, giving her dead, at last, the recognition of mourning other than her own. And when she told them of her husband's forcing his way off the ship, leaving its safety to be with her, they murmured to each other gravely. The fleet-captain put his hand on her arm. "He must have been a goodly man, your husband," he said.

They inspected the carved grave-markers, with their circled crosses and their inscriptions. This was, indeed, a Christian cemetery, they nodded to each other, and their last doubts of her, in her strange situation, seemed to disappear. Then they peered through the garden gate with interest, even entering it and stooping to feel the tilth of the soil.

As they did so, a few blackbirds flew up from the barley-stubble, even as they did in the fields of France. It seemed a good omen.

—2—

Some of the seamen returned to the cove and went back to their vessels. They had nearly filled them with fish, and with a good day's catch they had planned to start back for France that night, since no fishing-boats were left in these waters by the end of November, and they were eager to set sail for home.

With only this one day's grace, she had seen their boats, and they, her signal.

Some of the catch would have to be moved to make way for her baggage, they said, and even so, they laughingly assured her, she would arrive in France, like them, smelling strongly of fish.

But it was clear that they intended to make her as comfortable as they could, and to keep her belongings as safe as possible on the small, exposed vessels, and they conferrred back and forth in their harsh Breton accents as to how this could best be done.

Then, returning to the *logette,* they helped Marguerite gather her belongings together, packing the most delicate in the topmost parts of the sea-chests. The arquebuses were great marvels to them; costly and valuable as they were, they must be oiled and wrapped safely from exposure to the sea-water, they warned her.

And only then, with a start of amazement, did Marguerite remember that she had left her customary two weapons down on the shore, beside the signal-fire, when the vessels came ashore. Now two of the seamen walked down to retrieve them. No worries now about the beasts, thought Marguerite. Such a large party of men have probably scared them away to the northernmost reaches of the island.

*

The packing was completed before the meal had cooked, and Marguerite served it on both the blue and white plates from the mantel and on the pewter dishes used on the voyage. The fleet-captain, at the head of the table, recited the blessing over the food, at Marguerite's request, and as he finished the members of the crew murmured their *prou face.*

They ate hungrily, marveling that the island could have produced such a tasty variety of food. Had she had time, Marguerite told them proudly, she could even have made a pastry from her grain, but grinding it by hand took too long for her to do so at short notice.

One of the men chuckled. "You sound just like my goodwife, *ma Damoiselle,*" he said. After that the men seemed to be at ease with her, and treated her, Marguerite thought, as one of their own.

The offshore wind still held, but the tide was now coming in, so that there was now no need for haste. The men finished their meal and lounged around the fire, drying their clothing and drinking the hot potion Marguerite had prepared for them. For a moment their presence seemed unreal to her, as if they might be creatures of her lonely imaginings, as if they might vanish when she glanced away from their faces.

But in their rough, odorous garments, with their good-humored, weather-beaten faces, they were reassuringly real. Several of them helped her to clean her cooking pots and the dishes, and to pack them safely for the voyage home.

They decided to take all the food, since it would be tasty fare for the voyage, so they roasted the meat to be shared among the boats and eaten before it spoiled. The smoked meat could be cooked later, even in France, if the passage was as fast as they hoped. And Marguerite felt a thrifty satisfaction that none of her hoarded provisions would be wasted.

*

At last the packing had been completed, even to the hides from the floor, the stools, and the feather-beds. Goosefeathers were valuable, the men said. And as she had feared, Marguerite found that there was a considerable pile. But somehow it was all packed together and stowed aboard the vessel they had selected.

Then the men sauntered about the courtyard and *logette,* marveling at its snugness, and querying how such a cabin could have been built by one man, with the help of two women. And when Marguerite mentioned the cave they climbed up to see it, and to peer in. Wintering in such a tiny hole under the rock, with three people, one a woman about to bear her first child—it would be a tale long repeated through generations of fisher-folk, Marguerite suddenly realized, as she heard their shocked comments on their return.

At last the men tactfully withdrew to the shore, carrying the last of Marguerite's belongings with them, except for her own sea-chest.

Alone in the *logette,* now stripped of its homelike contents, Marguerite pulled on her warm quilted and fur-lined undergarments, and her husband's oiled hunting-boots. The small vessel would be wet and cold. Making a small bundle of her pewter dish, her spoon, a warm blanket and a washing-cloth, she packed the rest of her belongings into the *coffre de voyage.* Like the seamen, she thought, I will sleep in my clothing and eat as they do when occasion makes it possible.

Stepping outside, she called to the nearest seaman that her chest was ready, and after it had been carried down to the shore someone shouted that the tide was cresting. The vessels would have to leave on the outgoing tide, Marguerite knew, sailing out on the west wind through the very entrance by which she had come into this harbor, more than two years before. And they would be running with a fair wind, headed straight for France.

With a natural tact the seamen busied themselves at the cove, readying the vessels for the voyage, since they stood in some awe of this woman who had survived hardships they could well understand, and who had lost her husband, her child and her nurse as well. Horrible, to have lived on this savage island alone, for more than a year.

They did not look toward Marguerite, nor hurry her. She

would come, they seemed to be saying by their actions, in her own time.

*

Empty-handed for the first time in many months, Marguerite walked out of the *logette,* peering back into it for the last time. Only the fireplace now lighted it; even the pan-lamps had all been carried away. It contained only her bed, bare of its canopy and mattresses, the table, and the wood stacked along the western wall, hiding Damienne's bed.

Memories flooded over her. Strangely, the cabin still looked comfortable, homelike. It seemed to be her home, now that she must leave it. Her eyes dimming with tears, Marguerite slowly closed and barred the doors. Looking back for the last time, she closed the gate of the courtyard with its ample wood supply.

The fishermen can make good use of it when they return, thought Marguerite, as now they will be sure to do.

She walked slowly up to the grave-place, and stood before the high, stony mounds, now covered with moss. Even the wooden markers had begun to weather. No more flowers for them, she thought, reaching to the overhanging branches to lay an evergreen bough on each grave. Fir will last, she told herself sadly, for a while.

Eyes flowing with tears, she said her last prayers over the beings she had loved, whose resting-place she would never be able to visit again.

Then at last, slowly, she gathered her fur-lined cape about her in the chill wind and turned toward the shore, to the Breton fishing-boats, to return to France. And as she did so she was overwhelmed by a certain wish not to leave there, but to die in that solitary place, like her husband, her child and her servant, desiring to remain there, torn by sorrow as she was.